elementary
algebra
STRUCTURE
AND USE

elementary algebra

STRUCTURE AND USE

RAYMOND A. BARNETT
Merritt College

McGRAW-HILL BOOK COMPANY
*New York   St. Louis
San Francisco
Toronto   London
Sydney*

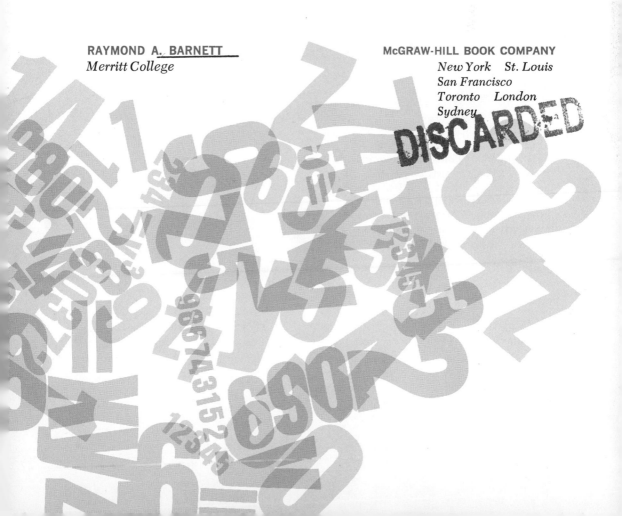

preface

This is an introductory course in algebra. It is written for students with no background in algebra and for those who need a review of algebra from a contemporary point of view. Recommendations and experimental texts from most of the well-known professional mathematical organizations and study-writing groups were carefully surveyed and had an influence on the content and emphasis in this book. However, the author assumes full responsibility for the material that appears in the text.

The text was successfully class-tested, in manuscript form, with students of varying interests and abilities. It provides a gradual transition from verbal forms to symbolic forms, from the concrete to the abstract (this is why the first chapters are longer than the later ones). Key theorems and definitions are stated both symbolically and verbally for increased understanding. Every effort has been made to lead the student from basic principles to normal operating procedures with minimum use of artificial devices. Many topics are developed by a questioning process which leads to a "discovery" of underlying general principles.

Set ideas are introduced early in a natural but not overly formal manner and are used where appropriate throughout the text. A postulational approach is used with substantial motivation. All axioms, definitions, and theorems are carefully stated and amply motivated.

The construction of the real-number system from the natural numbers forms the logical basis for the text. It is the spirit of this construction that is emphasized rather than each logical detail. It is assumed that the natural numbers with basic arithmetical operations are known.

The emphasis in the text is on names of numbers and operations on these names rather than on a precise knowledge of what a number is as an object. This avoids concepts such as equivalence classes which are better left to more advanced courses.

Special care is taken when the negative sign is introduced. Three uses of the sign (negation, subtraction, and part of a number symbol) are clearly identified and fully discussed. Inequalities and graphing are introduced early (Chapter 1). Concepts such as solution sets, equivalent equations, and equivalent inequalities are stressed. The straight-line and linear equations in one and two variables (with applications) receive more attention than in most texts at this level. The concept of function is developed carefully, but only after the student has gained facility in working with symbols and experience with ordered pairs of numbers through graphing. The postulational method is introduced in a natural but informal way at first; a more formal presentation is made in the last chapter, after the student has gained some mathematical maturity.

Simple necessary and sufficient conditions are stated for the factorability of second-degree polynomials with integral coefficients. This leads to an easy test for factorability. In the problem sets, quadratic forms that are factorable are mixed in with those that are not.

The problem sets form a very important part of the text and have been selected and arranged with care. They are designed to increase the student's skill with algebraic mechanics, as well as his understanding of algebraic structure. The exercises are graded, and problems are matched in pairs. Answers to odd-numbered problems are included in the text. At the end of each chapter is a comprehensive review exercise complete with answers to all problems. (The teacher's supplement contains an additional set of chapter review exercises.)

Contrived applications have been consciously avoided. Significant and interesting applications from many different fields have been used wherever possible. An important feature of the text is the inclusion of problems from the social and life sciences, as well as the physical sciences and business. Each student should find—from the extensive number and variety of applications included—a number of applications that are of particular interest to him. All problems are self-contained; they require no previous specialized knowledge of any given field.

A summary of key mathematical ideas is included at the end of each chapter.

If time is of concern, the following material may be treated briefly or omitted without loss of continuity: Sections 33, 36, 38, 41, 42, 52, 54, 59, 67, and 70; all of Chapter 11; and perhaps all of Chapter 10 (many instructors prefer to postpone the important topic of function until the next course rather than to treat it too hurriedly in this course).

Professor Kenneth O. May once said, "We know that students have two prime drives in studying mathematics: their belief that mathematics will be useful to them, and the joy that comes from mathematical insight and accomplishment." It is hoped that this book will appeal to students at both levels.

The author wishes to thank the several teachers who reviewed the text in manuscript form for their many useful suggestions and comments; Mr. Horacio H. Miller for his careful checking of examples, problem statements, and answers; and Mrs. Mary Faville for her excellent typing of the final manuscript.

RAYMOND A. BARNETT

contents

elementary
algebra
STRUCTURE
AND USE

natural numbers

1 WHY STUDY ALGEBRA?

Students enroll in an elementary algebra course for many reasons. Perhaps they are satisfying a prerequisite for a chosen major or meeting a general college requirement—and the sooner it is finished the better. Whatever your reason for studying algebra, your decision to take this course will be far more important to you than you may realize. You will not only gain a tool that will enable you to state and solve many types of problems which were heretofore out of reach, but you will be introduced to one of the great intellectual achievements of mankind: a method of inquiry known as the postulational method. The importance of the postulational method in the development of mathematics, science, and philosophy cannot be overemphasized.

The number of fields using mathematics (as well as the intensity of its use in any given field) has increased. In addition to the areas where mathematics has

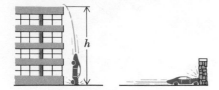

Figure 1   Energy and cars.

traditionally been used, such as physics, chemistry, engineering, and technology, we find a substantial increase in the use of mathematics (algebra and higher) in such unlikely places as historical research, political science, linguistics, biology, sociology, psychology, and economics, to name a few.

A remarkable feature of algebra, and mathematics in general, is that it owes no particular allegiance to any one subject; a single mathematical theory, by the very way it is developed, is free to be applied to many diverse problems from many different fields.   To give the reader an appreciation of the variety of the areas of application of elementary algebra, a few interesting problems will be presented here.   Each is relatively easily solved with the methods developed in this text, but the average person would find them very difficult without algebra.

PHYSICS–ENERGY AND CARS. At 20 mph a car collides with a stationary object with the same force it would have if it had been dropped $13\frac{1}{2}$ ft, that is, if it had been pushed off of the roof of an average one-story house.   In general, a car moving at r mph hits a stationary object with a force of impact that is equivalent to that force with which it would hit the ground when falling from a certain height h, given by the formula $h = 0.0336r^2$ (Fig. 1).   How fast would a car have to be moving if it crashed as hard as if it had been pushed off of the top of a 12-story building 120 ft high?

MUSIC.   The Greeks were aware of certain natural harmonies in music.   Pythagoras, with a one-string instrument known as the monochord (Fig. 2), found that by placing the bridge so that the string was divided in the ratio of 2 to 1, he could produce the chord known as the octave.   Similarly, the ratio of 3 to 2 produced a chord known as a fifth, and the ratio of 4 to 3 produced a fourth.   For an instrument with a 20-in. string, where are the three places that the bridge should be placed to produce the three chords mentioned?

COMMUNICATION. The number of telephone connections possible through a switchboard to which n telephones are connected is given by the formula

Figure 2   Monochord.

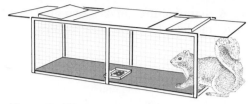

Figure 3   *Live trap.*

$c = n(n - 1)/2$.   How many telephones could be handled by a switchboard that had a capacity of 190 different connections?

BUSINESS–SIMPLE INTEREST. The amount of money A that a person would have coming to him after t years, if he invested P dollars at the simple interest rate r, is given by the formula $A = P + Prt$.   Show that $P = A/(1 + rt)$ is another form of the same formula.

ZOOLOGY–POPULATION SAMPLING. (This problem is also of interest to fish and game officials.)   The problem is to estimate the total population of a given species in a given region.   A technique that is very widely used because of its simplicity is the "capture-mark-recapture" technique.   A group of specimens (such as deer, fish, or birds) is collected from the population in such a way as to avoid any injury to them (Fig. 3), and these are marked in some distinctive way. The marked specimens are then released into the total population.   After a time period adequate for thorough mixing a new sample is captured, and the proportion of the marked specimens is determined.   Write an equation that can be used to estimate the total population.

CHEMISTRY–A GAS LAW. In the study of gases there is a simple law, called Boyle's law, that expresses a relationship between volume and pressure.   It states that the product of the pressure and volume, as these quantities change and all other variables are held fixed, remains constant (Fig. 4).   Stated as a formula, $PV = k$ (or $P_1V_1 = P_2V_2$).   If 500 cc of air at 70 cm of pressure were converted to 90 cm of pressure, what volume would it have?

Figure 4

ECONOMICS–LINEAR PRODUCTION MODEL. A manufacturer makes two grades of cameras, an economy model and a deluxe model. Each camera requires the following times in hours for production:

	Fabricating	Assembling	Finishing and packaging
Economy model	6	5	2
Deluxe model	10	6	4

The production in each department is limited, of course, by the number of man-hours available per week. These are 4,800 for fabricating, 3,500 for assembling, and 1,800 for finishing and packaging. What are the possible weekly production combinations of economy and deluxe cameras?

In addition to helping you solve problems of the types stated above, algebra may be of considerable use in helping you understand the technical writing that is appearing in increased amounts in newspapers, magazines, and textbooks. Consider the following two quotations. The first is from the biology text, "Principles of Animal Ecology," by W. C. Allee, and the second is from the article, *The Quantification of Sensation*, by the well-known Harvard psychologist, S. S. Stevens.

The oceans are the great reservoirs of water. They occupy 70.8 percent of the 510.1×10^6 square kilometers of the earth's surface and have an average depth of 3795 meters. Their total volume is about 1.37×10^9 cubic kilometers. The amount of water frozen into the ice of glaciers and ice sheets equals some 9.3% of this amount. That found in the air as vapor is only about 9×10^{-6} of that in the sea. In more direct terms, if all moisture in the air were precipitated and collected in the ocean, the sea level would be raised only 3.5 cm.

Some two dozen continua have been examined, always with the same outcome: the sensation magnitude y grows as a power function of the stimulus magnitude x. In terms of a formula, $y = kx^p$.... A law of this form seems to govern our reactions to light and sound, taste and smell, warmth and cold, vibration and shock ... equal stimulus ratios produce equal subjective ratios.... For example, it requires approximately a ninefold increase in energy to double the apparent brightness of light, no matter where we start from in the first place. Doubling the apparent intensity of an electric shock requires an increase in current of only about 20 percent, but this percentage increase is approximately the same all up and down the scale. On all continua governed by the power law, a constant percentage change in the stimulus produces a constant percentage change in the sensed effect.

Even if you do not plan to take any more mathematics after this course, you will find that a little knowledge of algebra is not a dangerous thing. You will be able to think on an entirely different level from that level attainable when you had only arithmetic to work with; in addition, many more areas of study will be opened to you.   For those who intend to continue their study of mathematics beyond this course, algebra will be the basic "language" for most of these studies.

There is nothing mysterious about algebra.   It does, however, place a demand and a responsibility on the reader to be precise.   A slow and careful approach pays the greatest dividends—one cannot read a mathematics text as if it were a novel.   In fact, for complete comprehension, several readings of the same material may often be necessary, including reviewing past material as one progresses through the text.   Mathematics is a cumulative subject.   To understand a current development, a preceding development must be understood.   It must be emphasized that mathematics is not a spectator sport; in order to understand, appreciate, and enjoy the subject one must do a great deal of thinking and problem solving—in short, do your homework!   A sharp pencil and plenty of paper are essential tools for learning mathematics; no mathematics text should be read without these.   Your careful attention to these details will be amply rewarded.   Good luck.   We hope you enjoy the course.

2   SETS AND SUBSETS

SETS

To begin the study and development of algebra, we will start with a very simple but mathematically important idea, the concept of set.   Our use of this word will not differ appreciably from the way it is used in ordinary everyday language.   Words such as "set," "collection," "bunch," and "flock" all convey the same idea.   We speak of a set of dishes, silverware, or glasses; an art or coin collection; a bunch of bananas or grapes; and a flock of geese.   The members or elements of these various sets are dishes, silverware, glasses, art objects, coins, bananas, grapes, and geese, respectively.   Hence,

An art collection is a set of art objects.
A bunch of grapes is a set of grapes.
A flock of geese is a set of geese.
A covey of quail is a set of quail.
A ski club is a set of people.
The digits from 0 to 9 is a set of numerals.

It is beyond the scope of this book to present a careful (axiomatic) development of set theory (a theory that enters into all branches of modern mathematics); we will be content, instead, to borrow a few very useful ideas from this far-reaching theory that will enable us to talk about certain algebraic concepts with increased clarity and meaning. We will not even attempt to give a general definition of the word "set"—from a mathematical point of view, defining "set" is a far more subtle task than it might at first appear.

Intuitively, we can think of a **set** as any collection of objects with the important property that given any object, it is either a member of the set or it is not. For example, if we define a particular set A to be the set of students in this class over 6 ft tall, then if you are over 6 ft tall, you are a member of set A, but if your height is 6 ft or less, then you are not a member of set A. If you are not a member of this class, you cannot be a member of set A no matter what your height is.

SET NOTATION

If an object a is in a set A, we say that a is a **member** or **element** of A and write $a \, \varepsilon \, A$; if an object a is not an element of A, we write $a \notin A$. Thus if A is the set of digits from 0 to 9, then $5 \, \varepsilon \, A$ and $11 \notin A$ (which is read, "5 is an element of A" and "11 is not an element of A"). The Greek letter for e is ε (epsilon); hence, ε is readily associated with the word "element." The words "element" and "member" will be used interchangeably.

Sets are frequently described by listing their elements within braces, $\{2, 4, 6\}$ is the set whose members are the three numbers 2, 4, and 6. One may write the elements of the set in any order; that is, $\{2, 4, 6\}$, $\{6, 2, 4\}$, and $\{4, 2, 6\}$ all represent the same set. A member of a set is not counted more than once, $\{1, 3, 3, 3\}$ and $\{1, 3\}$ are identical sets. These ideas are made precise in the following discussion.

EQUALITY

Two sets A and B are said to be **identical** or **equal,** and we write $A = B$ if and only if every element of set A is an element of set B, and every element of set B is an element of set A.

EXAMPLE 1. Identify the identical sets among the following:

$A = \{2, 4, 6, 8\}$

$B = \{2, 8, 4, 6\}$

$C = \{2, 4\}$

$D = \{4, 2\}$

$E = $ the set of digits from 1 to 9 that are exactly divisible by 2

$F = $ the set of digits from 1 to 5 that are exactly divisible by 2

SOLUTION: Sets A, B, and E are equal; sets C, D, and F are equal.

SUBSETS

We will occasionally be interested in sets within sets. If we define set Q to be the set of digits from 1 to 9, then set E in example 1 is a set within set Q. We will call E a *subset* of Q. Similarly, all of the other sets in example 1 are subsets of Q. In general we say that set A is a **subset** of set B if every element of A is an element of B. (Note that under this definition every set is a subset of itself.)

We will conclude this section by introducing a very special set (a set that, incidentally, is to be considered a subset of every set) called the **empty set** or **null set**. The empty set is a set without any elements in it. Visualizing an empty basket may help you to understand the concept. The null set functions in much the same way when one works with sets as the number zero does when one works with numbers. This set is usually represented by the Greek letter ϕ (phi). Consequently, when you are working with sets and you see the Greek letter ϕ, you will know that the empty set is involved in the discussion. Note that ϕ and $\{0\}$ are not the same set. Why?

EXAMPLE 2

ϕ = the set of all elephants that can fly

ϕ = the set of all monkeys enrolled in this class

ϕ = the set of all digits from 1 to 9 exactly divisible by 10

EXERCISE 1

1. Give an example of a set with five members. Name one member and one subset of the set.

2. State a rule that will determine a set with seven members. Name two members and two subsets of the set.

3. Let A be the set of counting numbers from 1 to 21 (inclusive) that are exactly divisible by 3. It is clear that $9 \varepsilon A$, but $11 \notin A$. Write down the elements of A within braces. Using ε notation, indicate how each of the following numbers is related to the set A: 1, 6, 7, 12, 14, 19, and 21.

4. Let Q be the set of counting numbers from 0 to 36 (inclusive) exactly divisible by 7. Write down the elements of Q within braces. Using ε notation, indicate how each of the following numbers is related to the set Q: 0, 5, 14, 18, 28, 32, 35, and 36.

5. Which of the following sets are equal?

$U = \{3, 6, 9, 12\}$

$V = \{9, 6, 3, 12\}$

$W = \{12, 3, 12, 6, 9, 3\}$

X = the set of counting numbers between 1 and 13 exactly divisible by 3
Y = the set of counting numbers between 1 and 13 exactly divisible by 6

6. Which of the following sets are equal?

$A = \{1, 3, 5, 7, 9\}$
$B = \{5, 7, 3, 9, 1\}$
$C = \{3, 5, 4, 3, 7, 3, 9, 1\}$
D = the set of odd digits from 0 to 9 (inclusive)
$E = \{9, 7, 5, 3\}$

7. The management of a company (president, vice-president, secretary, and treasurer) wish to select a committee of two persons from among themselves. How many ways can this committee be formed; that is, how many two-person subsets can be formed from the set of four officers of the company?

8. The Executive Committee, consisting of five members, of the Associated Students wishes to form a subcommittee of three members to study the problem of student-body cards. In how many ways can this subcommittee be formed? Hint: Replace the word "committee" with "set" every place that it appears.

9. Which of the following sets is the empty set ϕ?

A = the set of all teachers over 20 ft tall
B = the set of students in this class under 6 ft tall
C = the set of numbers from 0 to 9 (inclusive) exactly divisible by 6
D = the set of numbers from 1 to 9 (inclusive) exactly divisible by 10

10. State three different rules other than those used in this section that produce the empty set.

11. Which of the following are subsets of the set $\{0, 1, 2, 3, 4, 5, 6, 7, 8, 9\}$?

$A = \{2, 4, 6, 8\}$
$B = \{3, 7, 1\}$
$C = \{0\}$
$D = \{9, 8, 7, 6, 5, 4, 3, 2, 1, 0\}$
E = the set of digits from 1 to 5 (inclusive) exactly divisible by 6
    (Recall that the empty set is a subset of every set.)

12. Which of the following are subsets of the set whose elements are the days of of the week?

$A = \{$Friday, Wednesday, Monday$\}$
$B = \{$Sunday, Saturday, Friday, Thursday, Tuesday, Monday, Wednesday$\}$
$C = \{$Thursday$\}$
D = the days of the week whose names begin with the letter "R"

13. List all of the subsets of each of the following sets including the empty set and the set itself:

(A) $\{a, b\}$
(B) $\{a, b, c\}$
(C) $\{2, 4, 6\}$
(D) $\{a, b, c, d\}$

Do you observe a pattern relating the number of subsets in a given set with the number of elements in that set so that you might guess the number of subsets of a set containing five elements?

14. Do all sets have a finite number of members? State a rule that will determine a set with an infinite number of elements in it. Name a finite and an infinite subset of this set. (Intuitively, you can count the number of elements in a finite set but you cannot count the number of elements in an infinite set.)

15. How do the sets ϕ, $\{\phi\}$, and $\{0\}$ differ from one another?

16. Which of the following statements are false: (A) $\phi = \{0\}$, (B) $\{\phi\} = \{0\}$, (C) $\phi = \{\phi\}$?

3   THE SET OF NATURAL NUMBERS

NATURAL NUMBERS

By this time in your life you have had quite a bit of experience with a variety of different kinds of numbers: whole numbers, fractions, decimal fractions, irrational numbers such as square root of 2, and possibly even a little experience with negative numbers. Since algebra (at least at this level) has to do with manipulating symbols that represent numbers, it is essential that we go back and take a careful look at some of the properties of numbers that you might have overlooked or have taken for granted. We are going to uncover a short basic list of properties that all of the numbers with which you have had any experience share in common, and we are going to require that any new kind of number we introduce also have these properties. These properties, plus a few others we will add later, govern all of the manipulations of symbols that represent numbers in algebra.

The set of **counting numbers**

$$\{1, 2, 3, \ldots\}$$

will be our starting place.* All of the other number systems with which we are going to deal in this course (and these include some with which you have had no experience) can be defined in terms of the counting numbers.

The set of counting numbers is often referred to as the set of **natural numbers.** These two names will be used interchangeably with the latter getting the edge on frequency of use. When we talk about natural numbers, we are talking about the numbers used to count objects; the numbers 1, 5, 375, 5,567,324, and 3,000,000,000,000,007 are all natural numbers, but $\frac{2}{3}$, $\frac{345}{629}$, 7.297, 0.0000273, $\sqrt{2}$, and $\sqrt[3]{35}$, since they cannot be used to count objects, are not natural numbers.

We have not given a mathematically precise definition of the natural numbers.

---

* The three dots in $\{1, 2, 3, \ldots\}$ tell us that the numbers go on without end following the pattern indicated by the first three numbers. This is a convenient way of representing some infinite sets.

We have simply described them relative to your experience with other numbers in such a way that you should be able to recognize one when you encounter it. A careful definition of natural numbers is beyond the scope of this book. To define precisely what we mean by a number such as 5 is not as easy as it might first seem. Try it!

AN IMPORTANT ASSUMPTION ABOUT THE SET OF NATURAL NUMBERS

We are going to assume that the set of natural numbers together with the binary° operations of addition, subtraction, multiplication, and division are known; that is, we will assume that you know what natural numbers are, how to add and multiply them, and how to subtract and divide them when permitted.

Later in the chapter we will investigate basic properties of the natural numbers relative to the operations of addition and multiplication.

SOME IMPORTANT SUBSETS OF THE NATURAL NUMBERS

You have undoubtedly heard of even and odd numbers, and many of you have even heard of prime and composite numbers. Since these numbers will be used at various places in the text and to make sure that we are all starting with the same background, each of these important subsets of the set of natural numbers will be defined.

A natural number is an **even number** if its quotient when divided by 2 is a natural number; a natural number is an **odd number** if it is not an even number. Less precisely, an even number is exactly divisible by 2, and an odd number is not. The numbers 2, 4, 12, 478, and 5,000,006 are even numbers, whereas 1, 3, 17, 979, and 432,137 are odd numbers.

When we add or subtract two or more numbers, the numbers are called **terms;** when we multiply two or more numbers, the numbers are called **factors.** In the sum "3 + 5 + 8," 3, 5, and 8 are terms; in the product "3 × 5 × 8," 3, 5, and 8 are factors. Since $2 \times 3 = 6$ we call 2 and 3 factors of 6; similarly, 5 and 7 are factors of 35.

In mathematics, at the level of algebra and higher, parentheses or the dot "·" are usually used in place of the times sign "×". Thus (2) (3) (5), $2 \cdot 3 \cdot 5$, and $2 \times 3 \times 5$ all denote the product of 2, 3, and 5.

There are many places in mathematics where it is necessary or desirable to write a natural number as a product involving as many natural-number factors as possible other than 1. Perhaps you already have had some experience with

---

° A binary operation is an operation on two numbers that produces a single number. This number is the sum in case of addition, the difference in case of subtraction, the product for multiplication, and the quotient for division. Later in the book we will be interested in operations on single numbers, called unary operations, that produce single numbers.

this process in arithmetic when you reduced fractions to lowest terms or found least common denominators.

Suppose you were asked to write 30 as a product involving as many natural-number factors as possible other than 1, you might proceed as follows:

$$30 = 3 \cdot 10 = 3 \cdot 2 \cdot 5$$

and find that this is as far as you can go since neither 3, 2, nor 5 can be represented as the product of other natural numbers when 1 is excluded. Natural numbers, such as 3, 2, and 5, that cannot be factored any more when 1 is excluded play an important role in many branches of mathematics and are given the name of prime numbers. Except for 1, all other natural numbers are called composite numbers. Thus, a **composite number** is a natural number that can be represented as the product of two or more natural numbers excluding 1, and a **prime number** cannot be so represented.

EXAMPLE 3

(A) 2, 3, 5, 7, 11, 13, 17, and 19 are all of the prime numbers between 1 and 20.

(B) 4, 6, 8, 9, 10, 12, 14, 15, 16, 18, and 20 are all of the composite numbers between 1 and 20.

(C) Write 60 as a product of prime factors.

$$60 = 10 \cdot 6 = 2 \cdot 5 \cdot 2 \cdot 3$$
$$\text{or} \quad 60 = 5 \cdot 12 = 5 \cdot 2 \cdot 6 = 5 \cdot 2 \cdot 2 \cdot 3$$
$$\text{or} \quad 60 = 4 \cdot 15 = 2 \cdot 2 \cdot 3 \cdot 5$$
$$\text{or} \quad 60 = 3 \cdot 20 = 3 \cdot 4 \cdot 5 = 3 \cdot 2 \cdot 2 \cdot 5$$

In example 3(C) note that in spite of the fact that each factoring started differently, the completely factored forms involve the same prime numbers except for order. This example illustrates the fact that *each composite number has, except for order, one and only one set of prime factors.*°

EXERCISE 2

1. From the following list of numbers, identify the even numbers, the odd numbers, the composite numbers, and the prime numbers: 9, 17, 29, 37, 87, 306, and 1,008.

° This statement is called "the fundamental theorem of arithmetic." Its proof can be found in almost any book on number theory, e.g., H. Davenport, "The Higher Arithmetic," Hutchenson's University Library, New York, 1952.

2. List all of the even numbers, odd numbers, composite numbers, and prime numbers between 20 and 30 inclusive.

3. Is every even number a composite number? Is every odd number a composite number?

4. Is every even number a prime number? Is every odd number a prime number? Is every prime number an odd number?

5. Suppose that you know that 3 is not a factor of a given natural number, is it possible that 6 is a factor of that number?

6. Suppose that you know that 6 is not a factor of a given number, is it possible that 3 is a factor of that number?

7. Is 8 a factor of 24? Is 24 a factor of 8?

8. Is 1 a factor of 8? Is 1 a factor of every number?

9. Write each of the following numbers as a product of prime factors: 12, 18, 84, and 128.

10. Write each of the following numbers as a product of prime factors: 42, 51, 76, and 91.

11. Intuitively, a set is said to have a finite number of elements in it if the elements can be counted; otherwise, the set is said to be infinite. Tell which of the following sets are finite or infinite: (A) the set of natural numbers, (B) the set of even numbers, (C) the set of odd numbers, (D) the set of composite numbers, (E) the set of digits from 0 to 9, and (F) the set of all the grains of sand on all the beaches in the world.

4   VARIABLES, CONSTANTS, AND ALGEBRAIC EXPRESSIONS

In using ordinary English we frequently encounter words with double or even multiple meanings. The results are often amusing, occasionally confusing, and even sometimes embarrassing. The ambiguity of the meaning of many words provides the raw material for the output of many humorists, poets, and writers. In mathematics, however, ambiguous words and statements are to be avoided at all costs. It isn't that we want to eliminate humor from the subject. It is simply that for mathematics to survive as a useful subject, ambiguities must be avoided.

In this book you will be introduced to a number of new words. Some will be words that you will recognize from our everyday language, and others will be completely new to you. In either case these terms will be carefully defined for the technical purposes to which they will be employed, and these definitions will replace any other definitions that you might know as long as these words are used in a technical sense. Words such as "constant" and "variable" are words about which most of you have some idea from your use of them in ordinary language.

Both of these words are important mathematical terms which will be defined carefully and used accordingly.

It is very important that you read mathematical definitions with care and understanding or progress in and enjoyment of the course will be seriously impaired.

CONSTANTS AND VARIABLES

Earlier in this chapter it was suggested that, among other things, algebra has to do with symbols and the manipulation of symbols that represent numbers. This idea should not be new to most of you.   Who has not worked with formulas where letters are used as place holders for numerals?   All students by this time should be familiar with most if not all of the following formulas:

AREA OF A RECTANGLE (Fig. 5):

$$A = ab$$ area = base × height

Figure 5

PERIMETER OF A RECTANGLE (Fig. 5):

$$P = 2a + 2b$$ perimeter = 2 × base + 2 × height

VOLUME OF A RECTANGULAR SOLID (Fig. 6):

$$V = abc$$ volume = length × width × height

CIRCUMFERENCE OF A CIRCLE (Fig. 7):

$$C = \pi D$$ circumference = pi × diameter

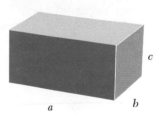

Figure 6

AREA OF A CIRCLE (Fig. 7):

$$A = \pi r^2$$ area = pi × radius × radius

SIMPLE INTEREST:

$$I = prt$$ interest = principal × rate × time

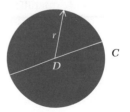

DISTANCE FORMULA:

$$d = rt$$ distance = rate × time

Figure 7

In the formula for the circumference of a circle we note that there are three letter symbols: C, D, and the Greek letter pi.   The letters C and D may be replaced with many different numerals, but π is a symbol that names only one number. We are going to call the letters C and D variables and the letter π a constant. In general, a **constant** is defined to be any symbol that names one particular thing; a **variable** is a symbol that holds a place for constants. In most of the cases we will be concerned with, constants will name numbers.

EXAMPLE 4: CONSTANTS. Each of the symbols 4, IX, IV, π, $4 + 7$, and $7 \cdot 5$ names one particular number. Thus, each is called a constant We note that one number may have more than one name; for example, 4, IV, $7 - 3$, $1 + 3$, $2 \cdot 2$, and $8 \div 2$ are different symbols naming the same number.

EXAMPLE 5: VARIABLES. The letters A, b, and h in the formula $A = bh$; C and D in the formula $C = \pi D$; and C and r in the formula $C = 2\pi r$ are all variables.

Usually some agreement is made ahead of time as to what set of constants may replace a given variable in a discussion, and this set is called the **replacement set** for the variable. For example, if a person earns \$135 per week, then his earnings in n weeks would be $135n$ dollars; 135 is a constant, n is a variable, and the replacement set for n would be understood to be some subset of the set of natural numbers.

The introduction of variables into mathematics as a systematic notational device occurred about A.D. 1600 or a little before. A Frenchman, Francois Vieta (1540–1603), is singled out as the one mainly responsible for this innovation. It is now clear that mathematics would not have developed nearly as far as it has without the important notion of the variable; in fact, many mark this point as the beginning of modern mathematics.

ALGEBRAIC EXPRESSIONS—THEIR FORMULATION AND EVALUATION

An **algebraic expression** is a symbolic form involving constants; variables; mathematical operations such as addition, subtraction, multiplication, and division (other operations will be added later); and grouping symbols such as parentheses ( ), brackets [ ], and braces { }.

EXAMPLE 6: ALGEBRAIC EXPRESSIONS.

$$prt \qquad 3x + 3y \qquad (u + 2v + 3w) \div 5$$
$$\pi D \qquad x(2x - 3y) \qquad y\{x + 3[x - (x + y)]\}$$

We have seen algebraic expressions used in formulas: another important use will be in the solution of problems such as those stated in Sec. 1. Before we can solve problems, we must have a better understanding of algebraic expressions—

how to interpret them, how to evaluate them for various values of the variables, and how to manipulate them to obtain alternate equivalent forms. By Sec. 20 in Chap. 2 we will have developed enough "machinery" to launch a profitable attack on practical problems using algebraic methods.

A number of examples will provide the fastest means to an understanding of the formation, interpretation, and evaluation of simple algebraic expressions. Go over these carefully before starting the problem set at the end of this section. Try working the examples on your own by covering the solutions, and then check your work when you have finished. Note that a^2 **means** $a \cdot a$, and a^3 **means** $a \cdot a \cdot a$ for any number a. (More general power forms will be considered later.)

EXAMPLE 7.   Evaluate each of the algebraic expressions for the values of the variables indicated (perform the operations within the grouping symbols first, if they are included, starting with the parentheses ( ), then the brackets [ ], and ending finally with the braces { }).

(A) $a + b$, $a - b$, $a \cdot b$, and $a \div b$, where $a = 6$ and $b = 2$.

SOLUTION: $6 + 2 = 8$, $6 - 2 = 4$, $6 \cdot 2 = 12$, $6 \div 2 = 3$.

(B) $(x + y) + z$ and $x + (y + z)$, where $x = 3$, $y = 4$, and $z = 2$.

SOLUTION: $(3 + 4) + 2 = 7 + 2 = 9$, $3 + (4 + 2) = 3 + 6 = 9$.

(C) $(xy)z$ and $x(yz)$, where $x = 3$, $y = 4$, and $z = 5$.

SOLUTION: $(3 \cdot 4) \cdot 5 = 12 \cdot 5 = 60$, $3 \cdot (4 \cdot 5) = 3 \cdot 20 = 60$.

(D) $ab + c$ and $a(b + c)$, where $a = 3$, $b = 2$, and $c = 7$.

SOLUTION: $(3)(2) + 7 = 6 + 7 = 13$, $3(2 + 7) = 3 \cdot 9 = 27$.

(E) $4[x + (y - z)]$, where $x = 5$, $y = 3$, and $z = 2$.

SOLUTION: $4[5 + (3 - 2)] = 4[5 + 1] = 4 \cdot 6 = 24$.

(F) $b\{b + 3[c - (a + d)] + 5\}$ where $a = 2$, $b = 3$, $c = 5$, and $d = 1$.

SOLUTION: $3\{3 + 3[5 - (2 + 1)] + 5\} = 3\{3 + 3[5 - 3] + 5\}$
$$= 3\{3 + 3 \cdot 2 + 5\} = 3\{3 + 6 + 5\} = 3 \cdot 14 = 42.$$

(G) $(x^2 - y^2) + w^3$ where $x = 3$, $y = 2$, and $w = 4$.

SOLUTION: $(3^2 - 2^2) + 4^3 = (9 - 4) + 64 = 5 + 64 = 69$.

EXAMPLE 8.   If x represents a natural number, write an algebraic expression that represents each of the expressed numbers. Evaluate each algebraic expression for $x = 11$.

(A) A number three times as large as x.

SOLUTION: $3x$ $3 \cdot 11 = 33$

(B) A number 3 larger than x.

SOLUTION: $x + 3$ (or $3 + x$) $11 + 3 = 14$

(C) A number 5 smaller than twice x.

SOLUTION: $2x - 5$ $2 \cdot 11 - 5 = 22 - 5 = 17$

(D) A number twice a number 3 larger than x.

SOLUTION: $2(x + 3)$ $2(11 + 3) = 2 \cdot 14 = 28$

(E) A number that is the sum of three consecutive numbers starting with x.

SOLUTION: $x+(x+1)+(x+2)$ $11+(11+1)+(11+2)=11+12+13=36$

EXERCISE 3

1. Indicate the variables and constants in each of the following formulas:

    (A) $P = 2a + 2b$ b  *Rectangle*

                                           a

    (B) $P = 4s$

    (C) $A = s^2$ s 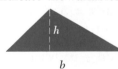 *Square*

                                             s

2. In each of the following formulas indicate the variables and constants:

    (A) $A = \tfrac{1}{2}bh$ *Triangle*

                                             b

    (B) $V = \pi r^2 h$ *Cylinder*

    (C) $V = \tfrac{1}{3}\pi r^2 h$ *Cone*

3. Evaluate each of the algebraic expressions for $a = 3, b = 9, c = 2,$ and $d = 1$:

(A) $b + c$ (B) $a - c$

(C) ab and ba (D) $3(b - c)$

(E) $ac + d$ and $a(c + d)$ (F) $ab - c$ and $a(b - c)$

(G) $(c - d) + (b + d)$ (H) $3a + 2(a + d)$

4. Evaluate each of the algebraic expressions for $x = 5, y = 1, z = 3,$ and $w = 2$:

(A) $x - z$ (B) $x + w$ and $w + x$

(C) zw and wz (D) $w(y + z)$ and $wy + z$

(E) $wy + wz$ (F) $w(8 + y) + x$

(G) $(z - y) + (z - w)$ (H) $4(y + w) - 2z$

5. Evaluate each of the following algebraic expressions for $u = 2, v = 3, w = 4,$ and $x = 5$:

(A) $2u + 3v^2$

(B) $2[x + 3(x - u)]$

(C) $2\{w + 2[7 - (u + v)]\}$

6. Evaluate each of the following algebraic expressions for $r = 2, s = 3, t = 7,$ and $u = 1$:

(A) $2r^3 - 8$

(B) $6[(t + u) - (r + u)]$

(C) $3\{4u + [4 + (s - u)]\}$

7. The distance s that an object falls in time t close to the surface of the earth is given approximately by the formula $s = 16t^2$, where s is in feet, and t is in seconds (Fig. 8). If the replacement set for t is $\{1, 2, 3, 4, 5\}$, what is the replacement set for the variable s; that is, how far will an object have fallen at the end of each of the first 5 sec?

8. An object thrown vertically with an initial velocity 96 fps has, at time t, a velocity given by the formula $v = 96 - 32t$ (when air resistance is neglected). If the replacement set for t is $\{0, 1, 2, 3\}$, what is the replacement set for the variable v? What do the elements of the replacement set for v signify?

9. Evaluate $t^2 + 2t + 1$ for each element of the replacement set for the variable t if the replacement set for t is the set of prime numbers between 1 and 10.

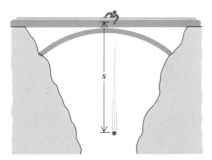

Figure 8

10. Evaluate $t^3 + t^2 + 3t + 5$ for each element of the replacement set for the variable t if the replacement set for t is the set of prime numbers between 1 and 6.

11. If x represents a natural number, write an algebraic expression that represents each of the following numbers and evaluate each expression for $x = 7$:
(A) 5 larger than x
(B) five times as large as x
(C) 5 less than x
(D) 3 more than twice x
(E) three times a number 3 smaller than x
(F) seven times a number 5 larger than x

12. If t represents an even number, write an algebraic expression that represents each of the following numbers and evaluate each expression for $t = 8$:
(A) 4 larger than four times t
(B) 4 less than four times t
(C) three times as large as the first even number smaller than t
(D) twice as large as the next even number larger than t
(E) the sum of three consecutive even numbers starting with t

13. A small steel ball is thrown straight downward, from the top of a very tall building, with an initial speed of 30 fps.   For each second that the ball falls its speed is increased by 32 fps. (A) Write a formula that indicates the speed v that the ball is traveling after t sec. (B) Identify the constants and variables. (C) How fast will the ball be traveling at the end of 8 sec?

14. The distance s that an object falls in t sec is 16 times the square of the time. (A) Write a formula that indicates the distance s that the object falls in t sec. (B) Identify the constants and variables.   (C) How far will the object have fallen at the end of 8 sec?

15. An earthquake produces several types of waves that travel through the earth.   One is called a shear wave, which travels at about 2 miles per sec and causes the earth to move at right angles to the direction of motion of the wave. (A) Write a formula that indicates the distance d that the wave travels in t sec. (B) Identify the constants and variables.   (C) How far will the wave have traveled in 10 sec?

16. Sound travels through the air at approximately 1,120 fps.   (A) Write a formula for the distance d that sound travels in t sec. (B) Identify the constants and the variables.   (C) How many feet more or less than a mile (5,280 ft) will sound from lightning travel in 5 sec?

17. A dress manufacturer has fixed costs of $100 per hr plus $10 for each dress he produces.   Let x represent the number of dresses produced per hour, and write a formula for the total cost C per hour in running the plant.   Identify the constants and variables.

18. A camera manufacturer has a fixed cost of $500 per day in addition to the cost of $15 for each camera he produces.   Let n denote the number of cameras produced per day, and write a formula for the total cost C per day in running the plant.   Identify the constants and variables in the formula.

5   EQUALITY

EQUALITY SIGN

In the preceding sections the equality sign "$=$" was used in a number of different places.   You are probably most familiar with its use in formulas such as $d = rt$, $A = \pi r^2$, or $I = prt$.   This sign is very important in mathematics, and you will be using it frequently.   Its mathematical meaning, however, is not as obvious as it might first seem.   For this reason we are devoting one section of this chapter solely to this sign so that you will use it correctly from the beginning.

The word "is" is a very familiar and often-used word in the English language, but a moment's thought will reveal that it is used in a number of different ways. For example, when we say, "Mt. Everest is the tallest mountain in the world," the word "is" is used to assert that Mt. Everest and the tallest mountain in the world are precisely the same object.   On the other hand, if one states, "The car is blue," then one would hardly mean that car and blueness are one and the same object, but rather that the car has blueness as a property.   The word "is" in the first sense is how we use "$=$" in mathematics.

In general, we will always use **equality** in the sense of logical identity; that is, an **equality sign** will be used to join two expressions if and only if the two expressions are names or descriptions of one and the same thing.   In this sense "$=$" means "is identical with."   In the first example above, "Mt. Everest is identical with the tallest mountain in the world"; hence, we may write, "Mt. Everest $=$ the tallest mountain in the world."   On the other hand, "car" is not identical with "blueness," and it doesn't make sense to write "The car $=$ blue."

Since the expression $a = b$ means a and b are names for the same object, it is natural that we define $a \neq b$ to mean a and b do not name the same thing; that is, a **is not equal to** b.   Thus we would write IX $\neq$ 5 since IX and 5 name two different numbers.

EXAMPLE 9.   Replace, where appropriate, the various forms of the verb "to be" ("is," "was," "are," "were," etc.) with the equality sign, remembering that $=$ means "is identical with":

(A) Abraham Lincoln was 6 ft 4 in. tall (true).

(B) Abraham Lincoln was "Honest Abe" (true).

(C) $3 + 5$ is 8.

(D) There exists at least one numeral x such that $x + 7$ is 13 (assume true).

(E) For all numerals x, $x + 3$ is $3 + x$ (assume true).

SOLUTION

(A) The equality sign does not replace "was" since the property of being 6 ft 4 in. tall is not the same thing as being Abraham Lincoln.

(B) Abraham Lincoln = Honest Abe. ("Abraham Lincoln" and "Honest Abe" are names for exactly the same object.)

(C) $3 + 5 = 8$. ("$3 + 5$" and "8" are names for the same number.)

(D) There exists at least one numeral x such that $x + 7 = 13$. (There exists at least one numeral x such that "$x + 7$" and "13" name the same number.)*

(E) For all numerals x, $x + 3 = 3 + x$. (For all numerals x, "$x + 3$" and "$3 + x$" name the same number.)

In examples (D) and (E) above $x + 7 = 13$ and $x + 3 = 3 + x$ are called algebraic equations. In general, if two algebraic expressions involving at least one variable are joined with an equality sign, the resulting form is called an **algebraic equation**. For example, $d = rt$, $P = 2a + 2b$, $a + b = b + a$, and $a(b + c) = ab + ac$ are algebraic equations in more than one variable; $2x + 3 = 5 + x$, $6t^2 + 2t + 3 = 0$, and $n(n + 3) = 4n - 5$ are algebraic equations, each in one variable.

Since a variable is a place holder for constants, an equation is neither true nor false as it stands; it doesn't become so until the variable has been replaced by a constant. As a consequence, equations are sometimes referred to as **open sentences** or **open statements**.

This brief discussion of equations will suffice for now; in succeeding sections the subject will be developed in detail.

LAWS OF EQUALITY

From the logical meaning of the equality sign a number of rules or laws can easily be established for its use. We will state and discuss these laws now and will rely on them many times throughout the book since they control a great deal of activity related to manipulating and solving equations. Once we can solve equations, we will be able to solve problems of the type discussed in the first section of this chapter.

---

* A *numeral* is a symbol that names a number. The numerals "4" and "IV" both name the abstract concept we call "four." The difference between number and numeral is essentially the same as the difference between you as a person and your name. The word "number" is often used by many where the word "numeral" should be used. From long incorrect usage, an insistence on a strictly correct use of these words throughout the text would make some statements seem awkward and unnatural. We will use the word "numeral" most of the time when we are referring to symbols that name numbers but will yield to the common (though strictly speaking not correct) use of the word "number" from time to time to avoid awkard or unnatural statements.

It is clear from the meaning of "$=$" that any thing is equal to itself; that is, for each x, $x = x$ (the equality relation is **reflexive**). Abraham Lincoln $=$ Abraham Lincoln.

For each x and each y, if $x = y$, then $y = x$ since if x and y name the same object, then y and x name the same object (the equality relation is **symmetric**). If Abraham Lincoln $=$ Honest Abe, then Honest Abe $=$ Abraham Lincoln; if IX $=$ 9, then 9 $=$ IX.

With the same kind of reasoning as above we can conclude that if $x = y$ and $y = z$, then $x = z$. (The equality relation is **transitive**.) If Honest Abe $=$ Abraham Lincoln and Abraham Lincoln $=$ the sixteenth president of the United States, then Honest Abe $=$ the sixteenth president of the United States.

For each object x and each object y, if $x = y$, then either may replace the other in any expression without changing the truth or falsity of the statement (**substitution principle**). Thus if $b = c$ and $a + b = 7$, then $a + c = 7$. To illustrate further, when we write "IX $=$ 9," we are asserting that "IX" and "9" are names for exactly the same object; any statement that is made about IX can be made with the same amount of truth about 9. A single object may have many names, and any name may be used in place of another for the same object.

The importance of these four laws will not be fully appreciated until we start solving equations and simplifying algebraic expressions. We will summarize them here for convenient reference.

LAWS OF EQUALITY (SUMMARY)

REFLEXIVE LAW: *For each x, $x = x$.*

SYMMETRIC LAW: *For each x and each y, if $x = y$, then $y = x$.*

TRANSITIVE LAW: *For each x, y, and z, if $x = y$ and $y \doteq z$, then $x = z$.*

SUBSTITUTION PRINCIPLE: *For each x and y, if $x = y$, then either may replace the other in any expression without changing the truth or falsity of the statement.*

EXERCISE 4

In problems 1 through 4 replace, where appropriate, the various forms of the verb "to be" ("is," "was," "were," "are," etc.) with "$=$" or "$\neq$" (remember that "$=$" means "is identical with" and "$\neq$" means "is not identical with").

1. (A) Charles Lindbergh was the first man to fly across the Atlantic alone.
   (B) Charles Lindbergh was a brigadier general. (Note that this statement is true but can we use the equality sign in place of "was"?)
   (C) $2 + 3$ is 5.

(D) $(5 + 7) + 2$ is $3 + (5 + 6)$.

(E) VII is 7.

(F) VII is a Roman numeral.

2. (A) Charles Lindbergh was the author of "The Spirit of St. Louis."

(B) Charles Lindbergh was an aviator.

(C) VIII is 3.

(D) 3 is an Arabic numeral.

(E) $5 + 7$ is $9 + 3$.

(F) $(7 - 3) + 5$ is $5 + (6 - 3)$.

3. (A) One fourth is twenty-five percent.

(B) The dress is red.

(C) Five is a natural number.

(D) $(2)(3)$ is $2 \cdot 3$ and $2 \cdot 3$ is 2×3.

(E) $3x$ is $3 \cdot x$.

(F) For all numerals x, $3x$ is $x3$ (assume true).

(G) There exists at least one numeral x such that 5 is $x + 3$ (assume true).

4. (A) Five is a prime number.

(B) The set of all natural numbers exactly divisible by two is the set of even numbers.

(C) ab is $a \cdot b$.

(D) For all numerals a and b, ab is ba (assume true).

(E) There exists at least one numeral x such that $x + 5$ is $9 - x$ (assume true).

(F) For all numerals a and b, $a + b$ is $b + a$ (assume true).

In problems 5 through 14 translate each statement into an algebraic equation. Do not use more than one variable in the final equation.

EXAMPLE 10.   Fifteen is nine more than a certain number.

SOLUTION: If we let the variable x represent the certain number (i.e., hold a place for the certain number), then we can write

$$15 = 9 + x$$

EXAMPLE 11.   Three times a certain number is seven more than twice the number.

SOLUTION: As above, if we let n represent the certain number, then the statement can be written as an equation as follows:

$$3n = 7 + 2n$$

EXAMPLE 12.   In a given rectangle of area 48 sq in. the base is three times the height.   Write an equation that relates the area with the base and height.

SOLUTION:

h

b

Let $h =$ the height of the rectangle.
Then $b = 3h =$ the base of the rectangle.

The formula for the area of a rectangle is
$A = bh$. Using $b = 3h$, $A = 48$, and the substitution principle for equality, we may write $48 = (h)(3h)$.

5. Seven more than twice a certain number is 49. HINT: Let x represent the certain number and write an appropriate equation.

6. Four times a given number is three more than three times that number. HINT: Introduce a suitable variable and write an appropriate equation.

7. The sum of four consecutive natural numbers is 54.

8. The sum of two consecutive even numbers is 54.

9. In a rectangle of area 50 sq ft the length is 10 ft more than the width. (NOTE: Length and width are other names for base and height.) Write an equation that relates the area with the length and the width.

10. In a rectangle of area 75 sq yd its length is five more than three times the width. Write an equation relating the area with the length and the width.

11. Pythagoras found that the octave chord could be produced (see Fig. 2 in Sec. 1) by placing the movable bridge so that a taut string is divided into two parts with the longer piece twice the length of the shorter piece. If the total string is 27 in. long and we let x represent the length of the shorter piece, write an equation relating the length of the two pieces and total length of the string.

12. A board 16 ft long is cut into two pieces so that the longer piece is 2 ft less than twice the length of the shorter piece. Write an equation relating the lengths of the two pieces with the total length.

13. According to Mendel's laws of heredity, if we mate two black guinea pigs, each of which is a carrier of the gene for white, then (since black dominates white in guinea pigs) the expected number of black offspring to white in a large litter would be in the ratio of 3:1 (Fig. 9). Suppose a number of matings of the type described produced 68 offspring. If we let x represent the number of expected white guinea pigs, then write an equation relating the number of expected black guinea pigs and the number of expected white guinea pigs with the total number of offspring.

14. One color trait does not necessarily dominate another in all animals. For example, in the shorthorn breed of cattle neither red nor white dominates for when a pure red is mated with a pure white a hybrid called a roan (red hairs intermingled with white hairs) is produced as an offspring. Roans are highly prized by cattle breeders, but unfortunately they never breed true. When two roans are mated, they yield reds, roans, and whites in the ratio of 1:2:1.

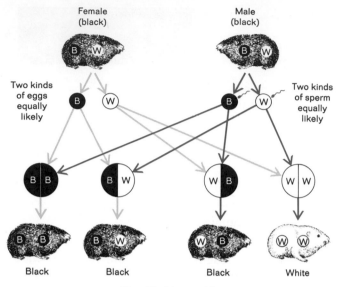

Female (black)

Male (black)

Two kinds of eggs equally likely

Two kinds of sperm equally likely

Black

Black

Black

White

Three black to one white

Figure 9

Suppose a large enough number of roans are mated to produce 1,752 offspring. If we let x represent the number of expected reds, write an equation relating the expected number of each type of offspring with the total number.

15. What is wrong with the following argument? The number 5 is a prime number and 7 is a prime number. Hence, we can write 5 = prime number and 7 = prime number. By the symmetric law for equality we can write prime number = 7 and conclude, using the transitive law for equality (since 5 = prime number and prime number = 7), that 5 = 7.

16. What is wrong with the following argument? John is a human and Mary is a human. Hence, we can write John = human and Mary = human. By the symmetric law for equality we can write human = Mary and conclude, using the transitive law for equality (since John = human and human = Mary), that John = Mary.

The material in the following problems will be taken up in detail near the end of Chap. 2 in the section on equations and applications. The more adventurous student might like to see what he can do with the problems now.

EXAMPLE 13. Show, using the laws of equality, that for any natural numbers x and y if $x = y$, then $x + 3 = y + 3$.

The proof is easy and can be done in three steps as follows:

$$x + 3 = x + 3 \qquad \text{reflexive law}$$

$$x = y \qquad \text{given}$$

$$x + 3 = y + 3 \qquad \text{substitution principle}$$

17. Show, using the laws of equality, that for any natural numbers x and y if $x = y$, then $3x = 3y$.

18. Show, using the laws of equality, that for any natural numbers x and y (where the subtraction can be accomplished), if $x = y$, then $x - 5 = y - 5$.

19. Show, using the laws of equality, that for any natural numbers a, b, and c, if $a = b$, then $a + c = b + c$, and $ac = bc$.

6   POSTULATES FOR ADDITION AND FOR MULTIPLICATION

You are now able to distinguish between constants and variables and recognize and form algebraic expressions and equations; in short, you have learned some of the basic language and processes of algebra.   However, you might ask, "What do I do with an algebraic equation or expression when I form one?"

One of the important objectives in algebra is to learn how to solve algebraic equations, that is, to learn how to find the set of numerical replacements for the variable(s), called the **solution set,** that make the equation true.   To solve equations, one must be able to manipulate algebraic expressions to produce equivalent expressions.   Procedures will be developed in the remaining part of this chapter and the first part of the next chapter with this end in mind.

In Sec. 2 we said that we would assume that you are familiar with the set of natural numbers and the basic arithmetical operations of addition, subtraction, multiplication, and division on this set.   In this section we will postulate (state without proof) and discuss six important properties of the natural numbers relative to the operations of addition and multiplication.   You have been using these properties in arithmetic for so long that you perform some arithmetical operations based on them in the same way that you walk or run—without thinking.

CLOSURE AXIOMS FOR ADDITION AND MULTIPLICATION

If we take two natural numbers, say 4 and 12, and add them, we obtain 16, a natural number; if we multiply them, we obtain 48, a natural number.   As a matter of fact, we cannot think of one single case where the sum and product of two natural numbers is not a natural number.   However, we are not in a position to prove that this is so for every pair of natural numbers. This is a property of the set of natural numbers that we feel so strongly about that we are willing to assume it is true for all natural numbers. We will, therefore, postulate that *for each natural number a and each natural number b, a + b and ab are natural numbers,* and call this postulate* the **closure axiom for addition and multiplication.**

In general, *any set of numbers is said to be closed with respect to a certain operation if the result of applying the operation to numbers in the set results only in numbers that are in the set.* Consider the following examples.

EXAMPLE 14. The set of numbers $\{1, 2, 3, 4, 5\}$ is not closed with respect to addition or multiplication since the sum of *any* two elements of the set is not always an element of the set and the product of *any* two elements of the set is not always an element of the set. For example, $2 + 4 = 6$, and 6 is not an element of the set; $2 \cdot 4 = 8$, and 8 is not an element of the set. Is any finite set of natural numbers closed with respect to addition or multiplication?

EXAMPLE 15. The set of natural numbers is not closed with respect to subtraction; $5 - 2$ is a natural number, whereas $1 - 3$ is not. (In Chap. 2 we will extend the natural-number system in such a way that the extended number system will be closed with respect to subtraction.)

EXAMPLE 16. The set of natural numbers is not closed with respect to division; $8 \div 4$ is a natural number, whereas $2 \div 3$ is not. (In Chap. 3 we will again extend the number system so that the extended number system will be closed with respect to all four arithmetical operations: addition, subtraction, multiplication, and division, division by zero excluded.)

COMMUTATIVE AXIOMS FOR ADDITION AND MULTIPLICATION

Another process in arithmetic that has become part of your subconscious has to do with the order in which you add or multiply numbers. You no doubt would readily accept as correct the relations $2 + 3 = 3 + 2$ and $2 \cdot 3 = 3 \cdot 2$. You have been told for so long that you get the same result whether you add 5 to 8 or 8 to 5 (or multiply 5 by 8 or 8 by 5) it now seems so obvious to you that you have shifted it out of your conscious thinking. We are not, however, in a position to prove this property for all natural numbers even though, as in the case for closure, we are not able to think of one single case where the order of addition or multiplication of natural numbers makes any difference. We will, therefore, postulate that *for each natural number a and each natural number b,*

---

*In modern mathematics no distinction is made between the words "postulate" and "axiom"; both words are used interchangeably to refer to unproved statements in a mathematical system. Proved statements are called theorems. See Chap. 11 for a detailed discussion of the postulational method.

$a + b = b + a$ and $ab = ba$ *(that is, "$a + b$" and "$b + a$" name the same number, and "ab" and "ba" name the same number)*, and call this postulate the **commutative axiom for addition and multiplication.**

In general, *when the result of applying an operation on any two numbers of a set is the same irrespective of the order in which the numbers are taken, then the operation is said to be commutative relative to that set.* Not all of the arithmetical operations are commutative relative to the set of natural numbers. $8 - 2 \neq 2 - 8$, showing that subtraction is not commutative; $8 \div 2 \neq 2 \div 8$, showing that division is not commutative.

The commutative axiom for addition and multiplication provides us with one of our first tools to change algebraic expressions from one form to other equivalent forms.

EXAMPLE 17.   On the basis of the commutative axiom (and in some cases with the help of the closure axiom) if a, b, x, and y are natural numbers, then

▶ $x + y = y + x$

▶ $(a + b) + x = x + (a + b)$

▶ $(a + b) + (x + y) = (x + y) + (a + b)$

▶ $xy = yx$

▶ $(ab)x = x(ab)$

▶ $(ab)(xy) = (xy)(ab)$

In each case the expression on the left of the equality sign names the same number as the expression on the right.*

The results of the commutative axiom may not seem so startling at the present, but when they are combined with the material that will be covered next in this section and the material of the next section, we will find that we have taken giant strides toward a general procedure for solving certain types of equations as well as for simplifying complicated algebraic expressions.

ASSOCIATIVE AXIOM FOR ADDITION AND MULTIPLICATION

When adding $5 + 8 + 7$ or multiplying $5 \cdot 8 \cdot 7$, why do we not need parentheses to show us which two numbers are to be added or multiplied first? You may answer that because of our past "experience" we assume that the grouping

---

* To be precise, we should add, ". . . for all replacements of the variables by names of natural numbers." Remember that, strictly speaking, a variable is a place holder for a name and does not name anything itself. However, we will often work with variables as if they were names for numbers; this seems to be psychologically more satisfying to most people, including many professional mathematicians, and no harm is done as long as one is able to recall the correct meaning of variable when necessary.

doesn't make any difference; we "know" that $(5 + 8) + 7 = 5 + (8 + 7)$ and $(5 \cdot 8) \cdot 7 = 5 \cdot (8 \cdot 7)!$

We seemed to have uncovered another "subconscious property" of natural numbers in which you have complete confidence since you have never seen even one exception to it. As before, we are not in a position to prove this property for all natural numbers so will postulate it as follows: *For all natural numbers a, b, and c, $(a + b) + c = a + (b + c)$, and $(ab)c = a(bc)$ [that is, "$(a + b) + c$" and "$a + (b + c)$" name the same number, and "$(ab)c$" and "$a(bc)$" name the same number].* This postulate is called the **associative axiom for addition and multiplication.**

Not all arithmetical operations are associative relative to the natural numbers. $(8 - 4) - 2 \neq 8 - (4 - 2)$, showing that subtraction is not associative; $(8 \div 4) \div 2 \neq 8 \div (4 \div 2)$, showing that division is not associative. We will want any new number system that is introduced later to satisfy the associative axiom for addition and multiplication. However, in addition to this, we now have another basic tool for transforming algebraic expressions into other equivalent forms.

EXAMPLE 18. On the basis of the associative axiom (and in some cases with the help of the closure axiom), if a, b, x, y and z are any natural numbers, then

▶ $(2 + x) + y = 2 + (x + y)$

▶ $x + (y + z) = (x + y) + z$

▶ $(a + b) + (x + y) = a + [b + (x + y)]$

▶ $(2x)y = 2(xy)$

▶ $x(yz) = (xy)z$

▶ $(ab)(xy) = a[b(xy)]$

In each case the symbol on the left of the equality sign names the same number as the symbol on the right.

The axioms presented in this section are very important since they regulate the manipulation of symbols that represent natural numbers when either addition or multiplication is involved. These axioms will be summarized here for convenient reference.

AXIOMS FOR ADDITION AND MULTIPLICATION (SUMMARY) *For all natural numbers a, b, and c*

$a + b$ *is a natural number*

closure axiom for addition

ab *is a natural number*

closure axiom for multiplication

$$a + b = b + a$$

commutative axiom for addition

$$ab = ba$$

commutative axiom for multiplication

$$(a + b) + c = a + (b + c)$$

associative axiom for addition

$$(ab)c = a(bc)$$

associative axiom for multiplication

When used in combination, the addition axioms permit us to rearrange and regroup symbols that represent natural numbers in any way that we please relative to the operation of addition; that is, we may change the order of addition at will and insert or remove symbols of grouping, such as parentheses ( ), brackets [ ], and braces { } as we wish as long as the resulting operations make sense. For this reason parentheses are often omitted in algebraic expressions or numerical operations involving only addition unless a particular emphasis is desired.

EXAMPLE 19. If we have an expression of the form $a + \{b + [(c + d) + e]\}$ where all of the letters represent natural numbers, then we may remove all symbols of grouping to obtain $a + b + c + d + e$. We may rearrange the letters in any other order we wish and regroup the terms to suit our needs. For example, we could write $e + [(b + c) + (d + a)]$ and be assured, because of the axioms discussed in this section, that this new expression is equal to the original.

Similarly, the multiplication axioms permit us to rearrange and regroup symbols that represent natural numbers in any way we please relative to the operation of multiplication. This means that we can change the order of multiplication as we please and insert or remove symbols of grouping at will as long as the resulting operations make sense. When only multiplication is involved, one often omits parentheses and other signs of grouping unless a particular emphasis is desired.

EXAMPLE 20. $(xy)[(uv)(ab)]$ may be written $xyuvab$ by removing all symbols of grouping, or we may rearrange the factors and insert symbols of grouping in any other way we may wish, for example, $b[y(xa)](uv)$. All three expressions are equal.

EXAMPLE 21. $(3x)(5y)(2z) = (3 \cdot 5 \cdot 2)(xyz) = 30xyz$. (Note the simplification achieved.)

The problem set for this section is designed to encourage you to think carefully about mathematical statements and processes and to give you practice in recognizing symbol groupings. A little effort now will be repaid many times throughout the course. After the next section our development will be less formal.

EXERCISE 5

If a, b, c, d, x, y, and z represent natural numbers, justify each of the statements in problems 1 through 6 on the basis of the axioms discussed in this section.

1. (A) $a + 7$ is a natural number. (B) xy is a natural number.
   (C) $8 + z = z + 8$.   (D) $bc = cb$.
   (E) $(a + 7) + b = a + (7 + b)$. (F) $(bc)x = b(cx)$.

2. (A) $13 + x = x + 13$.   (B) $(14c)a = 14(ca)$.
   (C) $17z$ is a natural number. (D) $(z + x) + y = z + (x + y)$.
   (E) $a + z$ is a natural number. (F) $cy = yc$.

3. (A) $53 \cdot 107 = 107 \cdot 53$. (B) $(a + b) + c = a + (b + c)$.
   (C) yz is a natural number.   (D) $(xy)z = x(yz)$.
   (E) $a + c$ is a natural number. (F) $y + z = z + y$.

4. (A) $(35a)b = 35(ab)$.   (B) $a + z = z + a$.
   (C) $az = za$.   (D) $(35 + a) + b = 35 + (a + b)$.
   (E) cx is a natural number. (F) $c + x$ is a natural number.

5. (A) $(2 + 3) + (5 + 7)$ is a natural number.
   (B) $(ab)(cd)$ is a natural number.
   (C) $(2 + 3) + (5 + 7) = (5 + 7) + (2 + 3)$.
   (D) $(ab)(cd) = (cd)(ab)$.

6. (A) $(z + x) + (c + a) = z + [x + (c + a)]$.
   (B) $(zx)(ca) = z[x(ca)]$.
   (C) $(x + y) + z = z + (x + y)$.
   (D) $(xy)z = z(xy)$.

In problems 7 and 8 we assume the following is known:

The sum of two even numbers is even.
The sum of two odd numbers is even.
The product of two even numbers is even.
The product of two odd numbers is odd.

7. Given the sets:

   A = the set of natural numbers
   B = the set of odd numbers
   $C = \{1, 2, 3, 4, 5, 6\}$
   $D = \{1, 3, 5, 7, 9, 11\}$

   (A) Which sets are closed with respect to addition?
   (B) Which sets are closed with respect to multiplication?

8. Given the sets:

   A = the set of natural numbers larger than 99 (We accept your intuitive notion of "larger" for now.)
   B = the set of even numbers
   C = the set of prime numbers

   (A) Which sets are closed with respect to addition?
   (B) Which sets are closed with respect to multiplication?

9. If in the set of natural numbers each of the four arithmetic operations were commutative, we would be able to write:

   For each natural number a and b

   $$a + b = b + a \qquad a - b = b - a$$
   $$ab = ba \qquad a \div b = b \div a$$

   For each case find, if you can, natural number replacements for a and b that will make the statement false. Conclusion?

10. If in the set of natural numbers each of the four arithmetic operations were associative, we would be able to write:

    For each natural number a, b, and c

    $$(a + b) + c = a + (b + c) \qquad (ab)c = a(bc)$$
    $$(a - b) - c = a - (b - c) \qquad (a \div b) \div c = a \div (b \div c)$$

    For each case find, if you can, natural number replacements for a, b, and c that will make the statement false. Conclusion?

In problems 11 through 18 each expression on the left can be transformed into the expression on the right of the equality sign in one to three steps using the axioms discussed in this section. State the axiom(s) used for each step. [It is important to recognize that this is a formal exercise; in the future we will rearrange terms and insert and remove parentheses relative to addition (or multiplication) as we please without stating relevant axioms each time. It is important, however, to know that our freedom in this respect is due to the axioms in this section.]

EXAMPLE 22. Show that $(a + b) + c = (b + c) + a$; that is, that "$(a + b) + c$" and "$(b + c) + a$" name the same number.

PROOF (Closure properties are assumed without statement throughout proof.)

$$(a + b) + c = a + (b + c) \qquad \text{associative axiom for addition}$$
$$a + (b + c) = (b + c) + a \qquad \text{commutative axiom for addition}$$

Therefore, $(a + b) + c = (b + c) + a$ transitive law for equality

EXAMPLE 23.   Show that $(xy)z = y(zx)$.

PROOF (Closure properties are assumed without statement throughout proof.)

$(xy)z = (yx)z$	commutative axiom for multiplication
$(yx)z = y(xz)$	associative axiom for multiplication
$y(xz) = y(zx)$	commutative axiom for multiplication
Therefore, $(xy)z = y(zx)$	transitive law for equality

11. $(a + 3) + c = (c + a) + 3$.
12. $(x3)z = (zx)3$.
13. $x + (y + z) = y + (z + x)$.
14. $(xy)b = y(xb)$.
15. $x(y + z) = (z + y)x$.
16. $(2x + 7)(3x + 5) = (3x + 5)(2x + 7)$.
17. $(xy)(a + b) = x[y(a + b)]$.
18. $a[b(x + y)] = (ab)(x + y)$.

In problems 19 and 20 rewrite each expression as an equivalent expression without symbols of grouping (see examples 19 and 20 in this section).

19. (A) $(ab)(cd)(ef)$.
    (C) $(uv)[w(xy)](ab)$.
    (B) $(a + b) + (c + d)$.
    (D) $[(a + b) + (c + d)] + (x + y)$.
20. (A) $u[v(xy)]$.
    (C) $3\{x[y(uv)]\}(wz)$.
    (B) $c + [d + (x + y)]$.
    (D) $w + \{a + [(c + d) + 5] + y\} + z$.

7   A POSTULATE INVOLVING BOTH MULTIPLICATION AND ADDITION

We have discussed commutative and associative axioms for addition and multiplication and found that these axioms allow us a considerable amount of freedom in manipulating symbols that represent natural numbers. We may rearrange and group terms and rearrange and group factors almost without restriction. A natural question is, "Are there similar sets of axioms for subtraction and division?" The answer is, "No," but this is not a serious problem since after the next two chapters we will be able to convert any subtraction problem into an addition problem and any division problem into a multiplication problem. Hence, the set of axioms that were stated for addition and multiplication will apply indirectly to subtraction and division.

There is, however, one more very important property of the natural numbers, tying addition and multiplication together, that we must discuss before we go

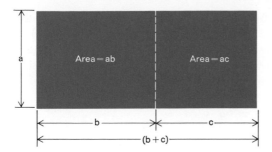

Figure 10

on.   It will provide us with another important tool to be used in changing algebraic expressions from one form to other equivalent forms.   The property is not as obvious as the others, but on the other hand it is not difficult to understand.   With a little experience you will be as familiar with it as you are with the others.   The property will be introduced by means of a simple geometric example.

Let *a*, *b*, and *c* be any three natural numbers.   Form a rectangle with the dimensions as indicated in Fig. 10.   The areas in Fig. 10 are related as follows:

$$\begin{array}{ccc} \text{area of} & \text{area of} & \text{area of} \\ \text{large rectangle} = \text{left rectangle} + \text{right rectangle} \end{array}$$
$$a(b + c) \quad = \quad ab \quad + \quad ac$$

In particular, if $a = 3$, $b = 5$, and $c = 2$, then $3(5 + 2) = 3 \cdot 7 = 21$, and $3 \cdot 5 + 3 \cdot 2 = 15 + 6 = 21$; if $a = 13$, $b = 23$, and $c = 57$, then $13(23 + 57) = 13 \cdot 80 = 1,040$, and $13 \cdot 23 + 13 \cdot 57 = 299 + 741 = 1,040$.   It appears that we have discovered another fundamental property of the natural numbers, namely, that for all natural numbers *a*, *b*, and *c*, "$a(b + c)$" and "$ab + ac$" name the same natural number.   You will find that you will not be able to discover even one single exception to this statement, but once again we are not in a position to prove it.   As before, we accept it as one of the fundamental properties of the natural numbers and call it the **distributive axiom.**   Thus *for all natural numbers a, b, and c,*

$$a(b + c) = ab + ac$$

Verbally, the axiom states that multiplication distributes over addition; that is, a multiplier is distributed over the terms of a sum.   We might ask if other pairs of operations have distributive properties.   For example, does addition distribute over multiplication?   Stated symbolically, for all natural numbers *a*, *b*, and *c*, do "$a + (b \cdot c)$" and "$(a + b) \cdot (a + c)$" name the same number?   You should not find it difficult to show that this last question must be answered in the negative.

This section will be concluded by several illustrations of the use of the distributive axiom. The axiom will be used in "both directions." If $a(b + c) = ab + ac$, then, by the symmetric law for equality, $ab + ac = a(b + c)$. Also, by use of the distributive axiom and the commutative axiom for multiplication we may write what is sometimes called the **right-hand distributive law:**

$$(b + c)a = ba + ca$$

EXAMPLE 24. $3(x + y) = 3x + 3y$ $5a + 5b = 5(a + b)$

EXAMPLE 25. $ax + ay = a(x + y)$ $ax + ay = (x + y)a$

(A common factor may be taken out either on the left or on the right.)

EXAMPLE 26. $3x + 2x = (3 + 2)x = 5x$

(Note the simplification!)

EXAMPLE 27. $xy + x \boxed{= xy + x \cdot 1} = x(y + 1)$

(NOTE: The middle step is usually done mentally.)

EXAMPLE 28. $x(x + 1) \boxed{= xx + x \cdot 1} = x^2 + x$

(NOTE: The middle step is usually done mentally.)

EXAMPLE 29. $(xy)(a + b) = xya + xyb$

EXAMPLE 30. $(x + y)(a + b) = (x + y)a + (x + y)b = xa + ya + xb + yb$

EXAMPLE 31. $(x + 2)(x + 1) = (x + 2)x + (x + 2)1$
$$= x^2 + 2x + x + 2$$
$$= x^2 + (2x + x) + 2$$
$$= x^2 + (2 + 1)x + 2$$
$$= x^2 + 3x + 2$$

The last example has made free use of many of the axioms we have considered. We are now beginning to see some of the power of these axioms when used in combination. We are arriving at the place where we are able to transform algebraic expressions into a rather large variety of other equivalent forms.

We state without proof the **generalized distributive law:** *Multiplication distributes over any finite sum.*° We will use this generalized form throughout the course without hesitation.

° The proof of this general form requires another fundamental property of natural numbers, called the induction property, that is beyond the scope of this course.

EXAMPLE 32

▶ $3(x + y + z + w) = 3x + 3y + 3z + 3w$

▶ $ma + mb + mc = m(a + b + c)$

▶ $2x(x + 3y + 2) = 2x^2 + 6xy + 4x$

The axioms that we have considered regulate a considerable amount of the activity in algebra. These are, so to speak, some of the rules of the game. However, like chess, knowing the rules of the game doesn't make one a good chess player. A great deal of practice in using the rules in a large variety of situations is necessary. The problem set for this section and the material covered in the next two sections will provide an opportunity for you to put some of these axioms to use. It is very important that you become experienced in using these axioms collectively and not just in isolation.

EXERCISE 6

1. Replace the question marks with appropriate numerals:
(A) $5(7 + 3) = 5 \cdot 7 + ? \cdot 3$ (B) $9(8 + 7) = ? \cdot 8 + ? \cdot 7$
(C) $?(3 + 6) = 3 \cdot 3 + 3 \cdot 6$ (D) $8(? + ?) = 8 \cdot 9 + 8 \cdot 7$
(E) $5 \cdot 7 + 5 \cdot 4 = ?(7 + 4)$ (F) $3 \cdot ? + 3 \cdot ? = 3(2 + 8)$

2. Replace the question marks with appropriate numerals:
(A) $13(27 + 39) = ? \cdot 27 + 13 \cdot ?$ (B) $27(18 + 87) = ? \cdot 18 + ? \cdot 87$
(C) $?(103 + 317) = 75 \cdot 103 + 75 \cdot 317$ (D) $56(? + ?) = 56 \cdot 368 + 56 \cdot 572$
(E) $27 \cdot 17 + 27 \cdot 32 = ?(17 + 32)$ (F) $43 \cdot ? + 43 \cdot ? = 43(3 + 13)$

3. Evaluate the expression on each side of the equality sign:
(A) $5(4 + 3) = 5 \cdot 4 + 5 \cdot 3$
(B) $9(7 + 8) = 9 \cdot 7 + 9 \cdot 8$
(C) $22(14 + 16) = 22 \cdot 14 + 22 \cdot 16$

4. Write as the sum of two terms and evaluate:
(A) $6(7 + 5)$ (B) $12(11 + 9)$
   Write as the product of two factors and evaluate:
(C) $6 \cdot 7 + 6 \cdot 5$ (D) $12 \cdot 11 + 12 \cdot 9$

In the following problems all letters represent natural numbers.

5. Write as the sum of two terms:
(A) $5(a + b)$ (B) $27(x + y)$
(C) $x(y + z)$ (D) $x(x + 5)$
(E) $y(7 + y)$ (F) $(ab)(c + d)$

6. Write as the sum of two terms:
(A) $4(U + W)$ (B) $5(s + 3)$
(C) $s(r + t)$ (D) $s(s + 5)$
(E) $t(3 + t)$ (F) $3r(2s + 4t)$

7. Write as the product of two factors:
(A) $3x + 3y$ (B) $cx + cy$
(C) $sr + st$ (D) $xy + 3y$
(E) $7y + 8y$ (F) $x^2 + x$

8. Write as the product of two factors:
(A) $as + at$ (B) $7s + 7t$
(C) $xa + ya$ (D) $8a + 7a$
(E) $3w + 9w$ (F) $u + u^2$

9. Write as a sum:
(A) $6(x + y + z)$ (B) $a(x + y + z)$
(C) $u(u + v + w)$ (D) $x(x^2 + x + 1)$
(E) $2y(y^2 + 3y + 4)$ (F) $(uv)(a + b + c + d)$

10. Write as a sum:
(A) $7(a + b + 5)$ (B) $a(u + v + w + x + y + z)$
(C) $u(u^2 + 2u + 1)$ (D) $3v(2v^2 + 5v + 7)$
(E) $(ab)(a + b + 1)$ (F) $(xy)(x^2y^2 + xy + 1)$

11. Write as a product taking out factors common to all terms:
(A) $4x + 4y + 4z$ (B) $ax + ay + az$
(C) $x^2 + xy + xz$ (D) $y^3 + y^2 + y$
(E) $3t^3 + 6t^2 + 9t$ (F) $u^2v + uv^2$
(G) $5x + 2x + 3x$ (H) $2ab + 4ab + 3ab$

12. Write as a product taking out factors common to all terms:
(A) $7a + 7b + 7c$ (B) $ua + ub + uc + ud$
(C) $st + t^2 + tu$ (D) $s^3 + 2s^2 + 3s$
(E) $12x^3 + 9x^2 + 3x$ (F) $a^2bc + ab^2c + abc^2$
(G) $9y + 12y + 8y + 3y$ (H) $3xyz + 5xyz + 7xyz$

13. Write as a sum:
(A) $(ab)(x + y)$ (B) $(u + v)(c + d)$
(C) $(m + n)(r + t)$ (D) $(m + 5)(m + 3)$
(E) $(x + 3)(x + 2)$

14. Write as a sum:
(A) $(uvw)(a + b + c)$ (B) $(s + t)(c + d)$
(C) $(t + 7)(t + 4)$ (D) $(3x + 2)(2x + 1)$
(E) $(4y + 5)(7y + 6)$

8   EXPONENTS AND THEIR FIRST LAW

In the preceding sections we encountered symbols of the form x^2 and y^3 in several different places. We found that these were convenient replacements for xx and yyy, respectively, and defined them as such. There is obviously no reason to stop here. You have no doubt already guessed how symbols such as 5^4 or t^8 should be defined. If so, you have anticipated the following general definition of a natural-number power of a number: For n a natural number and b any number, **b to the nth power,** denoted by b^n, is defined by the equation

$$b^n = \underbrace{bbb \cdots b}_{n \text{ factors of } b}$$

b is called the **base** and n the **power** or the **exponent.**

EXAMPLE 33. $r^2 = rr$ $t^5 = ttttt$

$3^4 = 3 \cdot 3 \cdot 3 \cdot 3$ $5x^3y^5 = 5xxxyyyyy$

EXAMPLE 34. $10^1 = 10$ $10^3 = 1,000$ $10^5 = 100,000$

$10^2 = 100$ $10^4 = 10,000$ $10^6 = 1,000,000$

EXAMPLE 35. $93,000,000 = 93 \cdot 10^6$

(Note the relationship between the number of zeros in the nonexponent form and the powers of 10 that are used in this and the preceding example.)

EXAMPLE 36.   Due to radiation of energy, the sun loses approximately $42 \cdot 10^5$ tons of solar mass per sec.

EXAMPLE 37.   In 1929 a biologist named Vernadsky suggested that all the free oxygen of the earth, about $15 \cdot 10^{20}$ grams, is produced by living organisms alone.

EXAMPLE 38.   "A human begins life as a single cell, the fertilized egg, which by successive cell divisions forms the 10^{13} cells contained in a grown man. The size of the fertilized egg is approximately the size of the cross section of a human hair. Yet a single fertilized egg, despite its minuteness, contains all of the potentialities of a Shakespeare or a Darwin. . . ." [*]

The last three examples are more or less typical statements one is likely to encounter in scientific writings. Knowing the meaning of a power symbol certainly adds to the meaning and interest of these statements.

[*] Edgar Altenburg, "Genetics," (rev. ed.), p. 1, Holt, Rinehart and Winston, Inc., New York, 1957.

In addition to increasing your understanding of scientific writings, the power symbol is a very useful symbol in algebra and will be used often. As a matter of fact because of its frequency of use we will establish several rules for manipulating power or exponent forms to produce new exponent forms. The first law of exponents will be introduced in this section; others will follow in later chapters.

We know that an exponent as a natural number indicates how many times the base is to be taken as a factor. If we were to write x^8y^9 in nonexponent form, we would have to write eight factors of x and nine factors of y. Something interesting happens if we multiply two exponent forms having the same base. If we were to write the product x^2x^3 in nonexponent form, we would write two factors of x times three factors of x, a total of five factors of x; that is, $x^2x^3 = x^5$. Reasoning in the same way,

$$a^3a^4 = (aaa)(aaaa) = aaaaaaa = a^7$$
$$y^5y^3 = (yyyyy)(yyy) = yyyyyyyy = y^8$$
$$tt^5 = (t)(ttttt) = tttttt = t^6$$

It appears that if we multiply two exponent forms with the same base, then the sum of the exponents indicates the total number of times the base is taken as a factor in the product. In general, for any natural numbers n and m and any number b we may write

$$b^nb^m = b^{n+m}$$

(since in b^nb^m there are n factors of b times m factors of b or a total of $n + m$ factors of b). We have just stated the **first law of exponents,** one of five very important exponent laws that you will get to know as well as your multiplication tables before the end of this book.

NOTE: In the following example, and throughout the text, dotted boxes are used to indicate steps that are usually done mentally.

EXAMPLE 39

▶ $x^5x^4 \;\boxed{= x^{5+4}}\; = x^9$

▶ $yy^3 \;\boxed{= y^{1+3}}\; = y^4$

▶ $2x^3(x^2 + 3x + 5) = 2x^5 + 6x^4 + 10x^3$

▶ $(2u^2v^3)(4uv^2) \;\boxed{= (2 \cdot 4)(u^2u)(v^3v^2)}\; = 8u^3v^5$

▶ $2x^2y(3xy^2 + x^2y^5) = 6x^3y^3 + 2x^4y^6$

▶ $(3 \cdot 10^4)(4 \cdot 10^8) = 12 \cdot 10^{12}$

EXERCISE 7

1. Write in nonexponent form and evaluate where possible:
(A) 2^5 (B) 3^4
(C) x^5 (D) y^7
(E) 5^3 (F) 10^4

2. Write in nonexponent form and evaluate where possible:
(A) 8^4 (B) 4^8
(C) $2^3 \cdot 3^2$ (D) x^3y^2
(E) x^4yz^3 (F) $4 \cdot 10^3$

3. Write in exponent form (write composite numbers in completely factored form first, that is, as a product of prime factors):
(A) $aaaaaa$ (B) 8
(C) $xxxyy$ (D) 27
(E) $8 \cdot 27$ (F) $uuuvwwww$

4. Write in exponent form (write composite numbers in completely factored form first):
(A) $tttttttttttttt$
(B) $uuu \cdots u$ (31 factors of u)
(C) 16
(D) 81
(E) $81 \cdot 16$
(F) $xxxxxyyyzwwwwwww$

5. Write as a single natural number in nonexponent form:
(A) 10^3 (B) 10^7
(C) $5 \cdot 10^8$ (D) $23 \cdot 10^6$
(E) $125 \cdot 10^{12}$
State a simple mechanical rule that can be used in this problem.

6. In each statement write each quantity as a single number in nonexponent form:
(A) The sun is $93 \cdot 10^6$ miles from earth.
(B) A grown man contains about 10^{13} cells.
(C) The estimated age of the earth is $5 \cdot 10^9$ years.
(D) The distance light travels in 1 year, called 1 light-year, is approximately $588 \cdot 10^{10}$ miles.

7. Simplify by combining as many factors as possible:
(A) $x^2 \cdot x^3$ (B) $y^5 \cdot y^4$
(C) $(a^2b)(ab^2)$ (D) $(2xy^3)(3x^3y)$
(E) $(4uvw)(v^2w)$ (F) $10^3 \cdot 10^8$
(G) $(4 \cdot 10^8)(24 \cdot 10^7)$

8. Simplify by combining as many factors as possible:
(A) t^5t^7 (B) $u^{12}u^{18}u^4$

(C) $(cd^2)(c^2d^2)$

(D) $(4x)(3xy^2z)$

(E) $r(7qst)(2r^2t^3)$

(F) $10^4 \cdot 10^7 \cdot 10^5$

(G) $(6 \cdot 10^3)(5 \cdot 10)(22 \cdot 10^4)$

9. Our galaxy is estimated to have a diameter of about 10^5 light-years and a thickness of about $2 \cdot 10^4$ light-years. If a light-year, the distance light travels in 1 year, is approximately $588 \cdot 10^{10}$ miles, what is the diameter and thickness of our galaxy in miles? (A) Express the answer in power-of-ten notation. (B) Express the answer as a single numeral without power-of-ten notation.

10. The 200-in. telescope at Palomar, California, can distinguish objects up to an estimated $6 \cdot 10^6$ light-years away. Express this distance in miles (see the preceding problem) (A) using the power-of-ten notation and (B) as a single numeral without power-of-ten notation.

11. The mass of the earth is approximately $66 \cdot 10^{20}$ tons. If one ton is $2 \cdot 10^3$ lb, what is the mass of the earth in pounds? Express the answer with and without power-of-ten notation.

12. If the area of the earth is approximately $197 \cdot 10^6$ sq miles, find the area of the earth in square feet if 1 sq mile contains approximately $279 \cdot 10^5$ sq ft. Express the answer with and without power-of-ten notation.

13. Write as the sum of two or more terms:

(A) $x(x + 1)$

(B) $x(x^2 + 2x + 3)$

(C) $(xy)(x^2y + y^3)$

(D) $3a^2b(2ab^2c + ab)$

(E) $5t^3(t^4 + 2t^2 + 3t + 6)$

14. Write as the sum of two or more terms:

(A) $y(y^2 + 3)$

(B) $c^2(c^4 + 3c^3 + 2c^2 + c + 4)$

(C) $(3a^2b)(4a^3b^3 + a^2b + 5ab^3)$

(D) $(x^2 + 1)(x^2 + x + 1)$

(E) $(2t^3 + 5)(4t^2 + 7)$

9 LIKE TERMS; SIMPLIFYING ALGEBRAIC EXPRESSIONS

We are almost at the place where we will be able to carry out rather extensive algebraic manipulations and simplifications—changing symbols that represent numbers from one form to simpler forms or more useful forms. In this section you will be introduced to three new technical terms, *coefficient*, *numerical coefficient*, and *like terms*, as well as to one more very useful operation, that of *"combining like terms."*

In a product of two or more factors any collection of factors is said to be the **coefficient** of the remaining factors. In the expression $5axy$, $5ax$ is the coefficient of y, $5xy$ is the coefficient of a, $5a$ is the coefficient of xy, 5 is the coefficient of axy, and so on.

In a product involving one or more variables as factors the constant factor is called the **numerical coefficient.** If no constant factor appears in the product, then the numerical coefficient is understood to be 1. In the expression $2x^3 + x^2y + 3xy^2 + y^3$, the numerical coefficient of the first term is 2, of the second term 1, of the third term 3, and of the fourth term 1. We will be mainly interested in numerical coefficients and will refer to them frequently throughout the book.

If two or more terms are exactly alike except for numerical coefficients, they are called **like terms.** In the expression $4x + 2y + 3x$ the first and third terms are like terms since they are exactly alike except for the numerical coefficients 4 and 3. In the expression $9x^2y + 3xy + 2x^2y + x^2y$ the first, third, and fourth terms are like terms since they all contain x^2y and no other variable factors. When we have an expression involving the addition of two or more like terms, the distributive axiom (including the generalized form) provides us with a tool that will enable us to simplify the expression (sometimes significantly).

COMBINING LIKE TERMS

The following example illustrates how expressions containing like terms can be simplified.

EXAMPLE 40

▶ $3x + 5x = (3 + 5)x = 8x$

▶ $5t + 4s + 7t = 5t + 7t + 4s = (5t + 7t) + 4s = (5 + 7)t + 4s$

$\qquad = 12t + 4s$

▶ $8xy + xy + 2x^2y + 9xy = 8xy + xy + 9xy + 2x^2y = (8xy + xy + 9xy) + 2x^2y$

$\qquad = (8 + 1 + 9)xy + 2x^2y = 18xy + 2x^2y$

It should be clear that free use was made of the axioms discussed earlier.

The above example illustrates a general principle: *Like terms under the operation of addition can always be combined into a single term.* Most of the steps written out in the above example, including the adding of the numerical coefficients, are usually done mentally as the following example illustrates.

EXAMPLE 41

▶ $5st + 8st = 13st$

▶ $12x + 4y + 3x = 15x + 4y$

▶ $(3x + 7y) + (4x + y) = 3x + 7y + 4x + y = 7x + 8y$

▶ $3x(x^2 + 6x + 2) + 2(x^3 + x) = 3x^3 + 18x^2 + 6x + 2x^3 + 2x$
$$= 5x^3 + 18x^2 + 8x$$

▶ $(x + 2)(x + 3) = (x + 2)x + (x + 2)3 = x^2 + 2x + 3x + 6$
$$= x^2 + 5x + 6$$

EXERCISE 8

All variables in the following problems represent natural numbers.

1. Write the numerical coefficient for each of the following terms: $4x$, $7ab$, x^2y^2, $8st^3$, and u^2w^2.

2. In the expression $7x^2y^3$ which numerals are called exponents, and which are called numerical coefficients?

3. Given the algebraic expression $2x^3 + 3x^2 + x + 5$:
(A) What is the numerical coefficient in the second term?
(B) What is the exponent of the variable in the second term?
(C) What is the numerical coefficient in the third term?
(D) What is the exponent of the variable in the third term?

4. Given the algebraic expressions $3x + 2y + 4z$, $x^2 + 2x + 3$, $3y^3 + 2y^2 + y + 7$, $s^4 + s^2 + s + 1$, and $x^3 + 2x^2y + xy^2 + y^3$:
(A) Write the numerical coefficient for the second term in each expression.
(B) Write the numerical coefficient for the first term in each expression.
(C) Write the exponent for the variable in the first term in each expression.

5. Which of the following terms are like terms: $2x$, $3y$, $4x$, $5y$, $6x^2$, $7y^2$, xy, $3x^2$, $2xy$, y^2?

6. Which of the following terms are like terms: $3x^2y$, $4t^3$, $2xy^2$, $3t^4$, $8x^2y$?

7. Combine like terms:
(A) $5x + 2x$ (B) $7t + 9t$
(C) $3y + y + 5y$ (D) $5x + 7x + 4y$
(E) $u + 2u + v + 3v$ (F) $7s + 2t + 4s + t$

8. Combine like terms:
(A) $6x + 3x + 7x$ (B) $2t^2 + t^2 + 3t^2$
(C) $9x^3 + 4x^2 + 3x + 2x^3 + x$ (D) $u^4 + v^4 + 2u^3 + 3v^4 + 2u^4 + u^2$

9. Combine like terms:

(A) $3x + 5y + x + 4z + 2y + 3z$

(B) $x^2 + xy + y^2 + 3x^2 + 2xy + y^2$

(C) $3x^2 + 2x + 1 + x^2 + 3x + 4$

(D) $(4x + 1) + (3x + 2) + (2x + 5)$

(E) $(4x^4 + 2x^2 + 3) + (x^4 + 3x^2 + 1)$

10. Combine like terms:

(A) $2r + 7t + r + 4s + r + 3t + s$

(B) $4x^2y + xy + 3xy^2 + 2xy^2 + 5xy + 7x^2y$

(C) $(t^2 + 5t + 3) + (3t^2 + t) + (2t + 7)$

(D) $(x^3 + 3x^2y + xy^2 + y^3) + (2x^3 + 3xy^2 + y^3)$

(E) $(2u^3 + uv^2 + v^3) + (u^3 + v^3) + (u^3 + 3u^2v)$

11. Multiply, using the distributive axiom, and combine like terms:

(A) $2(x + 5) + 3(2x + 7)$

(B) $5(t^2 + 2t + 1) + 3(2t^2 + t + 4)$

(C) $x(x + 1) + x(2x + 3)$

(D) $2t(3t + 5) + 3t(4t + 1)$

(E) $y(y^2 + 2y + 3) + (y^3 + y) + y^2(y + 1)$

12. Multiply, using the distributive axiom, and combine like terms:

(A) $3x(x + 5) + 2x(2x + 3) + x(x + 1)$

(B) $2y(y^2 + 2y + 5) + 7y(3y + 2) + y(y^2 + 1)$

(C) $2x(3x + y) + 3y(x + 2y)$

(D) $(x + y)x + (x + y)y$

(E) $(x + y)(x + y)$

13. Multiply, using the distributive axiom, and combine like terms:

(A) $2xy^2(3x + x^2y) + 3x^2y(y + xy^2)$

(B) $2x^3(2x^2 + 1) + 3x^2(x^3 + 3x + 2)$

(C) $(2x + 3)3x + (x + 4)2$

(D) $(2x + 3)(3x + 2)$

(E) $(x + 2y)(2x + y)$

14. Multiply, using the distributive axiom, and combine like terms:

(A) $3s^2t^3(2s^3t + s^2t^2) + 2s^3t^2(3s^2t^2 + st^3)$

(B) $(2x + 3)(x + 2)$

(C) $(t + 4)(3t + 2) + 2t(3t + 4)$

(D) $(r + s + t)r + (r + s + t)s + (r + s + t)t$

(E) $(r + s + t)(r + s + t)$

(F) $(x + 3)(x^2 + 2x + 5)$

15. If x represents a natural number, write an algebraic expression for the sum of four consecutive natural numbers starting with x. Simplify the expression by combining like terms.

16. If t represents an even number, write an algebraic expression for the sum of three consecutive even numbers starting with t. Simplify.

17. If y represents an odd number, write an algebraic expression for the product of y and the next odd number.   Write as the sum of two terms.

18. If y represents the first of four consecutive even numbers, write an algebraic expression that would represent the product of the first two added to the product of the last two.   Simplify.

19. An even number plus the product of it and the next even number is 180. Introduce a variable, and write as an algebraic equation.   Simplify the left and right sides of the equation where possible.

20. There exist at least two consecutive odd numbers such that five times the first plus twice the second is equal to twice the first plus three times the second. Introduce a variable and write as an algebraic equation.   Simplify the left and right sides of the equation where possible.

10   ORDER RELATIONS: "LESS THAN" AND "GREATER THAN"

Most students, if given any two natural numbers, would have little difficulty in stating which of the two is the smaller or the larger.   If, on the other hand, you were asked, "Given any two natural numbers a and b, is it always true that exactly one of the following three cases holds: a is less than b, a is equal to b, or a is greater than b?" you might have to stop and think for a moment about the exact meaning of the question.   However, after the meaning became clear, you would no doubt answer that the statement is true.   If we said that one natural number is less than a second and the second is less than a third, then you would probably accept the fact that the first is less than the third.   A set of numbers that has the properties just described is called an **ordered set.**

The ordered-set properties of the natural numbers are properties that you have "known" so long and feel so sure about that you probably accept them without question.   These additional important properties of the natural numbers have become a part of your "instinctive knowledge" of numbers.   Since we are not in a position to prove these properties for all natural numbers, we will accept as a postulate that *the set of natural numbers is an ordered set.*

These ideas will be discussed in more detail in Sec. 21.   In the meantime we will proceed somewhat informally and rely on your intuitive or instinctive knowledge of what is meant by "is less than" and "is greater than."

In this section you will be introduced to inequality symbols and a new way of representing sets; both will be used extensively throughout the text.

INEQUALITY SYMBOLS

Just as we found it convenient to replace "is equal to" or "is identical with" with "$=$," we will find it of equal value to replace "is less than" and "is greater than" with appropriate symbols, namely, "$<$" and "$>$," respectively.° Thus for "8 is less than 12" we will write "$8 < 12$," and for "28 is greater than 13" we will write "$28 > 13$." To avoid confusing these symbols, remember that the small end (the point) is directed toward the smaller of the two numbers.

For convenient reference we list the most commonly used equality and inequality symbols.

EQUALITY SYMBOL
$=$ means "is equal to" or "is identical with"

INEQUALITY SYMBOLS
$<$ means "is less than"
$\leq$ means "is less than or equal to"
$>$ means "is greater than"
$\geq$ means "is greater than or equal to"
$\neq$ means "is not equal to"

EXAMPLE 42

SYMBOLIC STATEMENTS	VERBAL STATEMENTS
$8 < 12$	8 is less than 12
$103 > 37$	103 is greater than 37
$5 \geq 2$	5 is greater than or equal to 2
$5 \geq 5$	5 is greater than or equal to 5
$4 \leq 7$	4 is less than or equal to 7
$4 \leq 4$	4 is less than or equal to 4
$6 \neq 1$	6 is not equal to 1
$3 + x < 5 - x$	$3 + x$ is less than $5 - x$
$x + 7 \geq 2 + 3x$	$x + 7$ is greater than or equal to $2 + 3x$

We will generally write "$a < x < b$" as an abbreviation for "$a < x$ and $x < b$." Thus if the replacement set for the variable x is the set of natural numbers, then the solution set for the inequality $2 < x < 7$ is the set $\{3, 4, 5, 6\}$; if x is replaced with any of the numerals 3, 4, 5, or 6, the inequality statement will be true. We do not write expressions such as $a < x > b$. Try a few specific examples replacing a and b with numerals to see why.

° Formally, we define "$<$" as follows: we write $a < b$ if and only if there exists a natural number n such that $a + n = b$. Statements "$a < b$" and "$a + n = b$" can be used interchangeably. We write $a > b$ if and only if $b < a$. This definition and its consequences will be discussed in greater detail in Chap. 2.

EXERCISE 9

1. Translate the verbal statements into symbolic statements using one of the inequality or equality symbols introduced in this section.
(A) 7 is greater than 3   (B) 7 is not equal to 3
(C) 5 is less than or equal to 5   (D) 11 is less than 12
(E) 11 is greater than or equal to 11   (F) 9 is equal to 9

2. Translate the verbal statements into symbolic statements using one of the inequality or equality symbols introduced in this section.
(A) 18 is greater than 4
(B) 103 is less than or equal to 103
(C) 342 is not equal to 543
(D) 2,347 is equal to 2,347
(E) 97 is greater than or equal to 97
(F) 875 is less than 932

3. Indicate which of the following statements are true:
(A) $8 > 9$ (B) $8 \geq 9$
(C) $8 < 9$ (D) $8 \leq 9$
(E) $8 = 9$ (F) $8 \neq 9$

4. Indicate which of the following statements are true:
(A) $18 > 81$ (B) $81 > 18$
(C) $75 \geq 75$ (D) $75 \leq 75$
(E) $130 \leq 103$ (F) $103 \leq 130$

5. Indicate which of the following statements are true:
(A) $5 \cdot 3 + 1 > 5 \cdot 1 + 3$ (B) $6(2 + 3) \leq 6 \cdot 2 + 6 \cdot 3$
(C) $6(2 + 3) \geq 6 \cdot 2 + 6 \cdot 3$ (D) $5 + (7 + 2) \neq (5 + 7) + 2$
(E) $4 \cdot 3 + 3 \cdot 7 < 3(4 + 7)$ (F) $4 \cdot 3 + 3 \cdot 7 \leq 3(4 + 7)$

6. Indicate which of the following are true:
(A) $7 + 9 \cdot 5 > 9 + 7 \cdot 5$ (B) $(7 + 9)5 > 7 \cdot 5 + 9 \cdot 5$
(C) $7 + 9 \cdot 5 > 7 + 5 \cdot 9$ (D) $6 \cdot 3 + 6 \cdot 9 \geq 6(3 + 9)$
(E) $(3 + 8)(4 + 3) \leq (3 + 8)4 + (3 + 8)3$
(F) $(3 + 8)(4 + 3) \geq 3(4 + 3) + 8(4 + 3)$

The solution set for an equation or inequality containing a variable is the set of replacements of the variable (from the replacement set) that makes the inequality or equality statement true. Equations and inequalities involving variables are neither true nor false until replacements of the variable are made by constants from the replacement set.

7. Find the solution set for each of the following inequalities or equations if the replacement set for the variable x is $\{2, 4, 6, 8\}$:
(A) $x > 5$ (B) $x \geq 5$ (C) $x < 6$
(D) $x \leq 6$ (E) $3x = 12$ (F) $3x \neq 12$

8. Find the solution set for each of the following inequalities or equations if the replacement set for the variable x is $\{1, 3, 5, 7, 9\}$:

(A) $3x > 9$ (B) $3x \leq 9$

(C) $x + 5 > 8$ (D) $2x - 1 \geq 9$

(E) $4x + 3 = 3(x + 1) + x$ (F) $4x + 3 \neq 3(x + 1) + x$

9. Find the solution set for each of the following inequalities if the replacement set for the variable t is $\{1, 2, 3, 4, 5\}$:

(A) $2 < t < 8$ (B) $2 \leq t \leq 8$

(C) $2 \leq 2t \leq 8$ (D) $3 \leq t + 2 < 7$

10. Find the solution set for each of the following inequalities if the replacement set for the variable y is the set of all natural numbers:

(A) $3 < y < 12$ (B) $3 < y \leq 12$

(C) $4 \leq 2y < 12$ (D) $7 \leq y + 5 \leq 12$

The following example and two problems are connected with an important business application known as "break-even analysis." This type of application will be treated more extensively in future chapters.

EXAMPLE 43. An optical company manufactures binoculars and wholesales them at $28 each. The company's annual fixed costs (which includes advertising, taxes, plant facilities, etc.) are $75,000, and the variable cost (the cost of producing each pair of binoculars in materials and labor) is $15. (A) Letting x represent the number of binoculars sold per year, write an inequality statement relating revenue and expenses in such a way that an annual profit will be guaranteed. (B) What conditions, stated in terms of an inequality statement, would have to be satisfied to keep the manufacturer from having a loss?

SOLUTION:

(A) Profit = revenue − expense. A profit will be realized if revenue > expense; that is, if

$$28x > 75,000 + 15x$$

(B) A loss will be prevented if revenue ≥ expense; that is, if

$$28x \geq 75,000 + 15x$$

11. A company engaged in the manufacturing of transistor radios sells each radio for $10. The fixed costs for running the plant are $40,000 per year, and the variable costs in labor and materials for producing each radio are $4. Let x be the number of radios sold per year. (A) Write an inequality statement relating revenue and expenses in such a way that an annual profit will be guaranteed. (B) What conditions, stated in terms of an inequality statement, would have to be satisfied to keep the manufacturer from having a loss?

12. A women's shoe store stocks three lines of shoes: sandals, flats, and dress. The revenue and expense breakdowns are

	Selling price per pair	Variable cost per pair
Sandals	$ 6	$ 3
Flats	9	5
Dress	18	10

Fixed costs = \$35,000 per year.

Let s = number of sandals sold per year
f = number of flats sold per year
d = number of dress shoes sold per year

Write an inequality statement relating revenue and expense in such a way that if the condition were satisfied no loss would occur.

The following two problems are related to another important area of applications in business and economics called "linear programming." This topic will be developed in greater detail in later chapters.

13. A company manufactures two models of skis, a racing model and a standard model. Each standard model requires 3 hr of finishing time, and each racing model requires 6 hr. Let S equal the number of standard models produced per week, and let R equal the number of racing models. If the manufacturer has a maximum of 800 man-hours he can use for finishing per week, write an inequality statement with two variables showing an appropriate restriction on the number of models the manufacturer is able to produce per week.

14. If in the preceding problem the manufacturer also has a maximum of 2,000 man-hours of fabricating time per week, each standard model requires 6 hr, and each racing model requires 9 hr for fabricating, write an inequality statement with two variables showing an appropriate restriction on the number of models the manufacturer is able to produce relative to fabricating.

15. A flat sheet of cardboard is used to make an open-topped box by cutting an x-in. square out of each corner and folding the remaining part appropriately.
(A) Show that the volume of the box is given by $V = (18 - 2x)(12 - 2x)x$ if the sheet of cardboard used was 18 by 12 in. to start with.
(B) What values can x assume so that a volume will result? State the restriction on x by use of a double-inequality statement. (Recall that replacement sets for variables are limited to natural numbers in this chapter.)

16. A rectangular lot is to be fenced with 400 ft of wire.

(A) If the lot is x ft wide, show that the area of the lot is given by the formula $A = x(200 - x)$.

(B) What values can x assume so that an area will result? State the restriction on x by use of a double-inequality statement. (Replacement sets for variables are limited to natural numbers in this chapter.)

SET NOTATION

You will recall that we described certain sets by listing their elements within braces. For example, $\{2, 4, 6\}$ is the set whose members are the three numbers 2, 4, and 6, and $\{1, 2, 3, 4, 5, 6, 7, 8, 9\}$ is the set whose numbers are the digits from 1 to 9 inclusive. We also introduced the Greek letter ϕ to represent the null (or empty) set, the set with no members.

The set notation introduced earlier is adequate for many purposes, but is awkward if the number of elements in the set is large or if we want to describe solution sets of equations or inequalities without actually listing the elements. It will be very convenient to be able to translate verbal statements of the form "the set of all natural numbers n such that $2n + 5 = 15$" or "the set of all natural numbers x such that $x + 5 \leq 10$" into more compact symbolic forms. There is a special set notation that has been designed for this purpose; it is sometimes referred to as "set-builder notation."

NOTE: We will assume in the following discussion and examples that all variables have as their replacement sets the set of natural numbers or one of its subsets; hence, we will not repeat this statement for every illustration.

The statement "A is the set of all natural numbers n such that $2n + 5 = 15$" is symbolized $A = \{n \mid 2n + 5 = 15\}$. This is not as forbidding as it first looks; each part of the symbol has a meaning as indicated in the diagram below.

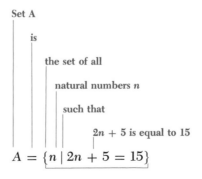

Set A
  is
    the set of all
      natural numbers n
        such that
          $2n + 5$ is equal to 15
$A = \{n \mid 2n + 5 = 15\}$

EXAMPLE 44

$G = \{t \mid t \leq 10\}$ is read, "G is the set of all natural numbers t such that t is less than or equal to 10."

$F = \{u \mid 3 \leq u \leq 8\}$ is read, "F is the set of all natural numbers u such that u is greater than or equal to 3 and less than or equal to 8."

$W = \{x \mid x + 3 = x(x + 2)\}$ is read, "W is the set of all natural numbers x such that $x + 3$ is equal to $x(x + 2)$."

EXAMPLE 45

▶ $\{y \mid y < 8\} = \{1, 2, 3, 4, 5, 6, 7\}$
▶ $\{t \mid 4 < t \leq 11\} = \{5, 6, 7, 8, 9, 10, 11\}$
▶ $\{x \mid x + 5 = 8\} = \{3\}$
▶ $\{n \mid n + 7 = 3\} = \phi$

Note that in each illustration in example 45, the set-builder notation used describes the solution set of the equation or inequality involved.

EXERCISE 10

In the following problems, the replacement set for all variables is the set of natural numbers.

1. Translate the following verbal statements into symbolic forms using set-builder notation:
(A) Set B is the set of all natural numbers x such that x is less than or equal to 7.
(B) Set C is the set of all natural numbers t such that t is greater than 13.
(C) Set D is the set of all natural numbers u such that u is greater than 4 and less than or equal to 10.

2. Translate the following verbal statements into symbolic forms using set-builder notation:
(A) Set G is the set of all natural numbers x such that $2x + 5$ is equal to $3x + 3$.
(B) Set D is the set of all natural numbers t such that $3t + 2$ is less than or equal to 8.
(C) Set F is the set of all natural numbers n such that $2n$ is greater than or equal to 4 and less than or equal to 10.

3. Translate each of the following symbolic statements into verbal statements:
(A) $F = \{x \mid x \leq 8\}$ (B) $B = \{t \mid 4 \leq t < 9\}$
(C) $C = \{n \mid 5 < n + 7 \leq 23\}$ (D) $A = \{y \mid 3y + 5 = 4(y + 2)\}$

4. Translate each of the following symbolic statements into verbal statements:

(A) $D = \{u \mid u > 14\}$

(B) $A = \{x \mid 5 < x \leq 11\}$

(C) $S = \{z \mid (z + 2)(z + 3) = z^2 + 5z + 6\}$

(D) $U = \{w \mid 3 < 2w + 3 < 10\}$

5. Replace the question marks with appropriate symbols:

(A) $\{x \mid x \leq 5\} = \{1, ?, ?, ?, 5\}$

(B) $\{t \mid 3 < t < 7\} = \{?, ?, ?\}$

(C) $\{t \mid 3 \leq t \leq 7\} = \{(\text{list elements})\}$

(D) $\{u \mid 4 ? u ? 9\} = \{4, 5, 6, 7, 8\}$

(E) $\{y \mid ? < ? \leq ?\} = \{3, 4, 5, 6, 7\}$

(F) $\{z \mid z ? 5\} = \{5, 6, 7, \ldots\}$

6. Replace the question marks with appropriate symbols:

(A) $\{s \mid ? < 8\} = \{1, ?, ?, ?, ?, ?, 7\}$

(B) $\{? \mid 100 < r \leq 103\} = \{(\text{list elements})\}$

(C) $\{z \mid ? \leq ? < ?\} = \{437, 438, 439, 440\}$

(D) $\{x \mid ? \geq ?\} = \{10, 11, 12, \ldots\}$

(E) $\{t \mid t \leq 10, t \text{ is even}\} = \{2, ?, ?, ?, ?\}$

(F) $\{t \mid 8 \leq t < 12, t \text{ is odd}\} = \{(\text{list elements})\}$

7. Use set-builder notation to indicate the replacement set for the variable x in problem 15, Exercise 9.

8. Use set-builder notation to indicate the replacement set for the variable x in problem 16, Exercise 9.

11   THE NUMBER LINE AND LINE GRAPHS

"A picture is worth a thousand words." How many times have you heard that statement? Did you ever think that it might apply to mathematics? Perhaps in an arithmetic course you learned how to represent certain kinds of information pictorially by such means as bar graphs, pie graphs, and broken-line graphs. In this and the next two chapters we will be interested in representing sets of numbers "pictorially" by means of graphs on number lines. This will be part of a more general process of representing algebraic ideas in simple visual form and eventually representing visual ideas in algebraic form. Both processes are of considerable importance in almost every area of mathematics the average reader is likely to encounter now or in the future.

To begin with, we will restrict our attention to the problem of associating each number in the set of natural numbers with a point on an extended line—a line that extends without end in either direction and is itself a set of geometric objects called points. This association results in what is called the **number line.**

Figure 11

The number line will look very much like the markings on a ruler or a household thermometer.

To construct the number line (see Fig. 11), select an arbitrary point on the extended line, and mark it. Next, divide the extended line to the right of the marked point into line segments of equal length. The arrow indicates that the process is assumed to continue without end. The size and number of line segments to be included on a sheet of paper is a matter of choice and will depend entirely on how many natural numbers you may wish to actually associate with points on your paper.

Finally, the set of natural numbers or one of its subsets is associated with the set of end points of the line segments. In general it is only necessary to show a few numbers associated with selected end points to establish a **scale** for the number line. The following example should make the process clear.

EXAMPLE 46

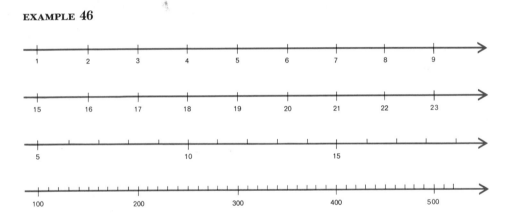

A line segment between two points associated with two consecutive natural numbers is said to be **one unit** in length. Thus, each indicated line segment on the first three number lines of example 46 is one unit in length, whereas each marked division on the fourth number line represents 10 units.

Once a number line is specified, any given natural number can be associated in one and only one way with a point on this line. The point associated with a particular number is called the **graph of the number** and is indicated by a darkened circle on the number line. On the other hand the number associated with a point on a number line is called the **coordinate** of the point. The **graph of a set of numbers** is the set of points on the number line that are the graphs of the individual numbers in the set.

EXAMPLE 47.   The graph of the set of numbers {3, 5, 8, 9} is

EXAMPLE 48.   The coordinates of the points a, b, c, and d on the number line below are 22, 23, 25, and 28, respectively.

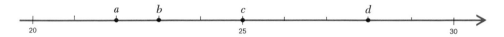

EXAMPLE 49.   The graph of the set of natural numbers {$x \mid 3 \leq x < 8$} is

EXAMPLE 50.   The graph of the set {$x \mid x \geq 6$, x a natural number} is

The relations "$<$" and "$>$" have a very clear geometric interpretation on a number line. If $a < b$, then the graph of a is to the left of the graph of b; if $a > b$, then the graph of a is to the right of the graph of b. For example, the graph of the solution set of the inequality statement $3 \leq x < 8$ is the set of points on or to the right of the point with coordinate 3 which are at the same time to the left of the point with coordinate 8 (see example 49 above).

The reader is undoubtably aware of the fact that we have ignored points to the left of the point with coordinate 1. In the next chapter we will extend the set of natural numbers to include zero and a new set of numbers called the negative integers. These new numbers will be associated with points to the left of 1 in much the same way as the points to the right of 1 have been associated with natural numbers.

EXERCISE 11

Graph each set in problems 1 through 8 using a separate number line for each graph.

1. (A) {2, 4, 6, 8}   (B) {5, 7, 9, 11}   (C) {85, 93, 102}
2. (A) {4, 12, 17}   (B) {42, 48, 53}   (C) {140, 170, 190}
3. (A) {Natural numbers less than 6}
   (B) {Natural numbers greater than or equal to 6}

4. (A) {Natural numbers between 5 and 9, inclusive}
   (B) {Natural numbers greater than 9}

5. (A) $\{x \mid 2 < x \le 7, x$ a natural number$\}$
   (B) $\{x \mid 2 \le x < 7, x$ a natural number$\}$

6. (A) $\{t \mid 23 < t < 28, t$ a natural number$\}$
   (B) $\{t \mid 23 \le t \le 28, t$ a natural number$\}$

7. Let N represent the set of natural numbers.
   (A) $\{n \mid n < 7, n \varepsilon N\}$
   (B) $\{n \mid n \ge 7, n \varepsilon N\}$

8. (A) $\{u \mid 70 \le u \le 85, u \varepsilon N\}$
   (B) $\{u \mid u \ge 100, u \varepsilon N\}$

9. Name the coordinate of each point marked a, b, and c, respectively.

(A)

(B)

10. Name the coordinate of each point marked r, s, and t, respectively.

(A)

(B)

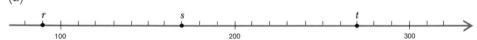

11. If the graph of set S is

then
(A) $S = \{$(list elements)$\}$.
(B) $S = \{t \mid ? \le t < ?, ?$ a natural number$\}$.

12. If the graph of set A (a subset of the set of natural numbers N) is

then

(A) $A = \{(\text{list elements})\}.$

(B) $A = \{x \mid ? < ? \le ?, ? \varepsilon ?\}.$

13. If the graph of the set B (a subset of the set of natural numbers N) is

then $B = \{x \mid ? \ge 7, ? \varepsilon ?\}.$

14. If the graph of the set G (a subset of the set of natural numbers N) is

then $G = \{y \mid ? > ?, ? \varepsilon ?\}.$

15. If $A = \{x \mid 3 \le x \le 8, x \varepsilon N\}$ and $B = \{x \mid 6 \le x \le 12, x \varepsilon N\}$, then

(A) $C = \{x \mid x \varepsilon A \text{ and } x \varepsilon B\} = \{(\text{list elements})\}.$

(B) $D = \{x \mid x \varepsilon A \text{ or } x \varepsilon B\} = \{(\text{list elements})\}.$

16. If $A = \{x \mid x < 9, x \varepsilon N\}$ and $B = \{x \mid x \ge 4, x \varepsilon N\}$, then

(A) $C = \{x \mid x \varepsilon A \text{ and } x \varepsilon B\} = \{(\text{list elements})\}.$

(B) $D = \{x \mid x \varepsilon A \text{ or } x \varepsilon B\} = ?$

12   CHAPTER SUMMARY

GENERAL

It is now very important to step back and take a look at the chapter as a whole to see how the parts are interrelated and to look into the future to see where we are going. A fairly large number of new concepts have been introduced that are basic to the rest of the development of the course. It follows, then, that you should not continue into the next chapter until you have reviewed this chapter and convinced yourself that you know the material presented. A comprehensive review exercise is provided at the end of this section to facilitate this review. The importance of this reviewing procedure cannot be overstressed, and it should be continued throughout the text.

The star of the show so far has been the set of natural numbers. In the next two chapters this set of numbers will have to share the spotlight with three other important and useful sets of numbers: the integers, rational numbers, and the set of real numbers. As we extend the natural numbers to these enlarged systems, we will require any new set of numbers to satisfy the same laws that we have stated relative to the natural numbers, namely, the closure laws, the commutative laws, the associative laws, all for addition and multiplication, and the distributive law. This means that multiplication and addition must be defined for these new sets of numbers so that these laws will continue to hold. As a consequence, we will still be able to manipulate symbols that represent these new numbers in the same way we manipulated symbols that represented natural numbers in this chapter; that is, we are going to continue to play the game with the same rules even though the replacement sets for the variables will have been enlarged. We will, of course, add to these rules, but the important thing to remember is that none of the present laws that we have stated will be thrown out.

We have now progressed to the place where we are able to formulate and simplify simple algebraic expressions, that is, translate certain verbal forms into symbolic statements and transform these statements into other (often simpler) forms. The next two chapters will provide us with the additional necessary background to launch a profitable attack on a large class of significant applications. These applications will be found in Chaps. 4 and 5. In addition, we will consider a limited number of simple but significant applications at the end of Chap. 2 and at the end of Chap. 3.

SPECIFIC

Key topics and related materials covered in this chapter are summarized below; you should know this material including the meaning of each term and symbol.

1. Sets

equal sets	empty set
subset	ϕ
element of a set	{(list of elements)}
member of a set	set-builder notation
$a \,\varepsilon\, A$	$\{x \mid (x \text{ satisfies some property})\}$
null set	

2. The Set of Natural Numbers

$\{1, 2, 3, 4, \ldots\}$	prime numbers
even numbers	composite numbers
odd numbers	completely factored
terms	product of prime factors
factors	$2 \cdot 3, 2 \times 3, (2)(3)$

3. Algebraic Expressions

constants	formulas
variables	algebraic expressions
replacement set	evaluation of algebraic expressions
the binary operation "$+$"	( ), [ ], { }
the binary operation "$\cdot$"	

4. Equality

a is equal to b

$a = b$

four laws of equality (reflexive, symmetric, transitive, substitution principle)

algebraic equation

5. Exponents

b^n	base
exponent	first law of exponents
power	$a^n a^m = a^{n+m}$

6. Postulates for Addition and Multiplication

closure laws	transforming algebraic expressions into equivalent forms
commutative laws	like terms
associative laws	combining like terms
distributive law	simplifying algebraic expressions

7. Order Relations

$a < b$	$a < x < b$
$a > b$	$a \leq x < b$
$a \leq b$	$a < x \leq b$
$a \geq b$	$a \leq x \leq b$

8. Line Graphs

number line	graph of a natural number
unit	coordinate of a point
scale	graph of a set of natural numbers

EXERCISE 12   CHAPTER REVIEW

The replacement set for all variables, unless otherwise stated, is the set of natural numbers.

1. Write down all of the prime numbers between 6 and 16. Is this set a subset of the set of natural numbers?

2. Translate the following word statements into symbolic statements:
(A) x is equal to y (B) x is not equal to y
(C) 4 is an element of set B (D) 5 is not an element of set C
(E) x is greater than y (F) x is less than or equal to y

3. Given the set $A = \{1, 2, 3, 4, 5, 6, 7, 8, 9\}$:
(A) If P is a set of four prime numbers and P is a subset of A, then $P = ?$
(B) If E is a set of four even numbers and E is a subset of A, then $E = ?$
(C) If C is a set of four composite numbers and C is a subset of A, then $C = ?$
(D) Factor each composite number in set A completely (as a product of prime factors).

4. Given the sets $A = \{1, 2, 3, 4, 5, 6, 7, 8, 9\}$, $B = \{4, 6, 8, 9\}$, $C = \{2, 3, 5, 7\}$, $E = \{1, 3, 5, 7, 9\}$, and $F =$ the set of prime numbers from set A, indicate which of the following statements are true:
(A) $5 \, \varepsilon \, C$ (B) $5 \notin F$
(C) $F \neq C$ (D) $F = C$
(E) C is a subset of E (F) A is a subset of C
(G) B is a subset of A (H) $F = \phi$

5. Let R be the set of natural numbers from 33 to 57 (inclusive) that contain 3 as a factor.
(A) Write down the elements of R within braces.
(B) Using ε notation, indicate how each of the following numbers is related to the set R: 33, 47, 51, and 57.
(C) Graph the set R on a number line.

6. A person has five friends and wishes to invite three of them to a weekend party. How many combinations has he to choose from; that is, how many three-person subsets can be formed from the set of five friends?

7. Evaluate each of the following algebraic expressions for $a = 5$, $b = 1$, $c = 8$, and $d = 2$:
(A) $ac + d$ (B) $a(c + d)$
(C) $3[ac + a(c - d)]$ (D) $2\{3[2 + (b + d)] + 2(a - d)\}$

8. If y represents a natural number, write an algebraic expression that represents a number:
(A) 5 more than three times y
(B) 3 less than five times y
(C) four times a number 3 smaller than y
Evaluate each expression for $y = 4$.

9.

(A) Replace the question mark in each expression with an appropriate inequality symbol: $a\,?\,b$, $b\,?\,c$, $a\,?\,c$, $b\,?\,a$, $c\,?\,b$.

(B) What are the coordinates of points a, b, and c?

10. If the area A of a square with side s is given by the formula $A = s^2$ and the replacement set for the variable s is $\{5, 6, 7\}$, find the replacement set for A. Graph the replacement set for A.

11. Find the solution set for the inequality $3x - 5 \geq x + 3$ if the replacement set for the variable x is $\{2, 4, 6, 8\}$. Graph the solution set.

12. (A) $\{x \mid 3 \leq x \leq 14,\ x \text{ is an odd number}\} = A$. List the elements of A within braces.

(B) Graph set A.

13. (A) Translate the following into a symbolic statement using set-builder notation: Set D is the set of all odd numbers u such that u is greater than 5 and less than or equal to 13.

(B) Translate the following into a verbal statement: $\{t \mid t > 13\}$.

14. Replace the question marks with appropriate symbols:

(A) $\{7, 8, 9, 10\} = \{x \mid 6\,?\,x\,?\,10\}$

(B) $\{4, 5, 6, 7\} = \{t \mid ?\, \leq\, ?\, <\, ?\}$

(C) $\{6, 7, 8, \ldots\} = \{u \mid ?\, >\, ?\}$

15. Is the set of natural numbers closed with respect to subtraction? Explain.

16. Find three natural numbers a, b, and c so that

$$(a - b) - c \neq a - (b - c)$$

thus showing that the natural numbers are not associative relative to the subtraction.

17. State which of the axioms for natural numbers justifies each statement:

(A) $2 + (x + y) = (x + y) + 2$

(B) $(a + b)(x + y) = (x + y)(a + b)$

(C) $(u + v) + (x + y) = u + [v + (x + y)]$

(D) $5(a + b) = 5a + 5b$

(E) $(u + v)(a + b) = (u + v)a + (u + v)b$

(F) $(ab)(xy) = a[b(xy)]$

18. State which of the axioms for natural numbers justifies each statement:

(A) $a + (b + c)$ is a natural number

(B) $(a + b)(x + y)$ is a natural number

(C) $[(u + v) + w] + x = (u + v) + (w + x)$

(D) $c + (a + b) = (a + b) + c$

19. Which axiom permits us to write the formula for the perimeter of a rectangle $p = 2a + 2b$ in the form $p = 2(a + b)$?

20. Combine like terms:
(A) $(3x^2 + 2x + 5) + (4x^2 + x + 1)$
(B) $2x^2 + 3xy + 4y^2 + xy + 3y^2 + x^2$
(C) $(3x + 2y) + (y + 5z) + (7x + 2z)$

21. Multiply, using the distributive axiom, and combine like terms:
(A) $5a(2a + b) + 3b(a + 4b)$
(B) $(2x^3 + 3)x^3 + (2x^3 + 3)5$
(C) $(3x + 2)(x + 3)$

22. Write as the product of two or more factors (removing factors common to all terms):
(A) $ax + ay$
(B) $2x^2 + 4xy$
(C) $3x^2y + 6xy^2 + 9xy$

23. In the algebraic expression $5t^4 + t^2 + 3t + 1$,
(A) What is the exponent of the variable in the second term?
(B) What is the numerical coefficient in the second term?
(C) What is the exponent of the variable in the third term?
(D) What is the numerical coefficient in the third term?

24. Simplify:
(A) $(2xy^3z^2)(4x^2yz^2)$ (B) $(3 \cdot 10^7)(12 \cdot 10^{13})$ (C) $(5u^2v^3)(2uv)(u^3v^2)$

25. If there are approximately 10^{13} cells in a grown man and an average-size cell contains about $2 \cdot 10^{14}$ molecules, approximately how many molecules are there in a grown man? Express the answer with and without power-of-ten notation.

26. Replace the words "is" and "was" with either "$=$" or "$\neq$" where appropriate:
(A) President Kennedy was the thirty-fifth president of the United States. (The statement is true.)
(B) IX is 9.
(C) IX is a Roman numeral.
(D) $5 + (8 - 3)$ is $(2 + 3) + (7 - 2)$.

27. Given the amount formula for simple interest $S = p + I$ and the simple interest formula $I = prt$. What principle of equality permits us to write $S = p + prt$?

28. Translate each statement into an algebraic equation using only one variable, and simplify the left and right sides where possible.
(A) The sum of two consecutive odd numbers is 36.
(B) Twice the sum of two consecutive natural numbers is five times the first.

29. Translate each statement into an algebraic equation using only one variable, and simplify the left and right sides where possible.

(A) The sum of two consecutive odd numbers is 5 more than the second odd number.

(B) In a rectangle with area 75 sq in. the length is 5 in. more than twice the width.   Write an equation relating the area with the length and the width.

30. A ski manufacturer has fixed costs of $400 per day in addition to the cost of $40 for each pair of skis produced.   (A) Let x denote the number of pairs of skis produced per day, and write a formula for the total cost C per day in running the plant.   (B) Identify the constants and the variables in the formula.   (C) If the replacement set for x is $\{30, 35, 40\}$, what is the replacement set for C?

31. Prove that if x and y are even numbers, then $x + y$ is an even number. HINT: Use the distributive law and the fact that an even number is two times an integer.

CHAPTER TWO **integers**

13 THE SET OF INTEGERS: POSITIVE INTEGERS, NEGATIVE INTEGERS, AND ZERO

In the last chapter we were primarily concerned with the set of natural numbers and some of its important subsets. Many other kinds of numbers within the reader's experience were obviously omitted. In this chapter we will partially remedy this situation by extending the set of natural numbers to include the familiar number zero and the not-so-familiar negative integers. In Chap. 3 the number system will again be extended to include other familiar numbers as well as to include more that are not familiar.

You may wonder why there is so much concern about number systems. We can answer this by stating that the manipulations of variables and constants that are needed to change algebraic expressions and to solve algebraic equations are controlled to a considerable extent by the properties of these number systems. To get the most out of algebra, the reader should acquire a number sense; that is, he should develop an awareness of the basic properties, including strengths and limitations, of the various number systems that are discussed in these first three chapters.

POSITIVE INTEGERS

It is convenient at this time to give the set of natural numbers another name. In the future we will use the names **positive integers** and "natural numbers" interchangeably.

To help us emphasize the difference between the positive integers (natural numbers) and the negative integers that are to be introduced shortly, we will often place a plus sign in front of a numeral used to name a natural number. Thus for every natural number a,

$$+a = a$$

that is, $+a$ and a name the same number.   Hence, for example, we may use either $+3$ or 3, $+25$ or 25, $+372$ or 372 as the situation dictates.

We may form a number line with the positive integers as with the natural numbers.   Thus we have

ZERO

Zero is a very special number and deserves special consideration.   Historically it has not been used as long as many believe.   Some form of the natural numbers have very likely been in use since before recorded time; in fact, some experimental evidence suggests that some animals have a natural-number sense.   Zero, on the other hand, did not arrive on the scene until some time between A.D. 300 and A.D. 700 and then only as a place holder so that one could distinguish between numerals such as 704 and 74.   It is generally agreed that this took place in India. Around A.D. 600 or 700 zero evolved into a number in its own right—a quantity that could be added, multiplied, and with few exceptions treated like other numbers.   These and other mathematical contributions from India were transmitted through the Arabs to Europe starting around the tenth century.   It is interesting to note that these ideas did not gain widespread use in Europe until well into the seventeenth century after the printing press was in general use.   It was during the time interval between the tenth and seventeenth centuries that the old and extremely cumbersome Roman numerals were finally abandoned.

There are many reasons why we in the modern world would want to extend the natural numbers (positive integers) to include zero.   Without zero we are not, for example, able to write an answer for $5 - 5$, nor solve the simple equation $5 + x = 5$.   We will not attempt to give a precise definition of the number zero but will accept your instinctive or intuitive notion of the concept.   We will, however, postulate the existence of zero as a number different from the positive integers (natural numbers), name it with the familiar symbol "0," and define how it is to be added and multiplied with itself and the positive integers.

On the number line, 0 will be assigned to the point one unit to the left of the point with coordinate $+1$. Thus we have

QUESTION: How should $+$ and $\cdot$ be defined over the sct $\{0, +1, +2, +3, \ldots\}$ so that

(A) $5 + x = 5$ will have a solution?
(B) the commutative laws will hold for $+$ and $\cdot$?
(C) the associative laws will hold for $+$ and $\cdot$?
(D) the distributive law will hold?

Consideration of questions of this type, in addition to a couple of others reserved for a more advanced treatment of the subject,° leads to the following definition.

DEFINITION 1: $+$ AND $\cdot$ OVER THE SET $\{0, +1, +2, +3, \ldots\}$.
(A) *If a and b are positive integers, then their sum and product are determined as in the set of natural numbers.*
(B) *If a is a positive integer or zero, then*

$$0 + a = a + 0 = a \quad and \quad 0 \cdot a = a \cdot 0 = 0$$

EXAMPLE 1

$$0 + 5 = 5 \quad 0 \cdot 5 = 0 \quad 0 + 0 = 0$$
$$5 + 0 = 5 \quad 5 \cdot 0 = 0 \quad 0 \cdot 0 = 0$$
$$3 \cdot 5 \cdot 7 \cdot 0 \cdot 6 = 0$$

Under this definition of $+$ and $\cdot$ one can show (though we won't) that *the set* $\{0, +1, +2, +3, \ldots\}$ *has the following properties:* (1) *it is closed with respect to* $+$ *and* $\cdot$, (2) $+$ *and* $\cdot$ *are associative and commutative,* (3) *multiplication is distributive over addition.*

Zero is often referred to as the **additive identity** for the reason that when it is added to any number, it produces that number back again. What number would be called the **multiplicative identity**; that is, what number, when multiplied by any other, produces that number back again? The answer, of course, is 1.

°Leon Henkin et al., "Retracing Elementary Mathematics," chap. 8, The Macmillan Company, New York, 1962.

NEGATIVE INTEGERS

About the same time that zero as a number came into being in India, Hindu mathematicians invented negative numbers. The growing importance of commercial activities seems to have stimulated this invention. Since business transactions involved decreases as well as increases, it was found that both transactions could be treated at once if the natural numbers represented amounts received and the negative numbers represented amounts paid out. Of course, since then negative numbers have been put to many other uses such as recording temperature below zero, indicating altitudes below sea level, and representing deficits in financial statements, to name a few that the reader is probably already aware of. In addition, without negative numbers it is not possible to perform the operation $7 - 12$ or to solve the simple equation $8 + x = 3$. Before this course is over many more uses of negative numbers will be considered.

As in the case of zero, we will not attempt to give a precise definition of each negative integer but will for the purposes of this course accept your intuitive notion of the concept. We will, however, postulate the existence of this set of numbers along with the following properties:

1. *No negative integer is zero or a positive integer.*
2. *To each positive integer there corresponds a unique (one and only one) number called a negative integer, and these are symbolized as follows:* $-1, -2, -3, -4, \ldots$. NOTE: *The minus sign is part of the number symbol.*

By collecting the positive integers and negative integers and zero into one set we obtain the set of numbers called the **integers;** symbolically,

$$\text{Integers} = \{x \mid x \, \varepsilon \text{ negative integers, } x = 0, \text{ or } x \, \varepsilon \text{ positive integers}\}$$
$$= \{\ldots, -4, -3, -2, -1, 0, +1, +2, +3, +4, \ldots\}$$

The negative integers are associated with points on the number line in essentially the same way as are the positive integers, but the points are located to the left of the point with coordinate zero. The point with coordinate zero is called the **origin.** Thus for each positive integer associated with a point to the right of the origin there is a negative integer associated with a point in the same relative position to the left of the origin.

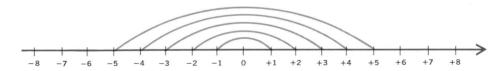

The basic arithmetical operations of addition, subtraction, multiplication, and division on the set of integers will be considered in detail in the following sections.

The invention of these new numbers—zero and the negative integers—and the definition of the arithmetical operations on these numbers to meet practical ends must be considered among the greatest advances of civilization.

EXERCISE 13

1. Write down the coordinates of points a, b, c, and d.

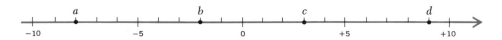

2. Given the graph of points a, b, and c,

write down the coordinate of the point
(A) eleven units to the left of c.
(B) eight units to the right of a.
(C) four units to the left of b.
(D) fourteen units to the left of b.

3. Graph each of the following sets of integers. Use a different number line for each set.
(A) $\{-4, -2, 0, +2, +4\}$
(B) $\{-25, -20, -15\}$
(C) $\{-10, -5, 0, +5\}$

4. Graph each of the following sets of integers. Use a different number line for each graph.
(A) $\{-5, -3, -1, +1, +3, +5\}$
(B) $\{-13, -5, -2, 0, +3, +8\}$
(C) $\{-35, -20, -5, +10, +15\}$

5. If $P =$ the set of positive integers
$N =$ the set of negative integers
$I \ =$ the set of integers
indicate which of the following are true:
(A) $-5 \, \varepsilon \, P$
(B) $-3 \, \varepsilon \, N$
(C) $-3 \, \varepsilon \, I$
(D) $+3 \, \varepsilon \, I$
(E) $+3 \, \varepsilon \, N$
(F) $0 \, \varepsilon \, N$
(G) $0 \, \varepsilon \, P$
(H) $0 \, \varepsilon \, I$
(I) P is a subset of I
(J) I is a subset of N

6. Each of the following sets is a subset of one or more of the sets P, N, and I defined in the previous problem; indicate of which sets the following are subsets:

(A) $\{+1, +5, +10\}$
(B) $\{-3, -7\}$
(C) $\{0\}$
(D) $\{-3, -2, -1, 0\}$
(E) $\{0, +1, +2, +7\}$
(F) $\{-6, -1, 0, +3, +8, +9\}$

7. Express each of the following quantities by means of an appropriate integer (see Fig. 1):

(A) A mountain height of 20,270 ft (Mount McKinley, highest mountain in United States).

(B) A valley depth of 280 ft below sea level (Death Valley, the lowest point in the Western Hemisphere).

(C) A mountain peak 29,141 ft high (Mt. Everest, highest point on earth).

(D) An ocean depth of 35,800 ft (Marianas Trench in the Western Pacific, greatest known depth in world).

8. Express each of the following quantities by means of an appropriate integer (see Fig. 2):

(A) 5° below freezing on Centigrade scale.
(B) 5° below freezing on Fahrenheit scale.
(C) 35° below freezing on Centigrade scale.
(D) 35° below freezing on Fahrenheit scale.
(E) 200° below boiling on Centigrade scale.
(F) 200° below boiling on Fahrenheit scale.

9. In each problem start at zero on a number line and give the coordinate of the final position:

(A) Move two units in the positive direction and four units in the negative direction.

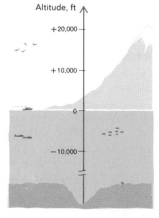

Figure 1

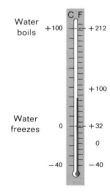

Figure 2

(B) Move three units in the negative direction, and move five more units in the negative direction.

(C) Move seven units in the negative direction, and move eleven units in the positive direction.

10. In each problem start at zero on a number line and give the coordinate of the final position:

(A) Move seven units in the positive direction, four units in the negative direction, five more units in the negative direction, and finally, three units in the positive direction.

(B) Move four units in the negative direction, seven units in the positive direction, and thirteen units in the negative direction.

11. Express each of the following quantities by means of an appropriate integer:

(A) A bank deposit of $25.   (B) A bank withdrawal of $10.

(C) A bank balance of $237.   (D) An overdrawn checking account of $17.

(E) A 23-yd gain in football.   (F) A 9-yd loss in football.

12. Express the net gain or loss by an appropriate integer:

(A) In banking: a $23 deposit, a $20 withdrawal, a $14 deposit.

(B) In banking: a $32 deposit, a $15 withdrawal, an $18 withdrawal.

(C) In football: a 5-yd gain, a 3-yd loss, a 4-yd loss, an 8-yd gain, a 9-yd loss.

(D) In an elevator: up two floors, down seven floors, up three floors, down five floors, down two floors.

14   THE NEGATIVE AND ABSOLUTE VALUE OF A NUMBER

In order to define the important binary operations of addition, subtraction, multiplication, and division on the set of integers it will be of help to define two unary° operations first. These unary operations are called "the negative of a number" and "the absolute value of a number" and will be developed in this section and used in the sections that follow as well as in many other places in the text.

THE NEGATIVE OF A NUMBER

It is important from the beginning to have a clear idea of the difference between "a negative number" and "the negative of a number." We have already discussed negative numbers; we will now define the negative of a number. The **negative of a number** N is the "mirror image" of N on the number line relative to the origin. We denote the negative of N by the symbol $-N$. The negative of

°A unary operation on a number is an operation on a single number that produces another number; contrast this with the binary operations of addition, subtraction, etc.

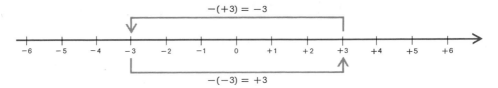

Figure 3

$+3$, denoted by $-(+3)$, is -3; the negative of -3, denoted by $-(-3)$, is $+3$ (see Fig. 3).

EXAMPLE 2

▶ $-(+37) = -37$

▶ $-(-34) = +34$

▶ $-[-(+8)] = -(-8) = +8$

▶ $-[-(-6)] = -(+6) = -6$

As a consequence of the definition of the "negative of a number," we note the following important properties: (1) *The negative of a number is not necessarily a negative number. The negative of a positive number is a negative number; the negative of a negative number is a positive number.* (2) *The negative of zero is zero.* (3) *The negative of the negative of a number is that number; that is, $-(-a) = a$ for all numbers a.* The last property is often called the "double negative principle."

It is perhaps unfortunate that the word "negative" is used in two different ways; however, with a little experience you should not have too much difficulty with the word as long as you are aware of these differences.

You are no doubt aware by now that the minus sign is also used in several distinct ways (three to be exact) as follows:

1. As the binary operation "subtract": $7 \overset{\downarrow}{-} 5 = 2$.
2. As the unary operation "the negative of": $\overset{\downarrow}{-}(-6) = +6$.
3. As a part of a number symbol: $\overset{\downarrow}{-}8$.

THE ABSOLUTE VALUE OF A NUMBER

Intuitively, we may think of the absolute value of a number as the distance of the number from the origin where this distance is expressed as a positive number (see Fig. 4). Thus the absolute value of $+5$ would be $+5$, and the absolute value of -5 would also be $+5$ since $+5$ and -5 are both the same distance from the origin.

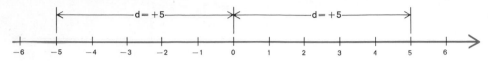

Figure 4

The notion of absolute value is made precise in the following definition.

DEFINITION 2   The **absolute value** of N, denoted by $|N|$, is defined as follows:
VERBAL FORM

If N is a positive number, then the absolute value of N is N.
If N is 0, then the absolute value of N is 0.
If N is a negative number, then the absolute value of N is the negative of N.

SYMBOLIC FORM $$|N| = \begin{cases} N & \text{if } N \text{ is a positive number} \\ 0 & \text{if } N = 0 \\ -N & \text{if } N \text{ is a negative number} \end{cases}$$

Even though the verbal form of the definition may be easier for you to understand, you should also try to understand the symbolic form since this is the form that will be most useful to us from a mathematical point of view. You will have less trouble with this concept if you simply remember the following important property:

The absolute value of a number is never negative.

EXAMPLE 3

▶ $|+7| = +7$

▶ $|-9| = \boxed{-(-9)} = +9$

▶ $|-(-3)| = |+3| = +3$

▶ $|-(+12)| = |-12| = +12$

▶ $-|+4| = -(+4) = -4$

▶ $-|-4| = -(+4) = -4$

The reader may wonder if we aren't leading him on. We went to all of the trouble to introduce negative numbers, and now we turn around and define an operation that makes negative numbers positive! We really aren't trying to make things difficult. The absolute-value operation has many uses in mathematics, and the reader will encounter it many times in this course and in the mathematics and science courses that follow.

EXERCISE 14

1. (A) Graph $-(-5)$, $-(-3)$, $-(-1)$, $-(0)$, $-(+2)$, and $-(+4)$ all on the same number line.

(B) Graph $|-5|$, $|-3|$, $|-1|$, $|0|$, $|+2|$, and $|+4|$ all on the same number line.

2. (A) Graph the negative of -5, -3, -1, 0, $+2$, and $+4$ all on the same number line.

(B) Graph the absolute value of -5, -3, -1, 0, $+2$, and $+4$ all on the same number line.

3. Replace the question marks with appropriate integers:

(A) $-(?) = +5$ (B) $-(+7) = ?$

(C) $|-5| = ?$ (D) $|?| = +5$

4. Replace the question marks with appropriate integers:

(A) $-(?) = -8$ (B) $-(-6) = ?$

(C) $|+5| = ?$ (D) $|?| = -5$

5. For $u = +2$ and $v = -3$, evaluate

(A) $|-u|$ (B) $-|u|$

(C) $-u$ (D) $-(-u)$

(E) $-|-u|$ (F) $|-v|$

(G) $-|v|$ (H) $-v$

(I) $-(-v)$ (J) $-|-v|$

6. For $x = +7$ and $y = -5$, evaluate

(A) $-x$ (B) $-y$

(C) $-|x|$ (D) $-|y|$

(E) $|-x|$ (F) $|-y|$

(G) $-(-x)$ (H) $-(-y)$

(I) $-|-x|$ (J) $-|-y|$

7. If $a = -5$, $b = -7$, $c = +8$, and $d = +3$, find

(A) $-(|a| + |b|)$ (B) $(|c| - |a|)$ (C) $-(|b| - |d|)$

8. If $x = -3$, $y = -9$, and $z = +5$, find

(A) $-(|x| + |y|)$ (B) $(|z| - |x|)$ (C) $-(|y| - |z|)$

9. If the replacement set for the variable x is the set of integers, what is the solution set for

(A) $-(|x| + |y|)$ (B) $|-12| = x$

(C) $|0| = x$ (D) $-|-4| = x$

10. If the replacement set for the variable x is the set of integers, what is the solution set for

(A) $|x| = 5$ (B) $|x| = 7$

(C) $|x| = -5$ (D) $|x| = 0$

11. Choose the right word:

(A) The negative of a number is (*always, sometimes, never*) a negative number.

(B) The absolute value of a number is (*always, sometimes, never*) a negative number.

12. Choose the right word:

(A) The negative of a number is (*always, sometimes, never*) a positive number.

(B) The absolute value of a number is (*always, sometimes, never*) a positive number.

13. For x an integer, describe the elements in each of the following sets:

(A) $\{x \mid -x = x\}$ (B) $\{x \mid x = |x|\}$

(C) $\{x \mid |x| = 0\}$ (D) $\{x \mid |-x| = x\}$

14. For x an integer, describe the elements in each of the following sets:

(A) $\{x \mid -x = |x|\}$ (B) $\{x \mid -x = 0\}$

(C) $\{x \mid -|x| = |x|\}$ (D) $\{x \mid -(-x) = x\}$

15. Show, using the definition of the negative of a number, that $-(-a) = a$ for all integers a (double-negative principle).

16. Explain, using the geometric interpretation of absolute value, why $|-x| = |x|$ for all integers x.

15   ADDITION OF INTEGERS

ADDITION OF INTEGERS GEOMETRICALLY DEFINED

In the beginning of this chapter it was pointed out that negative numbers were invented in India because of the growing importance of commercial activities. "Since business transactions involved decreases as well as increases, it was found that both transactions could be treated at once if the natural numbers represented amounts received and negative numbers represented amounts paid out." What was meant by "could be treated at once" is that a system of adding signed numbers was devised so that a running account of commercial activities could be maintained.

To be specific, if we wanted to keep a running account of bank deposits and withdrawals for a month by using positive numbers for deposits and negative numbers for withdrawals, we would need to define addition of signed numbers in such a way that at the end of the month we would be able to determine our balance by simply adding the signed entries. For example, if we started the month with a balance of $30 and made deposits and withdrawals of $+$$50, $-$$10, $-$$5, $-$$15, and $+$$10, we would expect the addition of these quantities to be defined so that the "sum" would reflect our balance at the end of the month, that is, $+$$60 dollars. If we made an additional withdrawal of $70 (indicated by $-$$70), we would expect the balance to be $-$$10, indicating an overdrawn account of $10. One may define the addition of signed numbers in many ways. We might start by thinking of addition in terms of points being moved "up and down" the number line—positive numbers indicating motion to the right and negative numbers indicating motion to the left.

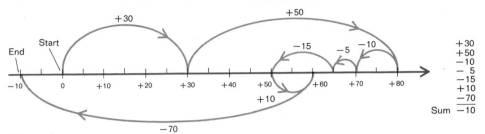

Figure 5

In the above example we would start at the origin and move 30 units to the right to indicate the balance at the first of the month, then move 50 units to the right for the first deposit, then 10 units to the left for the first withdrawal, five more units to the left for the second withdrawal, 15 more units to the left for the third withdrawal, 10 units to the right for the second deposit, and 70 units to the left for the last withdrawal, ending at -10, as we should. All of these transactions are clearly represented in Fig. 5.

This method of adding signed numbers certainly appears to be "simplicity itself." Practically speaking, however, it may prove very awkward—consider a case where fractional or decimal quantities (to be considered later) are involved. In spite of the practical limitations to this geometric method of adding signed numbers, the reader may still find the method of value as a stepping stone to a more useful, but less easily understood, nongeometric definition of addition which we will state shortly. The following examples illustrate integer addition using the number line.

EXAMPLE 4. $(+2) + (-4) = -2$

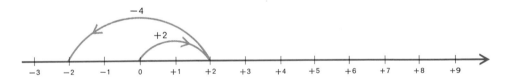

EXAMPLE 5. $(-2) + (-4) = -6$

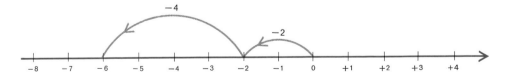

These examples may be interpreted in such terms as deposits and withdrawals and rise and fall in temperature, to name a few possibilities.

EXERCISE 15

1. Before daybreak the thermometer read $-14°$; what would be the reading if
(A) the temperature rose 20°?
(B) the temperature rose 8°?
(C) the temperature fell 6°?
(D) Illustrate parts (A), (B), and (C) geometrically on three different number lines, using appropriate integers for the changes in temperature.

2. If an elevator, starting at the 14th floor, dropped six floors, rose two floors, rose one floor, and dropped 13 floors, where would it be? Represent each motion with an appropriate integer and interpret the motion geometrically on a number line. (Let the ground floor be zero.)

3. A stock on the New York Stock Exchange closed at $18 on Monday, dropped $2 on Tuesday, dropped $3 on Wednesday, rose $2 on Thursday, and dropped $4 on Friday. What was the closing price on Friday? Represent each quantity with an appropriate integer, and illustrate the week's changes geometrically on a number line.

4. In a football game your team is on the 40-yd line and in the next four downs gains 7 yd, loses 12 yd, loses 3 yd, and gains 17 yd. Did the team make a first down (a first down requires a net gain of 10 yd)? Represent each motion with an appropriate integer, and interpret the motion geometrically on a number line.

Use the geometric method of adding in the problems that follow. (The standard but non-geometric method of adding will be defined and used after this exercise.)

5. Add, using a different number line for each problem:
(A) $(-3) + (+9)$ (B) $(-4) + (-3)$
(C) $(+5) + (+2)$ (D) $(+8) + (-12)$

6. Add, using a different number line for each problem:
(A) $(+7) + (+4)$ (B) $(+7) + (-4)$
(C) $(-7) + (+4)$ (D) $(-7) + (-4)$

7. Add, using a different number line for each problem:
(A) $(+2) + (+3) + (-8) + (+1)$ (B) $(-4) + (+9) + (-12) + (+3)$

8. Add, using a different number line for each problem:
(A) $(+5) + (-3) + (-7) + (+4)$ (B) $(-7) + (-4) + (+6) + (+5)$

9. Show that $(-3) + (+5) = (+5) + (-3)$ (suggesting that addition is commutative relative to the integers).

10. Show that $[(-4) + (+3)] + (-2) = (-4) + [(+3) + (-2)]$ (suggesting that addition is associative relative to the integers).

ADDITION OF INTEGERS FORMALLY DEFINED

It was mentioned above that the method of adding integers by using the number line, even though simple in concept, is generally awkward when put to practical use.   However, because of the preceding material, you should now have a good idea of what you would want a more formal definition of addition to accomplish.

It is clear from the examples on deposits and withdrawals that the final balance in one's bank account should not depend on the order in which one makes a series of deposits or withdrawals (assuming an overdrawn account is allowed). For example, if we start with $30, our final balance will be the same whether we deposit $5 and withdraw $7 or withdraw $7 and then deposit $5; the net effect on the account is the same in both cases.   Similarly, any regrouping of the same deposits and withdrawals should have the same net effect on the account. Examination of the other examples considered in the first part of this section leads us to the same conclusion; namely, *addition on the integers must be defined so that the operation is commutative and associative.*

We would also like addition to be defined so that we can answer questions of the following type: "If our bank account has $50 in it, what amount must be 'added' to produce a new balance of $37?"; or symbolically, "If the replacement set for the variable x is the set of integers, find the solution set for $50 + x = 37$."

All of this discussion leads up to the following important question.

QUESTION: How should $+$ be defined over the set of integers $\{\ldots, -4, -3, -2, -1, 0, +1, +2, +3, +4, \ldots\}$ so that

(A) equations of the type $8 + x = 3$ will have a solution?

(B) the set will be commutative relative to the operation $+$?

(C) the set will be associative relative to the operation $+$?

Consideration of questions of this type (in addition to several others reserved for a more advanced treatment of the subject) leads to the definition of addition that follows.   Here you will see why we introduced the absolute value of a number and the negative of a number first.   For increased understanding two forms of the definition of addition are given, a verbal form and a symbolic form. Following the statement of the definition we will observe that it has met our stated objectives, and we will then formulate simple mechanical rules that are consistent with the definition for routine everyday calculations.

DEFINITION 3:   ADDITION OVER THE SET OF INTEGERS $\{\ldots, -4, -3, -2, -1, 0,$ $+1, +2, +3, +4, \ldots\}$.

VERBAL FORM	SYMBOLIC FORM
Numbers with like sign. *If a and b are positive integers, add as in the set of natural numbers. If a and b are both negative, the sum is the negative of the sum of their absolute values.*	Numbers with like sign. *If a and b are positive integers, add as in the set of natural numbers. If a and b are negative numbers,* $$a + b = -(|a| + |b|)$$
Numbers with unlike signs. *The sum of two integers with unlike signs is a number of the same sign as the one with the larger absolute value. The absolute value of the sum is the difference of the absolute values of the two numbers found by subtracting the smaller absolute value from the larger. If the numbers have the same absolute values, their sum is zero.*	Numbers with unlike signs. *If a is positive and b is negative, then* $$a + b = (|a| - |b|) \quad if \ |a| > |b|$$ $$a + b = -(|b| - |a|) \ if \ |b| > |a|$$ $$a + b = 0 \qquad\quad if \ |a| = |b|$$ *In addition, we define* $$a + b = b + a$$
Zero. *The sum of any integer and zero is that integer; the sum of zero and any integer is that integer.*	Zero. *For any integer a,* $$a + 0 = a \qquad and \qquad 0 + a = a$$

EXAMPLE 6.   The definition of addition is used to find the following sums:

▶ $(+3) + (+5) = +8$

▶ $(-3) + (-5) = -(|-3| + |-5|) = -[(+3) + (+5)] = -8$

▶ $(+3) + (-5) = -(|-5| - |+3|) = -[(+5) - (+3)] = -(+2) = -2$

▶ $(+7) + (-7) = 0$

▶ $(-8) + 0 = -8$

All of these results agree with what we would have obtained using a number line in the first part of this section. The reader will no doubt object to the difficulty in applying the new definition to problems of the type illustrated by example 6. Fortunately, we will be able to mechanize the process so that you will be able to handle problems of this type without difficulty. You should not forget, however, that these mechanical rules or procedures that are to be discussed shortly are justified on the basis of the above definition and not vice versa. It is important that you understand Definition 3 since any property of the integers involving only addition is justified on the basis of this definition; it is the place where disputes involving addition of integers must be resolved.

The following important properties of addition are an immediate consequence of the definition of addition.

THEOREM 1   *For each integer a, b, and c*

▶ *a + b is an integer*   closure property

▶ *a + b = b + a*   commutative property

▶ *(a + b) + c = a + (b + c)*   associative property

As a consequence of this theorem we will have considerable freedom in manipulating symbols that represent integers relative to the operation of addition. This is essentially the same kind of freedom that we had with the natural numbers in rearranging terms and inserting or removing parentheses.

Now let us turn to the mechanics of adding signed numbers. It may relieve you to know that no one (not even the professional mathematician) in his every-day routine calculations involving the addition of signed numbers goes through the steps precisely as they are described in the formal definition of addition; mechanical shortcuts soon take over. The following process, or something close to it, is very likely used. We will restrict our attention to nonzero quantities since addition involving zero seems to offer few difficulties.

MECHANICS OF ADDING SIGNED NUMBERS

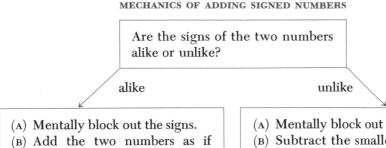

Are the signs of the two numbers alike or unlike?

alike   unlike

(A) Mentally block out the signs.   (A) Mentally block out the signs.
(B) Add the two numbers as if   (B) Subtract the smaller unsigned
    they were natural numbers.   number from the larger.
(C) Prefix the common sign of the   (C) Prefix the sign associated with
    original numbers to the sum.   the larger of the two unsigned
                                               numbers.

examples   examples

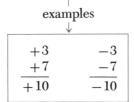

$$\begin{array}{rr} +3 & -3 \\ +7 & -7 \\ \hline +10 & -10 \end{array}$$

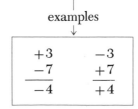

$$\begin{array}{rr} +3 & -3 \\ -7 & +7 \\ \hline -4 & +4 \end{array}$$

To add three or more integers, add all of the positive integers together, add all of the negative integers together (the commutative and associative properties of integers relative to addition justify this procedure), and then add the two resulting sums as above.

EXAMPLE 7

$$(+3)+(-6)+(+8)+(-4)+(-5) = [(+3)+(+8)]+[(-6)+(-4)+(-5)]$$
$$= (+11)+(-15)$$
$$= -4$$

or vertically,

```
                    ┌ ─ ─ ─ ─ ─ ─ ─ ─ ─ ─ ─ ─ ─ ─ ─ ─ ─ ─ ─ ┐
                    │         Done mentally or on scratchpaper      │
                    │                                          │
     +3             │   +3           -6            +11         │
     -6             │   +8           -4            -15         │
     +8             │  ───          ───          ───          │
     -4             │   +11          -5            -4          │
     -5             │               ───                       │
    ───             │               -15                       │
     -4 ────────────└ ─ ─ ─ ─ ─ ─ ─ ─ ─ ─ ─ ─ ─ ─ ─ ─ ─ ─ ─ ┘
```

REMARKS

It is at this point that some students will ask why we didn't start with these mechanical rules and avoid all of the discussion which led up to them. We have to answer this by stating that algebra (as well as other mathematics subjects) can be learned on several levels. One can learn a certain amount of useful algebra by simply memorizing a number of basic rules and working a lot of mechanical problems; perhaps for some people this is enough. For many, however, this superficial approach will prove unsatisfactory. Concepts which are memorized without understanding tend to be forgotten or confused early. A person who has an understanding of the background of the mechanical rules that he uses will be able to adjust to a variety of problem types and situations. In short, he will be aware of the power and limitations of these rules and will be able to approach unknown situations with a certain degree of confidence. On the other hand, the rote memory approach to algebra usually limits the student to a few memorized problem types and leaves him with a lack of confidence in new problem situations.

The situation is not black versus white, complete rote learning versus complete understanding. The average student should be able to handle algebraic mechanics with some understanding; the honor student will be able to handle the mechanics with considerably more understanding. Of course, complete understanding of algebra is not possible at the first-year level; we can only approach it as a desirable goal and reward those who make the effort.

ADDITIONAL PROPERTIES OF ADDITION

We will conclude this rather long section by stating, without complete proof, another (but less obvious) property of addition that follows from the definition of addition. We will refer to this property a number of times in developments that follow.

THEOREM 2   (A) *For each integer a the sum of it and its negative is zero; that is,* $a + (-a) = 0$. (B) *If the sum of two numbers is zero, then each must be the negative of the other; symbolically, if $a + b = 0$, then $b = -a$ and $a = -b$.*

PROOF OF PART (A)

   Case 1. Assume $a = 0$.

$$0 + [-(0)] = 0 + 0 = 0 \qquad \text{Can you supply the reasons?}$$

   Case 2. Assume $a \neq 0$.

By the definition of the negative of a number, a and $-a$ are numbers with unlike signs; by the definition of absolute value, $|-a| = |a|$. Therefore, by the definition of the sum of two numbers of unlike sign with the same absolute value, $a + (-a) = 0$.

EXAMPLE 8

▶ $(+3) + [-(+3)] = (+3) + (-3) = 0$

▶ $(-5) + [-(-5)] = (-5) + (+5) = 0$

▶ If $7 + b = 0$, then $b = -(+7) = -7$

▶ If $(-9) + c = 0$, then $c = -(-9) = +9$

EXERCISE 16

In problems 1 through 8 perform the indicated additions.

1. (A) $\begin{array}{r} +5 \\ +6 \\ \hline \end{array}$ (B) $\begin{array}{r} +7 \\ -4 \\ \hline \end{array}$ (C) $\begin{array}{r} -9 \\ +6 \\ \hline \end{array}$ (D) $\begin{array}{r} -3 \\ -8 \\ \hline \end{array}$ (E) $\begin{array}{r} -6 \\ +6 \\ \hline \end{array}$

2. (A) $\begin{array}{r} +13 \\ -\ 9 \\ \hline \end{array}$ (B) $\begin{array}{r} +11 \\ -23 \\ \hline \end{array}$ (C) $\begin{array}{r} -12 \\ -21 \\ \hline \end{array}$ (D) $\begin{array}{r} -307 \\ +231 \\ \hline \end{array}$ (E) $\begin{array}{r} +45 \\ +73 \\ \hline \end{array}$

3. (A) $(+5) + (+4) = ?$ (B) $(-8) + (+2) = ?$
   (C) $(-4) + (-7) = ?$ (D) $(+9) + (-4) = ?$

4. (A) $(-17) + (+4) = ?$ (B) $(-14) + (-23) = ?$
   (C) $(+54) + (-34) = ?$ (D) $(+13) + (+16) = ?$

5. (A) $+4$ (B) -6 (C) $+12$ (D) -354
       -3 -4 -18 -231
       -5 $+8$ -23 $+\ 45$
       -7 $+3$ $+\ 4$ $+517$
       $+9$ -5 -11 $-\ 73$

6. (A) -13 (B) -231 (C) -3152 (D) $+432$
       $+\ 9$ $-\ 27$ $+\ 326$ $-\ 12$
       $+11$ -159 -4398 -176
       -17 $-\ 8$ $+8991$ -328

7. (A) $(+5) + (-8) + (-9) + (+7) = ?$
    (B) $(+12) + (+7) + (-37) + (+14) = ?$
    (C) $(-23) + (-35) + (+43) + (-33) = ?$
8. (A) $(-8) + (-7) + (+3) + (+9) = ?$
    (B) $(-63) + (-18) + (+27) + (-12) = ?$
    (C) $(+381) + (-273) + (+88) + (-109) = ?$
9. Replace each question mark with an appropriate numeral:
    (A) $(+7) + (?) = (+12)$ (B) $(+8) + (?) = (+3)$
    (C) $(-12) + (?) = (+4)$ (D) $(?) + (-11) = (-18)$
    (E) $(?) + (-23) = (-14)$ (F) $(+33) + (?) = (-44)$
10. Replace each question mark with an appropriate numeral:
    (A) $(?) + (-4) = (-7)$ (B) $(-8) + (?) = (+11)$
    (C) $(-54) + (?) = (-33)$ (D) $(?) + (-14) = (+21)$
    (E) $(?) + (-12) = (-7)$ (F) $(+17) + (?) = (+3)$

11. Your football team is on the opponent's 10-yd line and in four downs gains 8 yd, loses 4 yd, loses another 8 yd, and gains 13 yd. Use addition of signed numbers to determine if a touchdown was made.

12. You own a stock that is traded on the New York Stock Exchange. On Monday it closed at $23 per share, it fell $3 on Tuesday and another $6 on Wednesday, it rose $2 on Thursday, and finished strongly on Friday by rising $7. Use addition of signed numbers to determine the closing price of the stock on Friday.

13. In a card game (such as rummy where cards held in your hand after someone goes out are counted against you) the following scores were recorded after four hands of play. Who was ahead at this time and what was his score?

Russ	Jan	Paul	Meg
$+35$	$+80$	-5	$+15$
$+45$	$+5$	$+40$	-10
-15	-35	$+25$	$+105$
-5	$+15$	$+35$	-5

14. A spelunker (cave explorer) had gone down 2,340 (vertical) ft into the 3,300-ft Gouffre Berger, the world's deepest pot-hole cave, located in the Isère province of France. On his ascent he climbed 732 ft, slipped back 25 ft and then another 60 ft, climbed 232 ft, and finally slipped back 32 ft. Use addition of signed numbers, starting with $-2,340$, to find his final position.

15. Evaluate each of the following using the definition of addition of integers (do not use the mechanical rules):

(A) $(+5) + (-9)$ (B) $(-12) + (-13)$
(C) $(-4) + (+12)$ (D) $(+12) + (-33)$
(E) $(+43) + (-43)$

16. Name the addition property that justifies each statement:

(A) $(-3) + (-7) = (-7) + (-3)$
(B) $[(+7) + (-3)] + (+3) = (+7) + [(-3) + (+3)]$

17. Evaluate each of the following:

(A) $|-3| + |+7|$ (B) $|-5| + [-(-8)]$
(C) $(-|-3|) + (-|+3|)$ (D) $[-(-3)] + [-(+3)]$
(E) $|(-8) + (+6)|$ (F) $|(-8)| + |(+6)|$

18. Evaluate each of the following for $x = -5$, $y = +3$, and $z = -2$:

(A) $(-x) + z$ (B) $-(|x| + |z|)$ (C) $|y| - |z|$
(D) $|-x| + |z|$ (E) $|(-x) + z|$ (F) $-(-x)$

19. (A) If x and y are negative integers, then $x + y$ is (*sometimes, never, always*) a negative integer.
(B) If x is a negative integer and y is a positive integer, then $x + y$ is (*sometimes, never, always*) a positive integer.

20. (A) If $|x| = |y|$ and x and y are integers of unlike sign, then what can you say about $x + y$?
(B) If $|x| > |y|$, then is $x + y$ a positive integer or a negative integer, or can you say?

21. In each statement replace the question mark with an appropriate numeral or expression:

(A) $(+7) + [-(+7)] = ?$ (B) $A + (-A) = ?$
(C) $? + (-5) = 0$ (D) $D + ? = 0$

22. In each statement replace the question mark with an appropriate numeral or expression:

(A) $? + [-(-12)] = 0$ (B) $(a + b) + [-(a + b)] = ?$
(C) $(-t) + ? = 0$ (D) $(-R) + R = ?$

23. Give a reason for each step:

$$[a + b] + (-a) = (-a) + [a + b]$$
$$= [(-a) + a] + b$$
$$= 0 + b$$
$$= b$$

24. Give a reason for each step:

$$(2a + c) + [3a + (-c)] = [(2a + c) + 3a] + (-c)$$
$$= [3a + (2a + c)] + (-c)$$
$$= [(3a + 2a) + c] + (-c)$$
$$= (5a + c) + (-c)$$
$$= 5a + [c + (-c)]$$
$$= 5a + 0$$
$$= 5a$$

25. If the temperature was $-3°$ this morning, how much gain or loss was required to produce a temperature reading of $+17°$? Let x be the amount that must be added to -3 to produce $+17$, and solve the equation $-3 + x = +17$, using your knowledge of addition of integers.

26. If Archimedes, the Greek mathematician, was born in 287 B.C. and died in 212 B.C., how long did he live? Let x represent his age at death, and solve the equation $(-287) + x = (-212)$ by using your knowledge of addition of signed numbers.

27. The United States Navy atomic-powered submarine, the Nautilus, rose from a depth of 327 ft below sea level to a depth of 197 ft below sea level. How far did it ascend? Write an equation (using signed numbers and a variable) that relates the known and unknown quantities, and solve as you did the last two problems.

28. Jerusalem, the Holy City, fell to the Babylonians in 586 B.C. and again to the Crusaders in A.D. 1099. How many years were spanned by these two events? Write an equation (using signed numbers and a variable) that relates the known and unknown quantities and solve using your knowledge of addition of signed numbers. NOTE: The Christian calender contains no year zero. Work the problem as if it did and then subtract 1 year from your answer.

29. Prove the following theorem: *If a and b are any integers, then the equation $a + x = b$ always has a solution in the integers, namely, $x = b + (-a)$. (Later we will show that this is the only solution.)*

16   SUBTRACTION OF INTEGERS

At the moment it is only assumed that you are permitted to subtract a smaller positive integer from a larger one. We would like to define subtraction for the integers so that we will always be able to subtract one integer from another no matter how they are chosen. For example, subtraction will be defined so that problems such as $(+3) - (+7)$, $(+7) - (-3)$, and $(-3) - (-7)$ will all have solutions in the integers.

From elementary school you recall that to check subtraction you added the difference and the subtrahend to see if the sum was equal to the minuend. Thus

CHECK:

$$
\begin{array}{rl}
237 & \text{minuend} \\
-148 & \text{subtrahend} \\
\hline
89 & \text{difference}
\end{array}
\qquad\qquad
\begin{array}{rl}
148 & \text{subtrahend} \\
+\ 89 & \text{difference} \\
\hline
237 & \text{minuend}
\end{array}
$$

We see that when we subtract one number from another, we are actually asking what number must be added to the subtrahend to produce the minuend. This point of view of subtraction will be of great use to us in extending the idea of subtraction to new number systems.

What do you think one should get if he were to subtract (-6) from $(+4)$? Writing the problem in elementary-school form, we get

$$
\begin{array}{rl}
(+4) & \text{minuend} \\
-(-6) & \text{subtrahend} \\
\hline
D & \text{difference}
\end{array}
$$

We see that if the subtraction properties of the natural numbers are going to continue to apply to the integers, then D must be a number so that when it is added to the subtrahend, the sum will be the minuend; that is, $(-6) + D = (+4)$, and D is clearly $+10$ from the definition of addition of integers.

We are now ready to give a general definition of subtraction that will apply not only to the integers, but to any new number system we will encounter in the future.

DEFINITION 4:   SUBTRACTION.   *We say that S subtracted from M is D if and only if the sum of S and D is M; in symbols,*

$$M - S = D \qquad \textit{if and only if} \qquad M = S + D$$

In elementary-school form we would write

$$
\begin{array}{rl}
M & \text{minuend} \\
-S & \text{subtrahend} \\
\hline
D & \text{difference}
\end{array}
\qquad \textit{if and only if} \qquad
\begin{array}{rl}
S & \text{subtrahend} \\
+D & \text{difference} \\
\hline
M & \text{minuend}
\end{array}
$$

EXAMPLE 9.   If a person was born in 1917 and died in 1966, we would normally have found his age, or how long he had lived, by subtracting his birth date, 1917, from the date he died, 1966 (that is, $1966 - 1917 = 49$). If the person was born in 535 B.C. and died in 467 B.C., we can still obtain his age at death by subtracting birth date from the date of his death, that is, by subtracting -535 from -467. From the definition of subtraction above, $(-467) - (-535) = +68$ since $(-467) = (-535) + (+68)$.

EXAMPLE 10.   Try to find the difference in each of the following problems by finding what must be added to the subtrahend to produce the minuend:

(A) $+7$	(B) $+3$	(C) $+7$	(D) -3
$+3$	$+7$	-3	$+7$
$?$	$?$	$?$	$?$

SOLUTION: (A) $+4$, (B) -4, (C) $+10$, and (D) -10.

You no doubt found the problems in example 10 a little troublesome; fortunately, we will be able to mechanize the process so that subtraction will be as easy as addition.   Nevertheless, you should still do the problems in example 10 to make sure you understand the definition of subtraction.   The mechanical rule that follows, as well as other properties of subtraction that will be considered in the future, is based on Definition 4.

The following useful and important theorem leads directly to a simple way of subtracting signed numbers.

THEOREM 3   *To subtract S from M, add the negative of S to M; symbolically,*

$$M - S = M + (-S)$$

PROOF

To prove the theorem, we must show that the sum of the subtrahend and the difference is equal to the minuend, that is, that $S + [M + (-S)] = M$. To this end, we make direct use of the properties of addition discussed in the last section (you should supply the reasons for each step).   Thus

$$S + [M + (-S)] = [M + (-S)] + S$$
$$= M + [(-S) + S]$$
$$= M + 0$$
$$= M$$

EXAMPLE 11

▶ $(+3) - (+9) = (+3) + [-(+9)] = (+3) + (-9) = -6$

▶ $(+8) - (-11) = (+8) + [-(-11)] = (+8) + (+11) = +19$

▶ $(-7) - (+4) = (-7) + [-(+4)] = (-7) + (-4) = -11$

If you look very carefully at the above example, you should be able to uncover a very simple **mechanical rule for subtraction,** namely, *to subtract one number from another, we simply change the sign of the subtrahend and add.*

EXAMPLE 12.   Subtract:

▶	$+\ 7$	▶	$-\ 4$	▶	$+\ 7$	▶	0
	$(+)$		$(-)$		$(-)$		$(+)$
	$-\ 8$		$+\ 5$		$+\ 9$		$-\ 6$
	$+\ 15$		$-\ 9$		$-\ 2$		$+\ 6$

EXAMPLE 13

▶ $(+5) - (+13) = (+5) + (-13) = -8$

▶ $(-9) - (-4) = (-9) + (+4) = -5$

▶ $0 - (+8) = 0 + (-8) = -8$

▶ $(-4) - 0 = (-4) + 0 = -4$

EXERCISE 17

Subtract and check problems 1 through 6.

1. (A) $\begin{array}{r} +9 \\ -4 \\ \hline \end{array}$ (B) $\begin{array}{r} +4 \\ +4 \\ \hline \end{array}$ (C) $\begin{array}{r} -2 \\ -2 \\ \hline \end{array}$ (D) $\begin{array}{r} -5 \\ +5 \\ \hline \end{array}$

2. (A) $\begin{array}{r} -1 \\ -8 \\ \hline \end{array}$ (B) $\begin{array}{r} +6 \\ +4 \\ \hline \end{array}$ (C) $\begin{array}{r} -5 \\ 0 \\ \hline \end{array}$ (D) $\begin{array}{r} 0 \\ +6 \\ \hline \end{array}$

3. (A) $\begin{array}{r} +24 \\ +39 \\ \hline \end{array}$ (B) $\begin{array}{r} -77 \\ -43 \\ \hline \end{array}$ (C) $\begin{array}{r} -98 \\ +33 \\ \hline \end{array}$ (D) $\begin{array}{r} -23 \\ -68 \\ \hline \end{array}$

4. (A) $\begin{array}{r} -312 \\ +\ 27 \\ \hline \end{array}$ (B) $\begin{array}{r} +\ \ 72 \\ +1386 \\ \hline \end{array}$ (C) $\begin{array}{r} 0 \\ -684 \\ \hline \end{array}$ (D) $\begin{array}{r} -692 \\ -892 \\ \hline \end{array}$

5. (A) $(+6) - (-8) = ?$ (B) $(-4) - (+7) = ?$
   (C) $(+10) - (+23) = ?$ (D) $(-13) - (-18) = ?$

6. (A) $0 - (-12) = ?$ (B) $(-23) - (-23) = ?$
   (C) $(-14) - (+14) = ?$ (D) $(+46) - (-63) = ?$

7. What theorem justifies the following statements:
(A) $(+4) - (-7) = (+4) + [-(-7)]$ (B) $a - b = a + (-b)$

8. Write down the reason for each step in the proof of Theorem 3 that was presented in this section.

9. Perform the indicated operations:
(A) $(-3) - (-4)$ (B) $(-4) - (-3)$
(C) $[(-2) - (+4)] - (-7)$ (D) $(-2) - [(+4) - (-7)]$

10. Perform the indicated operations:
(A) $[(+6) - (-8)] + [(-8) - (+6)]$
(B) $(-23) - [(-7) + (-13)]$
(C) $[(-23) - (-7)] + (-13)$

11. Is subtraction commutative relative to the integers? Explain. Is subtraction associative relative to the integers? Explain.

12. Which of the following hold for all integers a, b, and c? Illustrate each false statement with an example that shows that it is false.
(A) $a + b = b + a$ (B) $a - b = b - a$
(C) $a - b = (-b) + a$ (D) $(a - b) - c = a - (b - c)$
(E) $|a - b| = |a| - |b|$ (F) $|a + b| = |a| + |b|$

13. Evaluate for $x = +2$, $y = -5$, and $z = -3$:
(A) $(x + z) - y$ (B) $y - |z|$ (C) $x - |y - z|$
(D) $(x + y) - |z|$ (E) $-|-y|$ (F) $-|y|$
(G) $|(x - y) - (y - z)|$ (H) $(-y) - (-z)$ (I) $-(|y| - |x|)$
(J) $-(|y| + |z|)$ (K) $-(|x||y|)$ (L) $|y||z|$

14. Evaluate for $a = -1$, $b = +5$, and $c = -7$:
(A) $a - c$ (B) $|a - c|$ (C) $|a| - |b|$
(D) $-|b + c|$ (E) $-(b + c)$ (F) $-(-a)$
(G) $|a + (a - b) + c|$ (H) $|a - b| - c$ (I) $-(|c| - |b|)$
(J) $-(|a| + |c|)$ (K) $-(|b||c|)$ (L) $|a||c|$

15. Use Fig. 6 and subtraction of signed numbers to find
(A) The difference in height between the highest point in the United States, Mount McKinley, and the lowest point in the United States, Death Valley.
(B) The difference in height between the Salton Sea and Death Valley (both in California).

16. Use Fig. 6 and subtraction of signed numbers to find
(A) The difference in height between the highest point on earth, Mount Everest, and the deepest point in the ocean, Marianas Trench.
(B) The difference in height between the Dead Sea, the deepest fault in the earth's crust, and Death Valley.

17. If you had $56 in the bank, determine how much was withdrawn (by use of signed numbers) if your new balance is (A) $28, (B) $-$11.

18. If a person's bank statement read $-$23 at the end of last month and $123

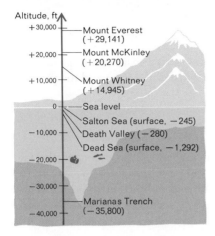

Figure 6

at the first of this month, use subtraction of signed numbers to determine the amount of the deposit that was made.

19. In a card game you are 35 points "in the hole." How many points are needed to get a score of 150? Use subtraction of signed numbers to get your answer.

20. There seems to be a relationship between carbon-14 activity and atmospheric temperature: "The two periods of high carbon-14 activity, 1200–500 B.C. and A.D. 1300–1860, were coincident with the two major periods of lower temperatures and glacial advance . . . . The long period of lower carbon-14 activity from A.D. 1 to 1200 was coincident with a well-documented period of glacial retreat or stagnation . . . ."* Use subtraction of signed numbers to

(A) determine the length of the first high carbon-14 period.

(B) determine the length of time between the end of the first period of high activity to the beginning of the second period of high activity.

NOTE: Since the Christian calendar does not have a year zero, work the problem as if it did. Then subtract 1 year from the answer.

21. Supply the reasons for each of the following steps (more than one reason may be required for each step):

$$(a + b) + [(-a) + (-b)] = [a + (-a)] + [b + (-b)]$$
$$= 0 + 0$$
$$= 0$$

Therefore, $\qquad -(a + b) = (-a) + (-b)$

* J. R. Bray, "Atmospheric Carbon-14 Content During the Past Three Millennia in Relation to Temperature and Solar Activity," *Nature*, vol. 209, no. 5028, March 12, 1966.

17   MULTIPLICATION OF INTEGERS

Having defined addition and subtraction for the integers, we now turn to multiplication.   Once again there are several cases to consider: the product of numbers with like sign, the product of numbers with unlike sign, and the product of any number and zero.

GENERAL DISCUSSION

By considering certain practical problems involving signed numbers and the fact that we wanted certain properties of the natural numbers to carry over to the integers, we were led rather naturally to the formal definitions of addition and subtraction of integers.   Similarly, we will investigate several situations involving signed numbers that will suggest how we should define multiplication on the integers.

1.   Suppose that we agree to let the number of hours after noon to be represented by positive numbers and the number of hours before noon be represented by negative numbers; the rate of a plane flying east by positive numbers and the rate of a plane flying west by negative numbers; and the distance that a plane, starting at zero, flies east by positive numbers and the distance west by negative numbers.   We will find that the familiar formula, (distance) = (rate) · (time), with this more general interpretation of distance, rate, and time, will suggest to us how we might define the product of signed numbers so that the plane's position (coordinate) on a number line will be determined if the plane's "directed rate" and "directed time" are given.   Consider the following cases where it is assumed that the plane is at the origin (zero) at noon:

West ————————————————————————————————— East

-500 .... 0 500

(A)   A plane flying east at 100 mph would be at $+400$ at 4 P.M.

$$+400 = (+100)(+4)$$

(directed distance) = (directed rate)(directed time)

(B)   A plane flying east at 100 mph would be at -200 at 10 A.M.

$$-200 = (+100)(-2)$$

(directed distance) = (directed rate)(directed time)

(C)   A plane flying west at 100 mph would be at -600 at 6 P.M.

$$-600 = (-100)(+6)$$

(directed distance) = (directed rate)(directed time)

(D) A plane flying west at 100 mph would be at $+500$ at 7 A.M.

$$+500 = (-100)(-5)$$

(directed distance) = (directed rate)(directed time)

It would appear from the above discussion that it might be natural to define the product of two numbers with like sign as a positive number, the product of two numbers with unlike sign as a negative number, and in all cases the product of the absolute values of the two numbers would be the absolute value of the product. The following illustration will provide added support for this proposal.

2. We would like to define multiplication of integers in such a way that closure, associative, commutative, and distributive properties hold. Let us assume for the moment that these properties do hold and investigate the consequences. Consider the following argument (assuming that $a \cdot 0 = 0$ for all integers a):

$(+3) + (-3) = 0$	Theorem 2, Sec. 15
$(+2)[(+3) + (-3)] = (+2)(0)$	property of equality
$(+2)(+3) + (+2)(-3) = 0$	assumed distributive property and $(+2)(0) = 0$
$(+2)(-3) = -[(+2)(+3)]$	Theorem 2, Sec. 15
$= -6$	definition of the negative of a number

What the preceding argument indicates is that if the multiplication properties of natural numbers carry over to the integers, then $(+2)(-3)$ has no choice but to be defined to be -6. A similar argument will show that $(-2)(-3)$ will have to be defined to be $+6$.

Neither of the two illustrations above prove anything in general. They simply provide very strong motivation for the formal definition of multiplication of integers that follows.

MULTIPLICATION OF INTEGERS FORMALLY DEFINED

The preceding general discussion leads us to the following question: How should multiplication be defined over the set of integers so that it will be commutative, associative, and distributive over addition, and, in addition, the integers will be closed relative to this operation? Consideration of this question, the foregoing general discussion, and several other questions reserved for a more advanced treatment of the subject, essentially dictate the following definition of multiplication.

DEFINITION 5:   MULTIPLICATION OVER THE SET OF INTEGERS $\{\ldots, -4, -3, -2,$ $-1, 0, +1, +2, +3, +4, \ldots\}$.

VERBAL FORM	SYMBOLIC FORM
Numbers with like sign. *The product of two integers with like signs is a positive number and is found by multiplying the absolute values of the two numbers.*	**Numbers with like sign.** *If a and b are integers with like sign, then* $$ab = |a||b|$$
Numbers with unlike signs. *The product of two integers with unlike signs is a negative integer and is found by taking the negative of the product of the absolute values of the two integers.*	**Numbers with unlike signs.** *If a and b are integers with unlike signs, then* $$ab = -(|a||b|)$$
Zero. *The product of any integer and zero is zero; the product of zero and any integer is zero.*	**Zero.** *For any integer a,* $$a \cdot 0 = 0 \qquad and \qquad 0 \cdot a = 0$$

EXAMPLE 14.   The definition of multiplication is used to find the following products:

▶ $(+2)(+3) = |+2||+3| = (+2)(+3) = +6$

▶ $(-2)(-3) = |-2||-3| = (+2)(+3) = +6$

▶ $(-2)(+3) = -(|-2||+3|) = -[(+2)(+3)] = -(+6) = -6$

▶ $(+5)(0) = 0$

Fortunately, as in the case with addition, we will be able to mechanize the process of multiplication of signed numbers so that you will be able to write down an answer immediately and with very little effort. However, as before, it is important that you understand the definition of multiplication since it is the basis for any mechanical rules that you may devise, as well as for the many useful general properties of multiplication that we will consider.

Before we mechanize the process of multiplying signed numbers, let us look at several very useful and important properties of multiplication that can be proved on the basis of the definition of multiplication given above. We will not carry out the general proof for all of these properties,[*] although special cases will be included as exercises in the problem set for this section.

[*] L. Henkin et al., "Retracing Elementary Mathematics," chap. 11, The Macmillan Company, New York, 1962.

THEOREM 4   *For each integer a, b, and c*

▶ *ab is an integer*   closure property

▶ *ab = ba*   commutative property

▶ *(ab)c = a(bc)*   associative property

▶ *a(b + c) = ab + ac*   distributive property

Because of this theorem we will continue to have the same kind of freedom in manipulating symbols that represent integers relative to multiplication that we did when we were limited to natural numbers. The theorem allows us, when multiplying, to rearrange factors at will and to insert and remove parentheses at will. You will be performing these operations almost subconsciously by the end of the course. The distributive property will be seen to be particularly powerful for simplifying algebraic expressions.

Returning now to the mechanics of multiplying signed numbers, we will start by stating that it is a rare person who, in daily use, multiplies signed numbers following the steps outlined in Definition 5. For routine calculations, the process is easily and quickly mechanized.

MECHANICS OF MULTIPLYING SIGNED NUMBERS

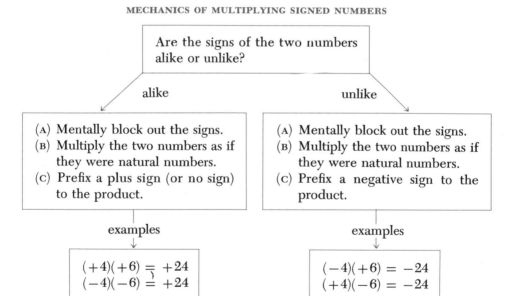

EXAMPLE 15.   Evaluate ab and ba for $a = -2$ and $b = +5$.

SOLUTION:

$$ab = (-2)(+5) = -10$$
$$ba = (+5)(-2) = -10$$

EXERCISE 18

1. Multiply:
(A) $(+2)(+7) = ?$ $\qquad$ (B) $(-6)(+8) = ?$
(C) $(+7)(-9) = ?$ $\qquad$ (D) $(-3)(-5) = ?$
(E) $(+1)(-8) = ?$ $\qquad$ (F) $(-1)(-8) = ?$
(G) $(0)(-5) = ?$ $\qquad$ (H) $(-6)(0)(-3) = ?$

2. Multiply:
(A) $(-4)(+3) = ?$ $\qquad$ (B) $(-12)(-3) = ?$
(C) $(+15)(-4) = ?$ $\qquad$ (D) $(+5)^2 = ?$
(E) $(-3)^2 = ?$ $\qquad$ (F) $(-2)(-4)(-1) = ?$
(G) $(-3)^2(-6) = ?$ $\qquad$ (H) $(+5)(-4)^3(0)(-7) = ?$

3. Find the value of each of the following:
(A) $(-4)(+7)$ $\qquad$ (B) $(+7)(-4)$
(C) $[(-3)(+2)](-6)$ $\qquad$ (D) $(-3)[(+2)(-6)]$
(E) $(-3)[(-4) + (+6)]$ $\qquad$ (F) $(-3)(-4) + (-3)(+6)$
(G) $(-2)[(+3) + (-5) + (-2)]$
(H) $(-2)(+3) + (-2)(-5) + (-2)(-2)$

4. Evaluate each of the following for $x = -5$, $y = +2$, and $z = (-7)$:
(A) xy $\qquad$ (B) yx
(C) $(xy)z$ $\qquad$ (D) $x(yz)$
(E) $x(y + z)$ $\qquad$ (F) $xy + xz$
(G) $(-2)(x + y + z)$ $\qquad$ (H) $(-2)x + (-2)y + (-2)z$

5. Find the products in problem $1a$ through $1d$ by using the definition of the product of integers (Definition 5).

6. Find the products in problem $2a$ through $2d$ by using the definition of the product of integers (Definition 5).

7. Replace the question marks with appropriate numerals:
(A) $(-3)(?) = +12$ $\qquad$ (B) $(+5)(?) = -15$
(C) $(-7)(?) = -42$ $\qquad$ (D) $(?)(+8) = +56$
(E) $(?)(-9) = -9$ $\qquad$ (F) $(-12)(?)(+3) = +36$
(G) $(?)(+7)(-3) = -42$ $\qquad$ (H) $(-8)(0)(+9) = ?$

8. Guess at the solution of each equation, assuming the replacement set for all variables involved is the set of integers:
(A) $(-4)x = -8$ $\qquad$ (B) $(+7)y = -21$
(C) $(-6)t = +54$ $\qquad$ (D) $(-9)z = +9$
(E) $(+12)y = +22$ $\qquad$ (F) $(-2)t(-3) = -24$
(G) $(+4)(-3)x = (-6)(+6)$ $\qquad$ (H) $(-4)x = -17$

9. Find the value of each of the following:
(A) $-(-2)^2$ $\qquad$ (B) $-(-2)^3$
(C) $-(|-3||+4|)$ $\qquad$ (D) $|-8||-9|$
(E) $(-5)^2(-1)^3$ $\qquad$ (F) $(-2)^3|-5|(-1)$

(G) $[(-3) - (+2)]^3$ (H) $(-3)^2 - (-2)^3$

10. Find the value of each of the following:

(A) $-(-1)^5$ (B) $-|-1|^5$

(C) $-|(-3)^3 - (-6)|$ (D) $[-(-3)](+4)$

(E) $-[(-3)(+4)]$ (F) $(-1)(-5)$

(G) $-(-5)$ (H) $[(-2)^3 - (-2)^2]^2$

11. Evaluate each of the following for $a = -1$, $b = +5$, and $c = -3$:

(A) abc (B) $|a|bc$

(C) $(-c)^2$ (D) $-c^2$

(E) $(-c)b$ (F) $-(cb)$

(G) $(-a)(-b)$ (H) ab

12. Evaluate each of the following for $x = -2$, $y = -4$, and $z = +3$:

(A) $(-x)^2$ (B) x^2

(C) $-x^2$ (D) $-(|y||z|)$

(E) $|x||y|$ (F) xy

(G) $x(x^2 - y^2)$ (H) $x^3 - xy^2$

13. (A) The product of an even number of negative numbers is (*sometimes, always, never*) negative.

(B) The product of an odd number of negative numbers is (*sometimes, always, never*) negative.

14. If the replacement set for the variable x is the set of integers, then $-x$ (*sometimes, always, never*) represents a negative integer.   Explain.

In the following problems assume that the replacement set for all variables is the set of integers.

15. Use the distributive property to write each as the sum of two terms:

EXAMPLE: $2a(2a + 3b) = 4a^2 + 6ab$.

(A) $x(x + 1)$ (B) $x^2(x + y)$

(C) $2xy(3x + 4y)$ (D) $(-2x)[(-3x^2) + (-4x)]$

16. Write as the product of two or more factors:

EXAMPLE: $4ac + 2bc = 2c(2a + b)$

(A) $ax + ay$ (B) $x^2 + xy$ (C) $x^2y + xy^2$ (D) $2ab + 4ac$

17. Simplify, combining like terms where possible:

EXAMPLE: $x^2(x + 3) + 2x(x^2 + 2x) = x^3 + 3x^2 + 2x^3 + 4x^2 = 3x^3 + 7x^2$.

(A) $3x^2 + 2x + 5x^2 + x$ (B) $2(x^2 + x) + 3x(x + 2)$

18. Simplify, combining like terms where possible:

(A) $4ab + c^2 + ab + 3c$ (B) $3a(a + 2b) + 4ab + 2b(2a + b)$

ADDITIONAL PROPERTIES OF MULTIPLICATION

We will complete this section by considering several additional properties of multiplication that will be very useful to us. To start, consider the effect of multiplying an integer by either $+1$ or -1. It is an immediate consequence of the definition of multiplication (Definition 5) that if we multiply any integer by $+1$, we will get that integer back again, and if we multiply any integer by -1, we will get the negative of the original integer. Thus for any integer a

$$(+1)a = a \qquad and \qquad (-1)a = -a$$

Because a quantity may be substituted for its equal in any expression (substitution principle for equality), $(+1)a$ and a may be used interchangeably, and $(-1)a$ and $-a$ may be used interchangeably. We now see why we say that a has an understood coefficient of $+1$, and $-a$ has an understood coefficient of -1. These are facts that will be used many times throughout the rest of the course.

EXAMPLE 16. Show that $3x - x = 2x$.

PROOF

$$\begin{aligned}
3x - x &= 3x + (-x) & &\text{Theorem 3, Sec. 16} \\
&= 3x + [(-1)x] & &\text{definition of multiplication} \\
&= [3 + (-1)]x & &\text{distributive and commutative properties} \\
&= 2x & &\text{definition of addition}
\end{aligned}$$

In Sec. 19 we will develop mechanical rules for simplifying expressions of the type found in example 16. Perhaps you can already guess a simple mechanical rule for combining $3x - x$ into $2x$.

The next property of integers we are going to discuss is often mistaken for the definition of the product of two integers; actually, it is a theorem.

THEOREM 5 *For each integer a and each integer b,*

(A) $(-a)b = -(ab)$

(B) $(-a)(-b) = ab$

In words this theorem states that the product of the negative of an integer and another integer is the negative of the product of the two integers, and the product of the negative of an integer and the negative of another integer is the product of the original integers.

PROOF OF PART (A)

$$\begin{aligned}
(-a)b &= [(-1)a]b & &\text{definition of multiplication} \\
&= (-1)(ab) & &\text{associative property} \\
&= -(ab) & &\text{definition of multiplication}
\end{aligned}$$

The proof of part (B) is left as an exercise.

EXAMPLE 17.   Evaluate $(-a)b$ and $-(ab)$ for $a = -5$ and $b = +4$.

SOLUTION

$$(-a)b = [-(-5)](+4) = (+5)(+4) = +20$$
$$-(ab) = -[(-5)(+4)] = -(-20) = +20$$

Expressions of the form "$-ab$" occur rather frequently in algebra and at first glance are often confusing to students.   If you were asked to evaluate $-ab$ for $a = -3$ and $b = +2$, how would you proceed?   Would you take the negative of a and then multiply it by b, or multiply a and b first and then take the negative of the product?   Actually it doesn't matter!   Because of Theorem 5 we get the same result either way since $(-a)b = -(ab)$.   If, in addition, we consider the first part of this discussion, we find that $-ab$ may even be replaced with a third form: $(-1)ab$.   Hence,

$$-ab = \begin{cases} (-a)b \\ -(ab) \\ (-1)ab \end{cases}$$

and we are at liberty to replace any one of these four forms with another from the same group.

EXAMPLE 18.   For $a = -2$ and $b = +3$ evaluate $-ab$ three different ways.

SOLUTION

$$-ab = (-a)b = [-(-2)](+3) = (+2)(+3) = +6$$
$$-ab = -(ab) = -[(-2)(+3)] = -(-6) = +6$$
$$-ab = (-1)ab = (-1)[(-2)(+3)] = (-1)(-6) = +6$$

We will conclude this section by observing two additional distributive properties that will be of use to us.

$$a(b + c + d + \cdots + f) = ab + ac + ad + \cdots + af$$
$$a(b - c) = ab - ac$$

The first distributive property is easily proved for any particular case by repeated use of Theorem 4 in this section; a general proof is beyond the scope of this course.   The proof of the second distributive property is left as an exercise (see problem 9, Exercise 19).

EXAMPLE 19

▶ $2x(3x^2 + 4x + 1) = 6x^3 + 8x^2 + 2x$

▶ $3xy(x - 2y) = 3x^2y - 6xy^2$

EXERCISE 19

1. Find the value of
(A) $(-1)(-7)$ and $-(-7)$
(B) $[-(-4)](-3)$, $-[(-4)(-3)]$, and $(-1)(-4)(-3)$
(C) $[-(+5)][-(-6)]$ and $(+5)(-6)$
2. For $x = -5$ and $y = +3$, evaluate
(A) $(-1)x$ and $-x$
(B) $(-x)y$, $-(xy)$, and $(-1)xy$
(C) $(-x)(-y)$ and xy
3. Find the value of
(A) $(-3)[(-1) + (+4) + (-7)]$ and $(-3)(-1) + (-3)(+4) + (-3)(-7)$
(B) $(-4)[(+3) - (+5)]$ and $(-4)(+3) - (-4)(+5)$
4. For $w = -2$, $x = -5$, $y = +8$, and $z = -1$, evaluate
(A) $w(x + y + z)$ and $wx + wy + wz$
(B) $w(x - z)$ and $wx - wz$
5. Write the following products as the sum (or difference) of two or more terms:
(A) $4t^2(2t^2 + 3t + 5)$
(B) $6xy(x^2 - y^2)$
(C) $3ab^2(2a + 6b + ab + b^2)$
(D) $4u^3(2u^2 - 3v)$
6. Write the following products as the sum (or difference) of two or more terms:
(A) $2yz(3y^2z - 5yz^2)$
(B) $4x^3(2x^4 + 3x^2 + x + 3)$
(C) $4t^3(t^5 - 2t^2)$
(D) $3x^2y^2(x^3 + 2x^2y + 3xy^2 + 2y^3)$
7. Prove $(-1)a = -a$ *for all integers a.*   HINT: Divide the proof into the following three cases: (1) assume a is a positive integer, (2) assume a is a negative integer, and (3) assume a is zero.
8. Prove part (B) of Theorem 5 [that is, $(-a)(-b) = ab$].   HINT: The proof of part (B) is very similar to the proof of part (A).
9. Supply the reasons for the proof of the distributive property $a(b - c) = ab - ac$.

PROOF

$$a(b - c) = a[b + (-c)] = ab + a(-c) = ab + (-c)a$$
$$= ab + [-(ca)] = ab + [-(ac)] = ab - ac$$

18   DIVISION OF INTEGERS

We have now discussed addition, subtraction, and multiplication of integers. Division, the last of the four fundamental arithmetical operations on integers, is the subject matter for this section.   After the next section, which includes a little more work with algebraic mechanics, we will be in a position to attack a number of useful and interesting applications.

GENERAL DISCUSSION

Preliminary to the definition of division of integers, we will review some of the properties of division of natural numbers that were first introduced to you in elementary school.   We will find that division is related to multiplication in much the same way that subtraction is related to addition.

From elementary school you recall that to check division, you multiplied the divisor and quotient to see if the product was equal to the dividend.   Thus

$$
\begin{array}{cl}
5 & \text{quotient} \\
\text{divisor} \quad 8\overline{)40} & \text{dividend}
\end{array}
\qquad
\begin{array}{cl}
5 & \text{quotient} \\
\underline{\times\ 8} & \text{divisor} \\
40 & \text{dividend}
\end{array}
$$

We see that when we divide one number by another, we are actually asking what number must be multiplied by the divisor to produce the dividend.   This approach to division will be of considerable use to us in generalizing the concept of division from natural numbers to new number systems.

What do you think one should get if he were to divide $+18$ by -3?   Writing the problem in elementary-school form,

$$
\begin{array}{cl}
Q & \text{quotient} \\
\text{divisor} \quad (-3)\overline{)(+18)} & \text{dividend}
\end{array}
$$

we see that if the division properties of the natural numbers are going to continue to apply to the integers, then Q must be a number so that when it is multiplied by the divisor, the product will be the dividend; that is, $(-3)Q = +18$. From the definition of the product of two integers, Q is clearly -6.

DIVISION FORMALLY DEFINED

Before a formal definition of division is given, a few remarks about division notation should be made.   The two symbols " $\div$ " and " $\overline{)}$ " that you have used so much in arithmetic are not used a great deal in algebra and higher mathematics. The horizontal bar "—" and slash mark "/" are the symbols for division we will use most frequently.   Thus, a/b, $\frac{a}{b}$, $a \div b$, and $b\overline{)a}$ all name the same number (assuming the quotient is defined).   Hence we can write

$$a/b = \frac{a}{b} = a \div b = b\overline{)a}$$

DEFINITION 6:   DIVISION.   *The quotient of two integers a and b, denoted by a/b (or any of the equivalent forms above), is a unique integer Q, if it exists, such that the product of b and Q is a.   Symbolically,*

$$\frac{a}{b} = Q \qquad \textit{if and only if} \qquad a = bQ \textit{ and } Q \textit{ is unique}$$

EXAMPLE 20.

▶ $\dfrac{+12}{-3} = -4$, since $(-3)(-4) = +12$.

▶ $\dfrac{-12}{-3} = +4$, since $(-3)(+4) = -12$.

▶ $\dfrac{+3}{-12}$ is not defined in the integers.

▶ $\dfrac{+4}{0}$ is not defined since the product of zero and any number is zero, not $+4$.

As in the case for the other three arithmetic operations, we will be able to mechanize the process for division.   The following theorem (which we will not prove) is a consequence of the definition of division and leads directly to this process.

THEOREM 6:   DIVISION OF INTEGERS.

(A) *If a and b are integers with like signs, then*

$$\frac{a}{b} = \frac{|a|}{|b|}$$

(B) *If a and b are integers with unlike signs, then*

$$\frac{a}{b} = -\frac{|a|}{|b|}$$

(C) *Zero.   If a is any nonzero integer, then*

(1) $\dfrac{0}{a} = 0$

(2) $\dfrac{a}{0}$ is not defined

zero cannot be used as a divisor—ever!

(3) $\dfrac{0}{0}$ is not defined

EXAMPLE 21.

▶ $\dfrac{-27}{-9} = \dfrac{|-27|}{|-9|} = \dfrac{+27}{+9} = +3$

▶ $\dfrac{-27}{+9} = -\left[\dfrac{|-27|}{|+9|}\right] = -\left[\dfrac{(+27)}{(+9)}\right] = -(+3) = -3$

▶ $\dfrac{0}{-4} = 0$

▶ $\dfrac{-4}{0}$ is not defined.

▶ $\dfrac{0}{0}$ is not defined.

You should have little difficulty formulating mechanical rules for dividing signed numbers since the sign properties for division are the same as the sign properties for multiplication; that is, *the quotient of two integers with like sign is positive, and the quotient of two integers with unlike sign is negative.*

EXAMPLE 22.   Evaluate a/b and b/a for $a = -8$ and $b = +2$.

SOLUTION

$$a/b = \dfrac{-8}{+2} = -4$$

$b/a = (+2)/(-8)$ is not defined in the integers.   (This form will be discussed in the next chapter.)

EXAMPLE 23.   Evaluate $(a/b)/c$ and $a/(b/c)$ for $a = -16, b = -8,$ and $c = -2$.

SOLUTION

$$\dfrac{a/b}{c} = \dfrac{(-16)/(-8)}{-2} = \dfrac{+2}{-2} = -1$$

$$\dfrac{a}{b/c} = \dfrac{-16}{(-8)/(-2)} = \dfrac{-16}{+4} = -4$$

These last two examples should make it clear that division is not closed, commutative, or associative relative to the integers.

EXERCISE 20

NOTE: *Recall that when symbols of grouping are used one generally performs the operations within the parentheses ( ) first, then the brackets [ ], and finally the braces { }; where symbols of grouping are absent, multiplication and division precede addition and subtraction.*

1. Divide as indicated and check:
(A) $(+8)/(+2) = ?$ (B) $(-8) \div (-2) = ?$

(C) $\dfrac{+8}{-2} = ?$ (D) $(-8)/(+2) = ?$

(E) $0 \div (+3) = ?$ (F) $0/(-3) = ?$

(G) $\dfrac{-4}{0} = ?$ (H) $0/0 = ?$

2. Divide as indicated and check:
(A) $(-36)/(-9) = ?$ (B) $(-12)/(+4) = ?$
(C) $0/(-12) = ?$ (D) $(+56)/(-8) = ?$
(E) $(-83)/0 = ?$ (F) $(+45)/(+15) = ?$
(G) $(-6)/(-1) = ?$ (H) $0/(-1) = ?$

3. Find the value of each of the following:
(A) $(-84)/(+7)$ (B) $(-2)/(-6)$
(C) $[(-3)(+5)]/(+3)$ (D) $[(-16)/(+2)] + [(-3)/(-1)]$
(E) $[(+27)/(-9)] - [(-21)/(-7)]$
(F) $(-2)\{[(-6)/(+2)] - [(-2)(-3)]\} + (-18)$

4. Evaluate each of the following for $w = +2, x = -3, y = 0,$ and $z = -24$:
(A) z/x (B) y/w

(C) $wx - z/w$ (D) $xyz + \dfrac{y}{z} + x$

(E) $x(z/x - z/w)$ (F) $(w^3x)/z$

5. Zero divided by any integer is (*always, sometimes, never*) zero.

6. Any integer divided by zero is (*always, sometimes, never*) zero.

7. Find the quotients in problems $1a$ through $1d$ by using the definition of the quotient of two integers.

8. Find the quotients in problems $2a$ through $2d$ by using the definition of the quotient of two integers.

9. Find the quotients in problems $1e$ through $1h$ by the use of Theorem 6 in this section.

10. Find the quotients in problems $2e$ through $2h$ by the use of Theorem 6 in this section.

11. Replace the question marks with appropriate numerals:
(A) $(+12)/(?) = +3$ (B) $(-18)/(?) = +3$

(c) $(?)/(-5) = -5$

(d) $(?)/(-14) = 0$

(e) $(-45)/(-9) = ?$

(f) $(-13)/(?) = +13$

(g) $(?)/(+27) = -1$

(h) $(+42)/(-3) = ?$

12. Guess at the solution of each equation assuming the replacement set for all variables involved is the set of integers:

(a) $x/(-4) = +12$

(b) $(-24)/y = -3$

(c) $z/(+32) = 0$

(d) $(-52)/(-13) = w$

(e) $(-1)/(+6) = x$

(f) $(+6)/(-1) = y$

(g) $t/(-3) = 0$

(h) $u^2/(-3) = +3$

13. Explain why $(-5)/0$ is not defined.

14. Explain why $0/(-5)$ is defined to be 0.

15. If the quotient x/y exists, is $\dfrac{x}{y}$ (*always, sometimes, never*) equal to $\dfrac{|x|}{|y|}$? Explain.

16. If the quotient x/y exists, is $\dfrac{x}{y}$ (*always, sometimes, never*) equal to $-\dfrac{|x|}{|y|}$? Explain.

19   ALGEBRAIC EXPRESSIONS: SIMPLIFICATION AND EVALUATION

We are almost at the place where we can start using algebra to solve problems. Before we start on applications, however, it will be worth our while to spend a short time developing techniques to speed up and improve our methods for manipulating symbols.

Up until now we have used parentheses and other symbols of grouping far more than they are generally used in practice. This was important for a careful development of the many basic concepts we considered in the beginning. In the future, for ease of reading and increased clarity, it will be desirable to reduce the number of symbols of grouping used in a given expression to a minimum.

In the discussions that follow we will need to refer to several important properties that were discussed earlier. We restate them here for easy reference.

1. $+5$ and 5 name the same number. In the future we will leave the plus sign off numerals that name positive integers unless a particular emphasis is desired.

2. $-5 = (-1)(+5) = (-1)5$

3. $-a = (-1)a \qquad a = (+1)a = 1a$

4. $a - b = a + (-b)$

5. $-ab = -(ab) = (-a)b = a(-b) = (-1)ab$

6. $a(b + c) = ab + ac \qquad a(b - c) = ab - ac$

THE MEANING AND MANIPULATION OF EXPRESSIONS SUCH AS $a - b + c$

Suppose you were asked to evaluate the expression

$$8 - 5 + 3$$

Some might subtract the 5 from the 8 first and then add the 3 to obtain 6, whereas others might subtract the sum of 5 and 3 from 8 to obtain 0. Which is right? Certainly, we would not want to allow two answers. We could, of course, have avoided any confusion if we had used parentheses to indicate what we had in mind in the first place. However, we said that we would like to introduce conventions (rules) that will enable us to reduce the use of parentheses. From now on we will use a generally accepted definition that allows for only one meaning for expressions of the type $8 - 5 + 3$, namely, *when three or more terms are combined by subtraction and addition and the order of operations is not indicated by symbols of grouping, then we proceed from left to right.*

EXAMPLE 24

▶ $8 - 5 + 3 = (8 - 5) + 3 = 3 + 3 = 6$

▶ $7 - 4 - 1 = (7 - 4) - 1 = 3 - 1 = 2$

▶ $a - b + c = (a - b) + c$

There will be occasions when we will want to rearrange the terms in expressions such as $a - b - c$. How should we proceed? We can, for example, rearrange the terms in the expression $a + b + c$ as we wish, but what do we do if the expression involves subtraction?

To start, we first note that $a - b - c$ can be written as $a + (-b) + (-c)$ as can be seen as follows:

$$a - b - c = (a - b) - c \qquad \text{why?}$$
$$= [a + (-b)] + (-c) \qquad \text{why?}$$
$$= a + (-b) + (-c) \qquad \text{why?}$$

Thus we have converted subtraction into addition and (because of associative and commutative properties of addition) we can rearrange the resulting terms as we please. For example,

$$a + (-b) + (-c) = (-b) + a + (-c)$$
$$= (-c) + (-b) + a$$
$$= (-c) + a + (-b)$$

or, returning to the nonparentheses form,

$$a - b - c = -b + a - c$$
$$= -c - b + a$$
$$= -c + a - b$$

Mechanically, we see that we can rearrange the terms in an expression such as $a - b - c$ if we associate each binary operation sign with the term on the right, and take it with the term when it is moved.

EXAMPLE 25.   Which of the following are equal to $a - b + c$?

(A) $a + (-b) + c$ (B) $a + c + (-b)$ (C) $a + c - b$

(D) $a + b - c$ (E) $-b + a + c$ (F) $-b + c + a$

SOLUTION: All are except (D).

EXAMPLE 26.   Which of the following are equal to $6x + 2y - 5y - 3x$?

(A) $6x - 3x - 5y + 2y$ (B) $6x - 3x + 2y - 5y$

(C) $2y - 5y + 6x - 3x$ (D) $-5y + 2y + 6x - 3x$

SOLUTION: All are.

The preceding discussion and examples illustrate the following theorem, which is a direct consequence of the associative and commutative properties of addition, the special theorem on subtraction, and the rule for combining terms when symbols of grouping are not used.

THEOREM 7   *When two or more terms are combined by addition or subtraction,* (A) *Any subtraction sign may be replaced with an addition sign if the term following it is replaced by its negative [thus, $a - b - c = a + (-b) + (-c)$].* (B) *The terms may be reordered without restriction as long as the sign preceding an involved term accompanies it in the process (thus, $a - b + c = a + c - b$).*

COMBINING LIKE TERMS

In the preceding chapter we learned how to combine like terms when addition is involved; in this section we will learn how to combine like terms in expressions involving both addition and subtraction. (Recall that two terms are said to be like terms if they are exactly alike except for numerical coefficients.) To start, we extend our concept of numerical coefficient as follows: *The numerical coefficient of a given term in an algebraic expression is to include the sign that precedes it.*

EXAMPLE 27. In the expression $3x^4 - 2x^3 + x^2 - x + 1$, the numerical coefficient of the first term is 3; of the second term, -2; of the third term, 1; and of the fourth term, -1.

This convention will seem more reasonable if you look at the algebraic expression in example 27 in the following equivalent forms:

$$3x^4 - 2x^3 + x^2 - x + 1 = (3x^4) + (-2x^3) + (x^2) + (-x) + (1)$$
$$= [(+3)x^4] + [(-2)x^3] + [(+1)x^2] + [(-1)x] + (+1)$$

Now let us proceed with the process of combining like terms. Consider the following example.

EXAMPLE 28

▶ $4 - 7 - 2 \boxed{= 4 + (-7) + (-2)} = -5$

▶ $2x - 3x = \boxed{(2-3)x = (-1)x} = -x$

▶ $-4x - 7x = \boxed{(-4)x + (-7)x = [(-4) + (-7)]x} = -11x$

▶ $3x - 5y + 6x + 2y \boxed{\begin{array}{l} = 3x + 6x + 2y - 5y \\ = (3+6)x + (2-5)y \\ = 9x + (-3)y \end{array}}$

$\qquad\qquad\qquad\quad = 9x - 3y$

This example suggests that we can continue combining like terms as we did in Chap. 1; see the following theorem.

THEOREM 8   *Two or more like terms can always be combined into a single term of the same type; the numerical coefficient of the single term is the sum of the numerical coefficients of the several like terms.*

This theorem follows from Theorem 7 in this section and the associative, commutative, and distributive properties of the integers. In practice we usually spot all of the like terms in a given expression, add the numerical coefficients mentally, and write down the result.

EXAMPLE 29

▶ $7xy - 12xy = -5xy$

▶ $3x^2 + 2y^2 - x^2 - 5y^2 = 2x^2 - 3y^2$

▶ $2t - 5 + 3t + 1 - 9t - 7 = -4t - 11$

▶ $x^3y^2 - 2x^2y^3 + 5x^2y^2 - 4x^2y^3 - x^3y^2 - 5x^2y^2 = -6x^2y^3$

EXERCISE 21

1. Which of the following are equal to $5 - 3 + 2$? (Answer the question without evaluating each expression.)

(A) $5 + (-3) + 2$ (B) $5 + 2 + (-3)$

(C) $(-3) + 5 + 2$ (D) $5 + 2 - 3$

(E) $-3 + 5 + 2$ (F) $5 - 2 + 3$

(G) $3 - 5 + 2$ (H) $2 - 3 + 5$

2. Which of the following are equal to $x - y - z$?

(A) $x + (-y) + (-z)$ (B) $(-y) + x + (-z)$

(C) $(-y) + (-z) + x$ (D) $y - x - z$

(E) $-y + x - z$ (F) $-y - z + x$

(G) $y - z - x$ (H) $z - y - x$

3. Evaluate:

(A) $5 + 7$ (B) $5 - 7$

(C) $3 - 2 + 4$ (D) $3 + 4 - 2$

(E) $4 - 8 - 9$ (F) $-3 + 2 + 5 - 6$

(G) $2 - 3 - 6 + 5$ (H) $5 + 2 - 6 - 3$

4. Evaluate:

(A) $6 - 8 - 3 + 5$ (B) $6 + 5 - 8 - 3$

(C) $-7 + 1 + 6 + 2 - 1$ (D) $9 - 5 - 4 + 7 - 6 + 10$

(E) $-5 - 3 - 8 + 15 + 1$ (F) $1 - 12 + 5 + 7 - 1 + 6 - 4$

5. Given the algebraic expression $3x^3 - 4x^2 + x - 8$, what is the numerical coefficient of (A) the second term, (B) the third term, (C) the first term?

6. Write down an algebraic expression of the same type as in the preceding problem but with numerical coefficients for the first, second, third, and fourth terms equal to -2, $+5$, -1, and $+4$, respectively.

7. Combine like terms:

(A) $2x + 5x + x$ (B) $2x - 5x + x$

(C) $4x + 3x - 5x - x$ (D) $-3y + 2y + 5y - 6y$

(E) $2y - 3y - 6y + 5y$ (F) $5y + 2y - 6y - 3y$

8. Combine like terms:

(A) $4t - 8t - 9t$ (B) $3xy + 4xy - xy$

(C) $3xy - xy + 4xy$ (D) $4x^2 - 3x^2 + x^2 - 5x^2$

(E) $-x^2y + 3x^2y - 5x^2y$ (F) $r^3t^3 - 4r^3t^3 - 7r^3t^3 + 12r^3t^3$

9. Simplify by combining like terms:

(A) $2x + 3y + 5x$

(B) $2a - 7a + 8b - 5b$

(C) $5s + 3t - s - 9t$

(D) $-x^2 + 3y^2 - y^2 - x^2 + 4x^2$

(E) $3xy + ab - 2ab - 4xy$

(F) $2x - 3y + 5x + 7y - x - y$

10. Simplify by combining like terms:

(A) $2a + 5b - a - b$

(B) $3x^2 - 2x + 5 - x^2 + 4x - 8$

(C) $y^3 + 4y^2 - 10 + 2y^3 - y + 7$

(D) $2x^2y + 3xy^2 - 5xy + 2xy^2 - xy - 4x^2y$

(E) $a^2 - 3ab + b^2 + 2a^2 + 3ab - 2b^2$

(F) $4x^2 - x + 12 + 3x^4 - 2x^3 + 5x - 9$

EXAMPLE 30. Evaluate (A) $2x - 3y + 5$ and (B) $x - y + z$ for $x = -3$, $y = -2$, and $z = -5$.

SOLUTION

(A) $2x - 3y + 5 = 2(-3) - 3(-2) + 5$

$$= 2(-3) + [(-3)(-2)] + 5$$

$$= -6 + 6 + 5$$

$$= 5$$

(B) $x - y + z = (-3) - (-2) + (-5)$

$$= (-3) + [(-1)(-2)] + (-5)$$

$$= -3 + 2 - 5$$

$$= -6$$

11. Evaluate each of the following for $x = -1$, $y = -3$, and $z = 8$:

(A) $2y - 5$

(B) $3x - 4y + 2$

(C) $2x + y - z$

(D) $x - y - 2z$

(E) $2x^2 - 3x - 5$

(F) $x^2 - x + 3$

12. Evaluate each of the following for $a = -2$, $b = -1$, and $c = 4$:

(A) $a - b$

(B) $a + b + c$

(C) $2b - 3c + 4$

(D) $a - b - c$

(E) $a^2 - b^2 + 2c^2$

(F) $a^3 - 3b^3 - 2c$

13. Evaluate each of the following for the same values of the variables used in the two preceding problems:

(A) $(2x + y)/(a - b)$

(B) $z/a + xyz + (4x + a)$

(C) $|a - b|/|b - a|$

(D) $|b - a|/|b - a|$

(E) $-b(a/x + z/c + xy + x^3)$

(F) $(x^3y + y^2z^2 + xc^2)/(x^2b)$

14. Evaluate each of the following for $x = -1$, $y = -12$, $z = 0$, $a = +4$, $b = -3$, and $c = +9$:

(A) $-|c/b|$

(B) $\dfrac{c}{b} + \dfrac{y}{x}$

(C) $-(y/b - c/x)$

(D) $-|c/x - y/b|$

(E) $xz\left(\dfrac{y}{a} - b\right)$

(F) $\dfrac{y}{|y + c|}$

(G) $(x^9 + b^3)/(b^2 - a^2)$

REMOVING PARENTHESES AND OTHER SYMBOLS OF GROUPING

The process of removing parentheses in algebraic expressions is primarily based on three principles: (1) any expression involving subtraction can be converted to addition, (2) multiplication distributes over addition, and (3) parentheses may be inserted and removed at will relative to the binary operation of addition (associative property). The following examples should make the process clear and, in addition, should suggest a mechanical procedure for its accomplishment.

EXAMPLE 31

$$(2a - 3b) + (4x - 2y) = [2a + (-3)b] + [4x + (-2)y]$$
$$= 2a + (-3)b + 4x + (-2)y$$
$$= 2a - 3b + 4x - 2y$$

EXAMPLE 32

$$-3(2a - 3b) - (-4a + b) = (-3)[2a + (-3)b] + (-1)[(-4)a + (+1)b]$$
$$= [(-6)a + 9b] + [4a + (-1)b]$$
$$= (-6)a + 9b + 4a + (-1)b$$
$$= -6a + 9b + 4a - b$$
$$= -2a + 8b$$

EXAMPLE 33

$$2x(3x - 5) - x(-x + 6) = 2x[3x + (-5)] + (-1)x[(-1)x + 6]$$
$$= [6x^2 + (-10)x] + [x^2 + (-6)x]$$
$$= 6x^2 + (-10)x + x^2 + (-6)x$$
$$= 6x^2 - 10x + x^2 - 6x$$
$$= 7x^2 - 16x$$

Mechanically, we notice that each term within parentheses (including the sign that precedes it) is multiplied by the coefficient of the parentheses. If the parentheses are preceded by a plus sign only, the parentheses are dropped without changing any of the signs within the parentheses; if the parentheses are preceded by a negative sign only, the parentheses are dropped, and the sign of each term within the parentheses is changed. Even though you will be using these mechanical steps to remove symbols of grouping, you should not lose sight of the basic principles behind these steps. These principles are the fundamentals to which you must always return when you are not sure if a mechanical process can be used.

The following example makes use of the mechanical process just outlined.

EXAMPLE 34

▶ $4x + (2x - 3) = 4x + 2x - 3 = 6x - 3$

▶ $(2x - 5) - (3x + 5) = 2x - 5 - 3x - 5 = -x - 10$

▶ $-3t^2(t^2 - 2t - 5) = -3t^4 + 6t^3 + 15t^2$

▶ $4x(-x - 2) - 3x(2x + 4) = -4x^2 - 8x - 6x^2 - 12x = -10x^2 - 20x$

▶ $(2x - 3y) - [x - 2(3x - y)] = (2x - 3y) - [x - 6x + 2y]$

$$= (2x - 3y) - (-5x + 2y)$$
$$= 2x - 3y + 5x - 2y$$
$$= 7x - 5y$$

EXERCISE 22

In problems 1 through 22 remove all symbols of grouping and simplify by combining like terms where possible.

1. $5x + (3x - 7)$
2. $3(2x^2 - x + 1)$
3. $4(2y - 3) + 2(3y + 6)$
4. $2t - (3t - 5)$
5. $-7(-t + 8)$
6. $-3(-t + 7) - (t - 1)$
7. $a + b - 2(a - b)$
8. $x - 3(x + 2y) + 5y$
9. $2(x - 1) + 3(2x - 3) - (4x - 5)$
10. $-2(y - 7) - 3(2y + 1) - (-5y + 7)$
11. $5t(2t - 3) + 3t(-2t + 4)$
12. $3x(2x^2 - 4) - 2(3x^3 - x)$
13. $2x^2 - 3x + 5 - 2x(x - 3) + 3$
14. $18x^3 - 3x - (x + 5) - 2x(8x^2 - 3)$
15. $3x - 2[x - (x - 7)]$
16. $2t - 3t[4 - 2(t - 1)]$
17. $2x[3x - 2(2x + 1)] - 3x[8 + (2x - 4)]$
18. $-2t(-t - 3) - [t^2 - t(2t + 3)]$

19. $x - \{x - [x - (x - 1)]\}$
20. $2t - 3\{t + 2[t - (t + 5)] + 1\}$
21. $3x^2 - 2\{x - x[x + 4(x - 3)] - 5\}$
22. $w - \{x - [z - (w - x) - z] - (x - w)\} + x$

23. Replace each question mark with an appropriate algebraic expression:
(A) $2 + 3x - y = 2 + (\quad ? \quad)$
(B) $2 + 3x - y = 2 - (\quad ? \quad)$
(C) $x - 4y - 8z = x - 4(\quad ? \quad)$

24. Replace each question mark with an appropriate algebraic expression:
(A) $2x - 6y - 3a + 12b = 2(x - 3y) - 3(\quad ? \quad)$
(B) $w^2 - x + y - z = w^2 - (\quad ? \quad)$
(C) $w^2 - x + y - z = w^2 + (\quad ? \quad)$

EXAMPLE 35.   A pile of 20 coins consists of nickels and dimes. If the pile has x nickels in it, write an algebraic expression that represents the value of the pile in cents and then simplify the expression.

SOLUTION

If $x =$ the number of nickels in the pile

then $20 - x =$ the number of dimes in the pile

value of pile $=$ value of nickels $+$ value of dimes

$$= 5x + 10(20 - x)$$
$$= 5x + 200 - 10x$$
$$= 200 - 5x$$

25. A coin purse contains dimes and quarters only. There are four more dimes than quarters. If x equals the number of dimes, write an algebraic expression that represents the value of the money in the purse. Simplify the expression. HINT: If x represents the number of dimes, then what does $x - 4$ represent?

26. A pile of coins consists of nickels, dimes and quarters. There are five less dimes than nickels and two more quarters than dimes. If x equals the number of nickels, write an algebraic expression that represents the value of the pile in cents. Simplify the expression. HINT: If x represents the number of nickels, then what do $x - 5$ and $(x - 5) + 2$ represent?

27. The width of a rectangle is 5 in. less than its length. If x is the length of the rectangle, write an algebraic expression that represents the perimeter of the rectangle and simplify the expression.

28. The length of a rectangle is 8 ft more than its width. If y is the length of the rectangle, write an algebraic expression that represents its area. Change the expression to a form without parentheses.

20   EQUATIONS AND APPLICATIONS

We have finally reached the place where we can discuss methods of solving equations other than by guessing. For example, you would not likely guess the solution to

$$2x + 2(x - 6) = 52$$

Finding a solution to this equation would lead to the solution of the following problem: Find the dimensions of a rectangle with a perimeter of 52 in. if its length is 6 in. more than its width.

We have encountered equations in a number of places in the preceding sections and have even mentioned such things as the replacement set for the variable and the solution set for the equation. These ideas will be discussed again in this section as part of a systematic development of a method of solving equations. We will divide our efforts into two parts: (1) techniques for solving equations and (2) applications.

Since our number system has been developed only as far as the integers, we will necessarily have to limit the types of equations and applications to those that have solutions in the set of integers. The methods that we will develop, however, will still serve us when we enlarge the number system in the next chapter; at that time we will be able to consider a less restricted class of equations and applications. Chapter 4 is devoted to an extensive treatment of the subject from a more general point of view.

TECHNIQUES FOR SOLVING EQUATIONS

You will recall that we defined a constant as a symbol that names one single thing and a variable as a symbol that is a place holder for constants. In this course constants will generally name numbers. The replacement set for a variable was defined to be the set of constants that are permitted to replace the variable. Since we use variables in equations as place holders for constants, an equation is neither true nor false until the variable is replaced with a constant. For this reason equations are frequently referred to as open statements. The solution set for an equation was defined to be those elements from the replacement set that make the equation a true statement. It is important to keep in mind that the solution set of an equation is always a subset of the replacement set. Any element of the solution set is called a **solution** or a **root** of the equation. To **solve an equation** is to find the solution set for the equation.

EXAMPLE 36.   If the replacement set for the variable x is the set of positive integers, then the solution set for the equation $x + 3 = -5$ is the empty set. If, on the other hand, the replacement set is the set of all integers, then the solution set is $\{-8\}$, and we call -8 a solution or root of the equation.

Knowing what we mean by the solution set of an equation is one thing. Finding it is another. Our objective now is to develop a systematic method of solving equations that is free from guesswork. To this end we will make use of the properties of equality discussed in the first chapter. We will learn how to perform mechanical operations on equations that will produce equivalent equations. Two equations are said to be **equivalent** if they both have the same solution set.

The basic idea of solving equations is to perform operations on equations that produce simpler equivalent equations and to continue the process until we reach an equation whose solution is obvious—generally, an equation such as $x = -3$. With a little practice you will find the methods that we are going to develop very easy to use and very powerful. Before proceeding further, it is recommended that you briefly review the properties of equality in Sec. 5.

The following theorem, which is a direct consequence of the properties of equality discussed in Sec. 5, is fundamental to the equation-solving process.

THEOREM 9:   PROPERTIES OF EQUALITY.

VERBAL FORM

(A) *If the same number is added to each of two equal numbers, the sums are equal.*   addition property

(B) *If the same number is subtracted from each of two equal numbers, the differences are equal.*   subtraction property

(C) *If two equal numbers are each multiplied by the same number, the products are equal.*   multiplication property

(D) *If two equal numbers are each divided by the same nonzero number, the quotients are equal.*   division property

SYMBOLIC FORM

For a, b, and c integers

(A) *If $a = b$, then $a + c = b + c$.*   addition property

(B) *If $a = b$, then $a - c = b - c$.*   subtraction property

(C) *If $a = b$, then $ac = bc$.*   multiplication property

(D) *If $a = b$ and $c \neq 0$, then $a/c = b/c$.*   division property

We will prove only one of the four properties since the proofs of the other three are similar.

PROOF OF (A)

$a + c = a + c$	identity property of equality
$a = b$	given
$a + c = b + c$	substitution principle

What has all of this to do with the process of obtaining equivalent equations? The next theorem, which we will freely use but not prove, provides us with our final instructions for solving simple equations.

THEOREM 10:   EQUIVALENT EQUATIONS.

(A) *If an equation is changed in any way by use of the properties in Theorem 9 (except for multiplication and division by zero), the new equation will be equivalent to the original.*

(B) *If any algebraic expression in an equation is replaced by its equal (substitution principle), then the altered equation is equivalent to the original.*

We are finally ready to solve equations!   Several examples will illustrate the process.   The set of integers is assumed to be the replacement set for all variables unless otherwise stated.

EXAMPLE 37.   Solve $x - 5 = -2$ and check.

SOLUTION   COMMENTS

$$x - 5 = -2$$

How can we eliminate the -5 from the left side?

$$x - 5 + 5 = -2 + 5$$

Add 5 to each side (addition property).

$$x = 3$$

Solution is obvious.

CHECK

$$3 - 5 \overset{?}{=} -2$$
$$-2 \overset{\vee}{=} -2$$

A solution for $x = 3$ should also be a solution for $x - 5 = -2$ since the two equations are equivalent.

EXAMPLE 38.   Solve $-3x = 15$ and check.

SOLUTION   COMMENTS

$$-3x = 15$$

How can we make the coefficient of x plus 1?

$$\frac{-3x}{-3} = \frac{15}{-3}$$

Divide each side by -3 (division property).

$$x = -5$$

Solution is obvious.

CHECK

$$(-3)(-5) \overset{?}{=} 15$$
$$15 \overset{\vee}{=} 15$$

The following examples will not be quite as easy as those just considered. However, all of them can be converted to the types just considered if you just remember one basic principle: *Perform operations on the equation that will get all of the terms involving the variable on one side of the equal sign and all of the other terms on the other side first, and then proceed as in the above examples.*

EXAMPLE 39.   Solve $2x - 8 = 5x + 4$ and check.

SOLUTION

$$2x - 8 = 5x + 4$$

$$2x - 8 + 8 = 5x + 4 + 8$$

$$2x = 5x + 12$$

$$2x - 5x = 5x + 12 - 5x$$

$$-3x = 12$$

$$\frac{-3x}{-3} = \frac{12}{-3}$$

$$x = -4$$

CHECK

$$2(-4) - 8 \overset{?}{=} 5(-4) + 4$$

$$-8 - 8 \overset{?}{=} -20 + 4$$

$$-16 \overset{\checkmark}{=} -16$$

EXAMPLE 40.   Solve $3x - 2(2x - 5) = 2(x + 3) - 8$ and check.

SOLUTION

This equation is not as difficult as it might at first appear; simplify the expressions on each side of the equal sign first, and then proceed as in the preceding example. Note that some of the following steps are done mentally.

$$3x - 2(2x - 5) = 2(x + 3) - 8$$

$$3x - 4x + 10 = 2x + 6 - 8$$

$$-x + 10 = 2x - 2$$

$$-x = 2x - 12$$

$$-3x = -12$$

$$x = 4$$

CHECK

$$3(4) - 2[2(4) - 5] \overset{?}{=} 2[(4) + 3] - 8$$

$$12 - 2(8 - 5) \overset{?}{=} 2(7) - 8$$

$$12 - 2(3) \overset{?}{=} 14 - 8$$

$$12 - 6 \overset{?}{=} 6$$

$$6 \overset{\checkmark}{=} 6$$

We conclude this part of the discussion by stating that equations of the type we are considering have at most one solution. We will discuss this point in greater detail in Chap. 4.

EXERCISE 23

Solve and check each equation in problems 1 through 34. The replacement set for all variables involved is the set of integers.

1. $x + 9 = -3$

2. $t - 11 = 10$

3. $y - 1 = -4$

4. $w + 33 = 12$

5. $y + 13 = 0$

6. $x - 5 = 0$

7. $4x = 32$

8. $3x = -21$

9. $-6x = 42$

10. $-12t = -24$

11. $3y = 0$

12. $-4u = 0$

13. $4x - 7 = 5$

14. $-3t + 8 = -13$

15. $2y + 5 = -1$

16. $2w - 18 = -8$

17. $2x - 7 = x + 1$

18. $3x - 8 = x + 6$

19. $4y + 8 = 2y - 6$

20. $2t + 9 = 5t - 6$

21. $w - 3 = w + 7$

22. $2x + 8 = 2x - 6$

23. $2x + 2(x - 6) = 52$

24. $5x + 10(x + 7) = 100$

25. $x + (x + 2) + (x + 4) = 54$

26. $10x + 25(x - 3) = 275$

27. $2(x + 7) - 2 = x - 3$

28. $5 + 4(t - 2) = 2(t + 7) + 1$

29. $-3(4 - t) = 7 - (t + 1)$

30. $5x - (7x - 4) - 2 = 5 - (3x + 2)$

31. $x(x + 2) = x(x + 4) - 12$

32. $x(x - 1) + 5 = x^2 + x - 3$

33. $t(t - 6) + 8 = t^2 - 6t - 3$

34. $x(x + 4) - 2 = x^2 - 4(x + 3)$

35. Which of the following are equivalent equations:

$$3x - 6 = 6 \qquad 3x = 12 \qquad 3x = 0 \qquad x = 4 \qquad x = 0$$

36. Which of the following are equivalent equations:

$$2x + 5 = x - 3 \qquad 2x = x - 8 \qquad 2x = x + 2 \qquad 3x = 2 \qquad x = -8$$

37. Which of the following are true:

(A) $\{x \mid 3x = 5, x \text{ an integer}\} = \phi$

(B) $\{t \mid 2t - 1 = 19, t \text{ an integer}\} = \{9, 10\}$

(C) $\{t \mid 2t - 1 = 19, t \text{ an integer}\} = \{9\}$

(D) $\{t \mid 2t - 1 = 19, t \text{ an integer}\} = \{10\}$

38. Which of the following are true:

(A) $\{y \mid -2y = 8, y \text{ a positive integer}\} = \{-4\}$

(B) $\{u \mid 2u - 5 = 11, u \text{ an integer}\} = \{3\}$

(C) $\{x \mid 3x + 11 = 5, x \text{ a positive integer}\} = \phi$

39. Prove the multiplication property in Theorem 9.

40. Prove the subtraction property in Theorem 9.

APPLICATIONS

At this time we will consider only a few different types of simple applications; hopefully, the reader will find some of them interesting as well as significant. A large variety of applications from many different fields will be considered in Chaps. 4, 5, and 6.

We will start by solving a fairly simple problem dealing with numbers. Through this problem you will learn a method of attack that can be applied to many other applications.

EXAMPLE 41.   Find three consecutive integers whose sum is 66.

SOLUTION   COMMENTS

Let x = the first integer   Identify one of the unknowns with a
then $x + 1$ = the next integer   letter, and then write other unknowns
and $x + 2$ = the third integer   in terms of this letter.

$$x + (x + 1) + (x + 2) = 66$$

Write an equation that relates the unknown quantities with other facts in the problem.

$$x + x + 1 + x + 2 = 66$$

Solve the equation.

$$3x + 3 = 66$$
$$3x = 63$$
$$x = 21$$

$$x + 1 = 22$$

Write all answers requested.

$$x + 2 = 23$$

CHECK

21
22   Thus we have found three consecu-
23   tive integers whose sum is 66.
——
66

Checking back in the equation is not enough since you might have made a mistake in setting up the equation; a final check is provided only if the conditions in the original problem are satisfied.

EXAMPLE 42.   Find three consecutive even numbers such that twice the second plus three times the third is seven times the first.

SOLUTION

Let x = the first even number
then $x + 2$ = the second even number
and $x + 4$ = the third even number

$$\underset{\text{even number}}{\text{twice the second}} + \underset{\text{third even number}}{\text{three times the}} = \underset{\text{first even number}}{\text{seven times the}}$$

$$2(x + 2) + 3(x + 4) = 7x$$

$$2x + 4 + 3x + 12 = 7x$$

$$5x + 16 = 7x$$

$$-2x = -16$$

$$x = 8$$

$$x + 2 = 10$$

$$x + 4 = 12$$

CHECK

8, 10, and 12 are three consecutive even numbers

$$2 \cdot 10 + 3 \cdot 12 \overset{?}{=} 7 \cdot 8$$

$$20 + 36 \overset{?}{=} 56$$

$$56 \overset{\vee}{=} 56$$

EXAMPLE 43. Find the dimensions of a rectangle with a perimeter of 52 in. if its length is 5 in. more than twice its width.

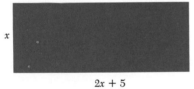

x

$2x + 5$

$2(\text{length}) + 2(\text{width}) = \text{perimeter}$ **CHECK**

$$2(2x + 5) + 2x = 52$$ 19 is 5 more than twice 7

$$4x + 10 + 2x = 52$$ $$2 \cdot 19 + 2 \cdot 7 \overset{?}{=} 52$$

$$6x = 42$$ $$38 + 14 \overset{?}{=} 52$$

$$x = 7 \qquad \text{width}$$ $$52 \overset{\vee}{=} 52$$

$$2x + 5 = 19 \qquad \text{length}$$

EXAMPLE 44. In a pile of coins containing only dimes and nickels, there are seven more dimes than nickels. If the total value of all of the coins in the pile is $1, how many of each type of coin is in the pile?

SOLUTION

Let $x =$ the number of nickels in the pile

then $x + 7 =$ the number of dimes in the pile

$$\underset{\text{in cents}}{\text{value of nickels}} + \underset{\text{in cents}}{\text{value of dimes}} = \underset{\text{in cents}}{\text{value of pile}}$$

$$5x + 10(x + 7) = 100$$
$$5x + 10x + 70 = 100$$
$$15x = 30$$
$$x = 2 \qquad \text{nickels}$$
$$x + 7 = 9 \qquad \text{dimes}$$

CHECK

9 dimes is seven more than 2 nickels

$$\text{value of nickels in cents} = 10$$
$$\text{value of dimes in cents} = 90$$
$$\text{total value} \quad \overline{100}$$

EXAMPLE 45.   An airplane flew out to an island from the mainland and back in 5 hr.   How far is the island from the mainland if the pilot averaged 600 mph going to the island and 400 mph returning?

SOLUTION
In this problem we will find it convenient to find the time out to the island first.

Let $\qquad x =$ the time it took to get to the island

then $\qquad 5 - x =$ the time to return (since round trip time is 5 hr)

$$\text{distance out} = \text{distance back}$$
$$600x = 400(5 - x)$$
$$600x = 2,000 - 400x$$
$$1,000x = 2,000$$
$$x = 2 \text{ hr} \qquad \text{time going}$$
$$5 - x = 3 \text{ hr} \qquad \text{time returning}$$

Since distance $=$ (rate) $\cdot$ (time), the distance to the island from the mainland is $600 \cdot 2 = 1,200$ miles.

CHECK

$$\text{time going} + \text{time returning} = 5$$
$$\frac{1,200}{600} + \frac{1,200}{400} \overset{?}{=} 5$$
$$2 \quad + \quad 3 \overset{\vee}{=} 5$$

You are now beginning to see the great power of algebra. It was an historic occasion when it was realized that a solution to a problem that was difficult to obtain by arithmetical computation could be obtained instead by a deductive process involving conditions that the solution was required to satisfy.

There are many different types of algebraic applications, so many, in fact, that no single approach will apply to all. The following suggestions, however, may be of help to you:

1. Read the problem very carefully—a second and third time if necessary.

2. Write down important facts and relationships on a piece of scratch paper.

3. Identify unknown quantities in terms of a single letter if possible.

4. Write an equation that relates these unknown quantities and the facts in the problem.

5. Solve the equation.

6. Write down all of the solutions asked for in the original problem.

7. Check the solution(s) in the original problem.

Remember, mathematics is not a spectator sport! Just reading examples is not enough; you must set up and solve problems yourself.

EXERCISE 24

1. Find three consecutive even numbers whose sum is 54.

2. Find three consecutive even numbers such that the product of the first and second is 12 less than the product of the first and third.

3. An 18-ft board is cut into two pieces so that one piece is 3 ft shorter than twice the length of the other piece. What is the length of each piece?

4. Find the dimensions of a rectangle with perimeter 128 in. if its length is 6 in. shorter than four times the width.

5. The area of a rectangle 64 ft long is the same as the area of a 16-ft square. Find the width of the rectangle.

6. You are asked to construct a triangle with two equal angles so that the third angle is twice the size of either of the two equal ones. How large should each angle be? NOTE: The sum of the three angles in any triangle is 180°

7. A chord called an octave can be produced by dividing a stretched string into two parts so that one part is twice as long as the other part. How long will each part of the string be if the total length of the string is 57 in.

8. If an adult with pure brown eyes marries an adult with blue eyes, their children, because of the dominance of brown, will all have brown eyes but will

be carriers of the gene for blue.   If the children marry others with the same type of parents, then according to Mendel's laws of heredity, we would expect the third generation (the children's children) to include three times as many with brown eyes as with blue.   Out of a sample of 1,748 third-generation children with second-generation parents as described, how many brown-eyed children and blue-eyed children would you expect?

9. A toy rocket shot vertically upward with an initial velocity of 160 fps, has at time t a velocity given by the equation $v = 160 - 32t$, where air resistance is neglected.   In how many seconds will the rocket reach its highest point?   HINT: Find t when $v = 0$.

10. Air temperature drops approximately 5°F per 1,000 ft in altitude above the surface of the earth up to 30,000 ft.   If T represents temperature and A represents altitude in thousands of feet and if the temperature on the ground is 60°F, then we can write

$$T = 60 - 5A \qquad 0 \le A \le 30$$

If you were in a balloon, how high would you be if the thermometer registered −50°F?

11. About eight times as much of an iceberg is under water as is above the water.   If the total height of an iceberg from bottom to top is 117 ft, how much is above and how much is below the surface?

12. The sun is about 390 times as far from the earth as the moon.   If the sun is approximately 93,210,000 miles from the earth, how far is the moon from the earth?

13. In a computer center two electronic card sorters are used to sort 52,000 IBM cards.   If the first sorter operates at 225 cards per min and the second sorter operates at 175 cards per min, how long will it take both sorters together to sort all of the cards?

14. A mechanic charges $6 per hr for his labor and $4 per hr for his assistant.   On a repair job his bill was $190 with $92 for labor and $98 for parts.   If the assistant worked 2 hr less than the mechanic, how many hours did each work?

15. How long would it take you to drive from San Francisco to Los Angeles, a distance of about 424 miles, if you could average 53 mph?

16. At 8 A.M. your father left by car on a long trip. An hour later you find that he has left his wallet behind. You decide to take another car to try to catch up with him. From past experience you know that he averages about 48 mph. If you can average 60 mph, how long will it take you to catch up to him?

17. One ship leaves England and another leaves the United States at the same time. If the distance between the two ports is 3,150 miles, the ship from the United States averages 25 mph and the one from England 20 mph, and they both travel the same route, how long will it take the ships to reach a rendezvous point, and how far from the United States will they be at that time?

18. You are at a river resort and rent a motor boat for 5 hr at 7 A.M. You are told that the boat will travel at 8 mph upstream and 12 mph returning. You decide that you would like to go as far up the river as you can and still be back at noon. At what time should you turn back, and how far from the resort will you be at that time?

19. If you have 20 dimes and nickels in your pocket worth $1.40, how many of each do you have?

20. In a pile of coins containing only quarters and dimes, there are three less quarters than dimes. If the total value of the pile is $2.75, how many of each type of coin is in the pile?

21. Find four consecutive even numbers so that the sum of the first and last is the same as the sum of the second and third. (Be careful!)

22. In a recent election involving five candidates, the winner beat his opponents by 805, 413, 135, and 52, respectively. If the total number of votes cast was 10,250, how many votes did each receive?

21   ORDER RELATIONS AND LINE GRAPHS

When we discussed order relations relative to the natural numbers, we leaned rather heavily on your common-sense notion of these ideas. Now, with the negative integers and zero, we will have to proceed more carefully. It may seem obvious to you that 2 is less than 3, but does it seem equally obvious that -3 is less than -2, -5 is less than 0, or -1 is greater than $-1,000$?

Before we formally define inequality relations for all of the integers, let us try to get an idea of what we want the definition to accomplish. Why is it reasonable to say that -3 is less than -2, -5 is less than 0, or -1 is greater than $-1,000$? We will answer this question by asking another question. If we think of the quantities mentioned as temperature readings, then which number indicates the warmer temperature: $-2°$ or $-3°$? $-5°$ or $0°$? $-1°$ or $-1000°$?

A similar kind of question can be asked about depth relative to sea level using the same number pairs. The inequality relation is made precise in the following definition.

DEFINITION 7:   ORDER RELATIONS.   *If a and b are integers, then we write $a < b$ if and only if there exists a positive integer p so that $a + p = b$. We write $a > b$ if and only if $b < a$.*

Intuitively, one would expect that if a positive integer were added to *any* number, the sum would be larger than the original number; that is essentially what the definition states. Thus $-3 < -2$ since $-3 + 1 = -2$, $-5 < 0$ since $-5 + 5 = 0$, and $-1,000 < -1$ since $-1,000 + 999 = -1$. In addition the second part of the definition allows us to write $-2 > -3$, $0 > -5$, and $-1 > -1,000$.

A simple geometric interpretation of Definition 7 is possible by considering the following number line:

Any number to the right of another number is larger than that number; thus $5 > 2$, $3 > -8$, and $-4 > -9$. Similarly any number to the left of another is less than that number; for example, $-5 < 3$, $-8 < 0$, and $-16 < -4$. Zero is greater than any negative integer and smaller than any positive integer.

In the example and exercise that follow you will need to recall that the solution set for an inequality in one variable is the set of replacements for the variable from the replacement set that makes the inequality statement true.

EXAMPLE 46.   Find and graph the solution set for the inequality $2x + 3 < -2$ if the replacement set for the variable x is $\{-5, -3, -1, 0, 3, 7\}$.

SOLUTION
Since the replacement set is finite and small, we can test the inequality for each value in the replacement set. We find that $\{-5, -3\}$ is the solution set for the inequality since -5 and -3 are the only numbers from the replacement set that make the inequality true. The graph of the solution set is:

If the replacement set in example 46 had been the set of all integers (an infinite set), then testing each integer in the inequality would be a futile undertaking since we would never exhaust the supply. As in the case for equations, we will be interested in developing systematic procedures for finding solution sets for inequalities when the replacement set for the variable is either large or infinite. We choose to postpone the development of these procedures until Chap. 5. We only wish to remark now that the procedures that will be developed then will be very similar to those we used in the last section to solve equations.

EXERCISE 25

1. Replace each question mark with an appropriate inequality symbol:
(A) 7 ? 5   (B) 0 ? 8
(C) −2 ? 3   (D) −2 ? 0
(E) −3 ? −7   (F) −21 ? −2
(G) 8 ? −32   (H) −28 ? 2

2. Replace each question mark with an appropriate inequality sign:

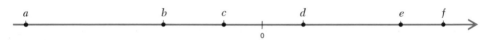

(A) a ? d (B) e ? a
(C) b ? a (D) 0 ? d
(E) e ? f (F) d ? e
(G) c ? e (H) 0 ? a

3. Replace each question mark with an appropriate inequality symbol:
(A) $2 - 3$? $5 - 5$ (B) $2(7 - 3)$? $2(3 - 7)$
(C) $3(-8) + 5$? 0 (D) $5(2) - 13$? $3 - (5 - 7)$

4. Indicate which of the following are true:
(A) $8 - 2 - 5 < 5 - 2 + 7$ (B) $3 - 2(-7) > 4(6 - 9)$
(C) For any integer n, $|n| \geq 0$ (D) $|3 - 5| > |3| + |-5|$
(E) $|3 - 5| < |3| - |5|$

5. Find the solution set for each of the following inequalities if the replacement set for the variable x is $\{-6, -4, -2, 0, 2, 4, 6, 8\}$:
(A) $x \leq 2$ (B) $x > 10$
(C) $x > -4$ (D) $x < 0$
(E) $-4 < x \leq 6$ (F) $-6 < x \leq 0$

6. Find the solution set for each of the following inequalities if the replacement set for the variable x is $\{-7, -5, -1, 0, 5\}$:
(A) $3x > 0$ (B) $2x \leq -4$
(C) $x - 5 < 2x - 3$ (D) $4 - x > 0$
(E) $0 < 4 - x \leq 9$

7. Graph each set on a separate number line.
(A) $\{x \mid -6 < x \leq 3, x \text{ an integer}\}$
(B) $\{x \mid -8 \leq x \leq 0, x \text{ an integer}\}$

8. Graph each set on a separate number line where I is the set of integers.
(A) $\{x \mid -3 < x < 3, x \, \varepsilon \, I\}$
(B) $\{x \mid -10 < x \leq -5, x \, \varepsilon \, I\}$

9. If we add a positive number to any integer, will the sum be an integer to the left or right of the original number on the number line?   Will the sum be greater than or less than the original number?

10. Show, using Definition 7, that if $a < b$, then $b - a$ is a positive integer; and, conversely, if $b - a$ is a positive integer, then $a < b$.

11. Prove, using Definition 7, that for all integers a, b, and c, if $a < b$ and $b < c$, then $a < c$.

12. Prove that for all integers a, b, and c, if $a < b$, then $a + c < b + c$.

22   CHAPTER SUMMARY

GENERAL

With these first two rather long chapters we have laid the foundation for the rest of the course.   You have now had experience with two of the most basic processes of algebra: transforming algebraic expressions into equivalent forms and solving algebraic equations.   In addition you have had experience in applying these algebraic processes to real-life applications.   This has all been carried out within the framework of first the natural numbers and now the integers.   It was the assumed and defined properties of these two sets of numbers that dictated our course of action.

The properties and procedures discussed in these first two chapters will not become obsolete as we continue to extend our number system.   On the contrary, the extensions of the number system are made in such a way that practically all of the properties and procedures we have discussed will continue to be valid in the new number systems.   Your success and ease of understanding during the rest of the course will depend to a considerable extent on how well you understand these first two chapters.

SPECIFIC

Key topics and related materials covered in this chapter are summarized below. You should know this material, including the meaning of each term and symbol.

1. **The set of integers.**

positive integers	zero
negative integers	the number line

2. Operations on integers.

the negative of an integer	$-N$
the absolute value of an integer	$\|N\|$
addition	$a + b$
subtraction	$a - b$
multiplication	ab
division	$\dfrac{a}{b}$

3. Algebraic expressions.

rearranging signed terms   simplifying algebraic expressions

combining like terms   evaluating algebraic expressions

removing grouping symbols

4. Solving equations.

properties of equality   solution or root

equivalent equations   checking solutions of equations

replacement set   applications

solution set   checking solutions for applications

5. Order relation for integers.

less than $<$ replacement set

greater than $>$ solution set

                             graph of a solution set

EXERCISE 26   CHAPTER REVIEW

The replacement set for all variables is assumed to be the set of integers unless otherwise stated.

1. If $P =$ the set of positive integers
    $N =$ the set of negative integers
    $I =$ the set of integers
indicate which of the following are true:

(A) $-7 \notin I$ (B) $0 \,\varepsilon\, P$

(C) $-8 \,\varepsilon\, I$ (D) I is a subset of P

(E) N is a subset of I (F) $\{-2, +1\}$ is a subset of I

2. Express each of the following quantities by means of an appropriate integer:
(A) A checking account balance of $48.
(B) An overdrawn account of $12.
(C) Salton Sea's surface at 245 ft below sea level.
(D) Mount Whitney's height of 14,495 ft.

3. Graph $-(+2)$, $-(-2)$, $|-2|$, and $|+2|$ all on the same number line.

4. Evaluate for $x = -4$ and $y = +8$:
(A) $-x$ (B) $-|y|$ (C) $|-y|$ (D) $-(-y)$

5. Find the sum, difference, and product of each of the following:

(A) -9 (B) $+8$ (C) -2 (D) $+1$
    -5 -2 $+8$ $+1$

6. Find the quotient of each of the following:

(A) $-25 \div -5$ (B) $(-52)/(+13)$ (C) $\dfrac{+16}{-4}$

7. The treasurer of a ski club had the following entries for income and expenditures in his record book: a debt of $7 carried over from last year; income from dues, $150; ski movie rentals, $55; cost of refreshments, $60; income from dance, $28; cost of ski trophies, $32; and publicity costs, $15. Use addition of signed numbers to find the financial position of the club at the end of the school year.

8. Evaluate for $x = -3$, $y = -5$, and $z = -1$:
(A) $x - z$ (B) xyz (C) y/z (D) $x + y$

9. Evaluate for $x = -12$, $y = 2$, and $z = -6$:

(A) $-(|x||y|)$ (B) $\dfrac{|x|}{|y|}$ (C) $-(|x| + |z|)$

10. Use subtraction of signed numbers to find the difference in altitude between Mount Everest, 29,141 ft above sea level, and the Dead Sea, 1,292 ft below sea level.

11. Replace each question mark with an appropriate inequality symbol:
(A) $2 + 8 - 5 \ ? \ 3 - 5 - 7$ (B) $-2(3 - 7) \ ? \ 8(2 - 9)$

12. In each statement replace the question mark with an appropriate numeral:
(A) $(-5) - \ ? \ = 0$ (B) $? - (-14) = +23$
(C) $(-3) + [-(?)] = 0$ (D) $(?)/(11) = -3$

13. Find all natural number solutions for
(A) $|x| = 7$ (B) $-x = -3$

14. If the replacement set for the variable x is the set of integers, what is the solution set for
(A) $|-3| = x$ (B) $|x| = 5$ (C) $|x| = x$

15. The absolute value of a number is (*always, sometimes, never*) negative.

16. Define the negative of a number.

17. Give examples of three different uses of the minus sign.

18. Which of the operations of addition, subtraction, multiplication, and division are associative relative to the set of integers?

19. The set of integers is closed with respect to which of the following operations: addition, subtraction, multiplication, and division?

20. Which of the following are true for all integers a, b, and c?
(A) $a + b = b + a$
(B) $(a + b) + c = a + (b + c)$
(C) $|a + b| = |a| + |b|$

For each statement that is false, find a set of values for the variables that show that it is false.

21. Using the definition of division explain why division by zero is not defined.

22. Evaluate:
(A) $3 - 2 - 5 + 7 - 1$
(B) $2(-1)^2 - 3(-1) + 5$
(C) $4[2(-3) - 3(+2)] - [(-3) - (+2)]$

23. Evaluate $3x^3 - 2x^2 + x - 7$ for $x = -2$.

24. Evaluate each of the following for $x = -4$, $y = +3$, $z = -9$, $a = -1$, $b = +12$, and $c = 0$:
(A) $(2a - b - c)/|x - y|$
(B) $(x + y)^3 - (z + b)^2$
(C) $axbycz$

25. Remove all grouping symbols and simplify:
(A) $2x + (3x - 9) + (x + 5)$ (B) $2x - (3x - 9) - (x + 5)$

26. Remove all grouping symbols and simplify:
(A) $-[t^2 - t(t - 2)] + 3t(t - 5)$ (B) $x - \{x + [x - (x - 3)]\}$

27. Replace the question mark with an appropriate algebraic expression:
(A) $x^3 - x^2 - x + 1 = (x^3 - x^2) - (\ \ ?\ \ )$
(B) $(x - y)^2 - x + y = (x - y)^2 - (\ \ ?\ \ )$

28. Solve and check:
(A) $3x - 9 = -15$ (B) $4x + 3 = 15 - 2x$

29. Solve and check:
(A) $2(x - 3) + x = x - (x + 8)$ (B) $2x + 3(x - 1) = 5 - (x - 4)$

30. Which of the following are equivalent equations:

$$4x + 6 = -2 \quad 4x = 4 \quad x = 1 \quad x = -2 \quad 4x = -8$$

31. Find and graph the solution set of each of the following inequalities if the replacement set for the variable x is $\{-8, -5, -4, -1, 0, 3, 5\}$:
(A) $3x \le -2$ (B) $x + 2 > 3 - x$

32. Describe the elements in each of the following sets:
(A) $A = \{x \mid 7x + 3 = -11, x$ a natural number$\}$

(B) $B = \{x \mid 3x - 9 = 6, x \text{ an integer}\}$

33. Graph the set $\{x \mid -3 < x \le 4, x \text{ an integer}\}$.

34. The sum of four consecutive natural numbers is 54. Find the four numbers.

35. An 18-ft rope is cut into two pieces so that the larger piece is 6 ft shorter than three times the length of the smaller piece. Find the length of each piece.

36. The perimeter of a rectangle is 170 in. If the length is 1 in. longer than five times the width, what is the area of the rectangle?

37. An unmanned space capsule passes over Cape Kennedy at 8 A.M. traveling at 17,000 mph. A manned capsule, attempting a rendezvous, passes over the

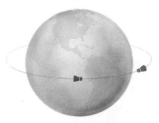

same spot at 9 A.M. traveling at 18,000 mph. How long will it take the second capsule to catch up with the first? How many miles will the second capsule have traveled by that time?

38. In the shorthorn breed of cattle neither red nor white dominates; when a pure red is mated with a pure white, a hybrid called a roan (red hairs intermingled with white hairs) is produced. Roans are highly prized by cattle breeders, but unfortunately they never breed true. When two roans are mated, they yield an equal number of reds and whites and twice as many roans as either reds or whites. Suppose a large enough number of roans are mated to produce 1,752 offspring. How many each of reds, roans, and whites would be expected?

39. Find four consecutive even numbers such that the product of the first and last is the same as the product of the middle two. (Be careful!)

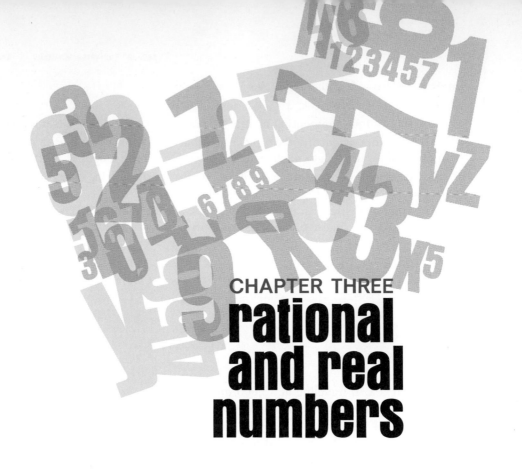

CHAPTER THREE

rational and real numbers

23 THE SET OF RATIONAL NUMBERS

In the last chapter we formed the set of integers by extending the natural numbers to include zero and the set of negative integers. With this extension came more power to perform the four basic arithmetical operations on more numbers and more power to solve more equations. In spite of this added power, we are still not able to solve the simple equation $2x = 3$ or divide -2 by 5. By now you have no doubt guessed the direction of the next extension of the number system. It is obvious that we need fractions.

You will recall that in the last chapter we said that we would use $a \div b$, a/b, and $\dfrac{a}{b}$ interchangeably; hence, $4 \div 2$, $4/2$, and $\frac{4}{2}$ are to be taken as different names for the same number (namely, the number 2). However what does $\frac{3}{2}$ name? Certainly not an integer. We are going to extend the set of integers so that $\frac{3}{2}$ will name a number; division will always be possible (except by zero), and equations of the type $ax + b = 0$ ($a \neq 0$), where a and b are numbers from the extended system, will always have a solution. The extended number system will be called the set of rational numbers; the set of integers will be a subset of this system.

RATIONAL NUMBERS

We will proceed as we did when we added zero and the negative integers to the natural numbers; that is, we will not attempt to give a precise definition of a rational number. We will, instead, accept the intuitive notion of rational numbers that you acquired through your experience with fractions in arithmetic. We will postulate their existence and name them with appropriate symbols. (Actually, it is how we work with symbols that name numbers that interests us most at this point rather than what we really mean by number. The precise definition of number will be left to more advanced courses.)

POSTULATE 1   *There exists a set of numbers called the rational numbers. Every fractional form a/b where a and b are names of integers with b $\neq$ 0 names a rational number; every rational number has a fractional form of the type described as a name. (In short, a number is called a rational number if and only if the number can be expressed as the quotient of two integers, division by zero excluded.)*

Thus, $\frac{1}{3}$, $\frac{3}{5}$, $\frac{8}{1}$, $(-2)/7$, $10/(-5)$, and $(-3)/(-2)$ all name rational numbers.

It is to be noted, since every integer can be expressed as the quotient of two integers (the integer itself divided by 1), that the set of integers is a subset of the set of rational numbers. Every integer is a rational number, but not every rational number is an integer!

It would seem reasonable, from our experience with multiplying and dividing signed quantities in the preceding chapter, to define the quotient of *any* two integers with like sign as a **positive rational number** and the quotient of *any* two integers with unlike sign as a **negative rational number**. We will symbolize positive and negative rational numbers as illustrated in the following examples:

$$\frac{+2}{+3} = \frac{2}{3} \qquad \frac{-2}{-3} = \frac{2}{3} \qquad \frac{-2}{+3} = -\frac{2}{3} \qquad \frac{+2}{-3} = -\frac{2}{3}$$

Identifying the rational numbers with points on a number line proceeds as one would expect; the positive numbers are to the right of the origin and the negative numbers are to the left of the origin. To locate the point associate with $\frac{7}{4}$, divide the line segment from 0 to 7 into four equal parts, and label the right end of the first line segment with $\frac{7}{4}$; $-\frac{7}{4}$ is located similarly, but to the left of the origin. (One can also divide the line segment from 0 to 1 into four equal parts and take seven of them to locate $\frac{7}{4}$.)

Proceeding as described, every rational number can be associated with a point on the number line.

The **negative of a rational number** and the **absolute value of a rational number** are defined as in the integers. Thus,

$$-\left(\frac{2}{3}\right) = -\frac{2}{3} \qquad -\left(-\frac{2}{3}\right) = \frac{2}{3} \qquad \left|\frac{2}{3}\right| = \frac{2}{3} \qquad \left|-\frac{2}{3}\right| = \frac{2}{3}$$

24   MULTIPLICATION AND EQUALITY FOR RATIONAL NUMBERS

MULTIPLICATION

We will define multiplication for rational numbers in terms of multiplication for integers. Thus the **product of any two rational numbers** a/b and c/d, where a, b, c, and d are integers, is defined by formula

$$\frac{a}{b} \cdot \frac{c}{d} = \frac{ac}{bd}$$

EXAMPLE 1

▸ $\dfrac{2}{5} \cdot \dfrac{3}{7} = \dfrac{2 \cdot 3}{5 \cdot 7} = \dfrac{6}{35}$

▸ $(-8) \cdot \dfrac{9}{5} = \dfrac{-8}{1} \cdot \dfrac{9}{5} = \dfrac{(-8)(9)}{(1)(5)} = \dfrac{-72}{5} = -\dfrac{72}{5}$

▸ $\dfrac{2x}{3y^2} \cdot \dfrac{x^2}{5y} = \dfrac{(2x)(x^2)}{(3y^2)(5y)} = \dfrac{2x^3}{15y^3}$

The following important properties of the rational numbers are a direct consequence of the definition of multiplication and the properties of the integers.

THEOREM 1 *The rational numbers are closed, associative, and commutative relative to the operation of multiplication.*

Because of these important properties we will still continue to enjoy the same type of freedom with the rational numbers that we had with the natural numbers and integers; that is, in a product involving two or more rational numbers as factors we may regroup and reorder the factors at will.

EQUALITY

A single rational number may have many different names, in fact, infinitely many names. We will discuss several properties of the rational numbers that will enable us to change expressions that represent rational numbers to different (but equivalent) forms.

First it will be helpful to identify two elementary properties of the rational numbers before we state and prove the next important theorem. For any non-zero integers a and c and any integer b,

$$\frac{a}{a} = 1 \qquad and \qquad 1 \cdot \frac{b}{c} = \frac{b}{c}$$

The first property follows from the definition of the quotient of two integers. The second property follows from the first and the definition of the product of two rational numbers; that is

$$1 \cdot \left(\frac{b}{c}\right) = \left(\frac{1}{1}\right) \cdot \left(\frac{b}{c}\right) = \frac{1b}{1c} = \frac{b}{c}$$

THEOREM 2   *For each integer a and nonzero integers b and k,*

$$\frac{ak}{bk} = \frac{a}{b}$$

PROOF

$$\frac{ak}{bk} = \frac{a}{b} \cdot \frac{k}{k} = \frac{a}{b} \cdot 1 = \frac{a}{b}$$

You should supply the reasons for each step

This theorem provides the basis for reducing fractions to lowest terms. It is also important to note that the theorem can be used to change fractions to "higher terms," a process we will often use when adding or subtracting rational numbers.

EXAMPLE 2:   REMOVING COMMON FACTORS FROM NUMERATOR AND DENOMINATOR.

▶ $\dfrac{27}{18} = \dfrac{3 \cdot \cancel{9}}{2 \cdot \cancel{9}} = \dfrac{3}{2}$

▶ $\dfrac{-5}{15} = \dfrac{(-1)\cancel{(5)}}{(3)\cancel{(5)}} = \dfrac{-1}{3} = -\dfrac{1}{3}$

▶ $\dfrac{-12}{-27} = \dfrac{4(-3)}{9(-3)} = \dfrac{4}{9}$

▶ $\dfrac{-6xy^2}{3x^2y} = \dfrac{(-2y)(3xy)}{(x)(3xy)} = \dfrac{-2y}{x}$

You might note that canceling common factors from the numerator and denominator is the same as dividing the numerator and denominator by the same nonzero quantity—think of how division of integers is defined in terms of multiplication.

The next and last theorem in this section, pertaining to rational numbers and signs, is used with great frequency in mathematics; its misuse is a major contributor to errors.

THEOREM 3*   *For each integer a and each nonzero integer b,*

(A) $\dfrac{-a}{-b} = \dfrac{a}{b}$

(B) $\dfrac{-a}{b} = \dfrac{a}{-b} = -\dfrac{a}{b}$

(C) $(-1)\dfrac{a}{b} = -\dfrac{a}{b}$

(D) $-\left(-\dfrac{a}{b}\right) = \dfrac{a}{b}$

The theorem is not difficult to prove. The following special cases will indicate the procedure. (You should be able to supply the reasons for each step.)

(A) $\dfrac{-a}{-b} = \dfrac{(-1)a}{(-1)b} = \dfrac{a}{b}$

(B) $\dfrac{-a}{b} = \dfrac{(-1)a}{(1)b} = \dfrac{(-1)}{1} \cdot \dfrac{a}{b} = \dfrac{1}{(-1)} \cdot \dfrac{a}{b} = \dfrac{(1)a}{(-1)b} = \dfrac{a}{-b}$

We will conclude this section by presenting an example that illustrates most of what we have been talking about.

EXAMPLE 3

$$\dfrac{-3x}{2y} \cdot \dfrac{6y^2}{9x^2} = \dfrac{(-3x)(6y^2)}{(2y)(9x^2)} = \dfrac{(-y)(18xy)}{(x)(18xy)} = \dfrac{-y}{x} = -\dfrac{y}{x}$$

* You should note that this theorem does not say that the quotient of two integers with like sign is positive or that the quotient of two integers with unlike sign is negative. All of the minus signs in the theorem, except for one, represent the unary operation "the negative of."

or (thinking of Theorem 2 in terms of dividing out common factors),

$$\frac{-3x}{2y} \cdot \frac{6y^2}{9x^2} = \frac{\overset{-1}{\cancel{(-3x)}}\overset{3y}{\cancel{(6y^2)}}}{\underset{1}{\cancel{(2y)}}\underset{3x}{\cancel{(9x^2)}}} = \frac{-y}{x} = -\frac{y}{x}$$

or (even more briefly),

$$\frac{\overset{-1}{\cancel{-3x}}}{\underset{1}{\cancel{2y}}} \cdot \frac{\overset{3y}{\cancel{6y^2}}}{\underset{3x}{\cancel{9x^2}}} = \frac{-y}{x} = -\frac{y}{x}$$

EXERCISE 27

1. What are the coordinates of points a, b, and c?

2. What are the coordinates of points c, d, and e?

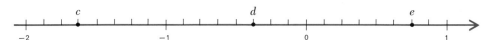

3. Graph the following set of rational numbers:

$$\left\{ \frac{5}{4}, -\frac{5}{4}, \frac{2}{-1}, \frac{-7}{4} \right\}$$

4. Graph the following set of rational numbers:

$$\left\{ \frac{3}{2}, \frac{-3}{2}, \frac{-1}{-2}, -\frac{1}{2} \right\}$$

5. Evaluate:

(A) $\left| -\frac{7}{8} \right|$ (B) $-\left(-\frac{7}{8} \right)$ (C) $\left| \frac{3}{4} \right|$ (D) $-\left(\frac{3}{4} \right)$

6. Evaluate:

(A) $-\left| -\frac{1}{2} \right|$ (B) $-\left(-\frac{1}{2} \right)$ (C) $-\left(\frac{7}{3} \right)$ (D) $-\left(\frac{-2}{3} \right)$

7. Reduce to lowest terms by removing common factors from the numerator and denominator:

(A) $\dfrac{6}{9}$

(B) $\dfrac{-3}{12}$

(C) $\dfrac{18}{-8}$

(D) $\dfrac{-9x}{-6x}$

(E) $\dfrac{-2abc}{6bcd}$

(F) $\dfrac{12a^2b}{-3ab^2}$

8. Reduce to lowest terms:

(A) $\dfrac{27}{15}$

(B) $\dfrac{25}{-15}$

(C) $\dfrac{-6x^2}{-15x}$

(D) $\dfrac{2y^2}{-8y^3}$

(E) $\dfrac{-21x^2y^3}{35xy}$

(F) $\dfrac{-3(x+y)}{-9(x+y)}$

9. Replace the question marks with appropriate expressions:

(A) $\dfrac{3}{5} = \dfrac{?}{15}$

(B) $-\dfrac{2}{3} = \dfrac{?}{12}$

(C) $\dfrac{3x}{5} = \dfrac{-6x^2}{?}$

10. Replace the question marks with appropriate expressions:

(A) $\dfrac{7}{3} = \dfrac{-21}{?}$

(B) $-\dfrac{2}{3x} = \dfrac{-8x}{?}$

(C) $-\dfrac{3u}{2v} = \dfrac{12uv}{?}$

11. Multiply and reduce to lowest terms:

(A) $\dfrac{2}{3} \cdot \dfrac{4}{5}$

(B) $\dfrac{-3}{7} \cdot \dfrac{14}{9}$

(C) $\dfrac{-2}{3} \cdot \dfrac{3}{-4}$

(D) $\dfrac{10}{-9} \cdot \dfrac{12}{15}$

(E) $\dfrac{2x}{-3yz} \cdot \dfrac{-6y}{4x}$

(F) $\dfrac{6a^2}{7c} \cdot \dfrac{21cd}{12ac}$

12. Multiply and reduce to lowest terms:

(A) $\dfrac{4}{5} \cdot \dfrac{15}{16}$

(B) $\dfrac{8}{3} \cdot \dfrac{-12}{24}$

(C) $\dfrac{-6}{-5} \cdot \dfrac{-50}{24}$

(D) $\dfrac{-2a}{3bc} \cdot \dfrac{9c}{a}$

(E) $\dfrac{-x}{yz} \cdot \dfrac{-z}{x}$

(F) $\left(-\dfrac{2}{3}\right)\left(\dfrac{6}{4}\right)$

13. Multiply and reduce to lowest terms:

(A) $\dfrac{-21}{16} \cdot \dfrac{12}{-14} \cdot \dfrac{8}{9}$

(B) $\dfrac{2x^2}{3y^2} \cdot \dfrac{-6yz}{2x} \cdot \dfrac{y}{-xz}$

14. Multiply and reduce to lowest terms:

(A) $\dfrac{18}{15} \cdot \dfrac{-10}{21} \cdot \dfrac{3}{-1}$

(B) $\dfrac{-a}{-b} \cdot \dfrac{12b^2c}{15ac} \cdot \dfrac{-10}{4b}$

15. Solve the following equations by guessing; the replacement set for the variable is the set of rational numbers:

(A) $2x = 1$ (B) $3x = -5$ (C) $-4x = 3$ (D) $\tfrac{2}{3}x = 1$

16. Solve the following equations by guessing; the replacement set for the variable is the set of rational numbers:

(A) $5x = 1$ (B) $-2x = 3$ (C) $7x = -5$ (D) $\tfrac{2}{3}x = \tfrac{1}{2}$

17. An easy way to test whether two rational numbers are equal is given in the following theorem: *Given two rational numbers a/b and c/d; we can write a/b = c/d if and only if ad = bc (b ≠ 0, d ≠ 0).* Prove this theorem.

25   DIVISION OF RATIONAL NUMBERS

When studying fractions in arithmetic, you might have been told, "To divide one fraction by another, invert (or take the reciprocal of) the divisor and multiply." It is not difficult to see why this mechanical rule is valid. Before we look into the matter, however, you might find it helpful to briefly reread the material on the division of integers in the first part of Sec. 18.

As with the integers we will define the **division of rational numbers** in terms of multiplication. If r and s are any two rational numbers, then we may write

$$\frac{r}{s} = Q \qquad \textit{if and only if } r = sQ, \textit{ and } Q \textit{ is unique}$$

As a consequence of this definition, we can convert division of rational numbers into multiplication of rational numbers.

THEOREM 4   *If a, b, c, and d are integers with b, c, and d different from zero, then*

$$\frac{a}{b} \div \frac{c}{d} = \frac{a}{b} \cdot \frac{d}{c}$$

PROOF

To prove this theorem, all that we have to do is to show that the product of the divisor (c/d) and the quotient $[(a/b) \cdot (d/c)]$ is equal to the dividend (a/b). Thus

$$\frac{c}{d} \cdot \left(\frac{a}{b} \cdot \frac{d}{c}\right) = \left(\frac{c}{d} \cdot \frac{d}{c}\right) \cdot \frac{a}{b} = \frac{a}{b}$$

We can now conclude because of Theorem 4 and the fact that the rational numbers are closed with respect to multiplication that *the rational numbers are closed with respect to division, except for division by zero.*

EXAMPLE 4

▶ $\dfrac{-6}{14} \div \dfrac{21}{2} = \dfrac{-6}{14} \cdot \dfrac{2}{21} = -\dfrac{2}{49}$

▶ $\dfrac{12x}{-5y} \div \dfrac{9y}{8x} = \dfrac{12x}{-5y} \cdot \dfrac{8x}{9y} = -\dfrac{32x^2}{15y^2}$

▶ $\dfrac{18a^2b/(-15c)}{12ab^2/(-5c)} = \dfrac{18a^2b}{-15c} \cdot \dfrac{-5c}{12ab^2} = \dfrac{a}{2b}$

▶ $\dfrac{-3x}{yz} \div 12x = \dfrac{-3x}{yz} \div \dfrac{12x}{1} = \dfrac{-3x}{yz} \cdot \dfrac{1}{12x} = -\dfrac{1}{4yz}$

Two numbers are said to be **reciprocals** of each other if their product is 1.

▶ The reciprocal of $\frac{2}{3}$ is $\frac{3}{2}$ since $\frac{2}{3} \cdot \frac{3}{2} = 1$.

▶ The reciprocal of 5 is $\frac{1}{5}$ since $(5)(\frac{1}{5}) = 1$.

▶ The reciprocal of $\frac{a}{b}$ is $\frac{b}{a}$ since $\frac{a}{b} \cdot \frac{b}{a} = 1$ $(a \neq 0, b \neq 0)$.

It should now be clear that the **mechanical rule for division** of rational numbers that was stated at the beginning of this section is valid; that is, *to divide one rational number by another, take the reciprocal of the divisor and multiply.*

SIMPLE EQUATIONS

In the preceding chapter we were not able to solve all equations of the form $ax = b$, where a and b are integers. For example, $2x = 3$ has no solution in the set of integers. By extending the integers to the rational numbers, we are now in a position to solve this equation and many others. In fact, we are in a position to solve any equation of the form $ax = b$, where a and b are any rational numbers with $a \neq 0$.

The laws of equality in Sec. 5 and Theorems 9 and 10 in Sec. 20 apply equally well to the set of rational numbers. This means that we can solve equations involving rational numbers using the same formal procedures that we used in the preceding chapter. A few examples should make the process clear.

EXAMPLE 6.   Solve $2x = 3$.

SOLUTION

Our objective, of course, is to find replacements for x that will make the statement true. Mechanically, we will think in terms of an operation on the equation that will make the coefficient of x a $+1$. In this example this can be accomplished in two ways: divide both members of the equation by 2, or multiply both members of the equation by the reciprocal of 2, that is, $\frac{1}{2}$:

1.

$$2x = 3$$

$$\frac{2x}{2} = \frac{3}{2}$$

$$x = \frac{3}{2}$$

2.

$$2x = 3$$

$$\tfrac{1}{2}(2x) = \tfrac{1}{2}(3)$$

$$x = \tfrac{3}{2}$$

CHECK

$$2(\tfrac{3}{2}) \stackrel{?}{=} 3$$

$$3 \stackrel{\vee}{=} 3$$

EXAMPLE 7. Solve $x/3 = -2$.

SOLUTION

$$\frac{x}{3} = -2$$

$$3\left(\frac{x}{3}\right) = (3)(-2)$$

$$x = -6$$

CHECK

$$\frac{-6}{3} \stackrel{?}{=} -2$$

$$-2 \stackrel{\vee}{=} -2$$

EXAMPLE 8. Solve $-\frac{2}{3}x = \frac{4}{9}$.

SOLUTION

$$-\tfrac{2}{3}x = \tfrac{4}{9}$$

$$(-\tfrac{3}{2})(-\tfrac{2}{3}x) = (-\tfrac{3}{2})(\tfrac{4}{9})$$

$$x = -\tfrac{2}{3}$$

CHECK

$$(-\tfrac{2}{3})(-\tfrac{2}{3}) \stackrel{?}{=} \tfrac{4}{9}$$

$$\tfrac{4}{9} \stackrel{\vee}{=} \tfrac{4}{9}$$

EXERCISE 28

Perform the indicated operations and reduce answers to lowest terms. All variables represent nonzero integers.

1. $\frac{2}{3} \div \frac{4}{9}$

2. $\frac{5}{11} \div \frac{55}{44}$

3. $\dfrac{\frac{7}{3}}{\frac{2}{3}}$

4. $\dfrac{-1/(-25)}{15/4}$

5. $\dfrac{7}{\frac{7}{5}}$

6. $\dfrac{\frac{5}{3}}{3}$

7. $\dfrac{0}{\frac{1}{3}}$

8. $\dfrac{-2/3}{0/4}$

9. $\dfrac{-8/9}{24/15}$

10. $\dfrac{36/21}{20/(-35)}$

11. $7 \div \dfrac{21}{-2}$

12. $\frac{16}{15} \div (-32)$

13. $\dfrac{a^2/(-b)}{b^2/a}$

14. $\dfrac{d/c^2}{d/(-c^2)}$

15. $\dfrac{2x}{3y} \div \dfrac{4x}{6y^2}$

16. $\dfrac{-a}{4c} \div \dfrac{-a^2}{12c^2}$

17. $\dfrac{3uv^2/(-5)}{6u^2v/(-15)}$

18. $\dfrac{-21x^2y^2/12cd}{14xy/9d}$

19. $\dfrac{-2xy}{x/y}$

20. $\dfrac{-x/3y}{3y}$

21. (A) $\left(\frac{9}{10} \div \frac{4}{6}\right) \cdot \frac{3}{5}$ (B) $\frac{9}{10} \div \left(\frac{4}{6} \cdot \frac{3}{5}\right)$

22. (A) $\left(\frac{a}{b} \div \frac{c}{d}\right) \cdot \frac{e}{f}$ (B) $\frac{a}{b} \div \left(\frac{c}{d} \cdot \frac{e}{f}\right)$

23. (A) $\dfrac{\frac{2}{3}}{\frac{5}{3}}$ (B) $\dfrac{\frac{5}{3}}{\frac{2}{3}}$ (C) $\dfrac{a/b}{c/d}$ (D) $\dfrac{c/d}{a/b}$

CONCLUSION: Division is not commutative.

24. (A) $\left(\frac{3}{4} \div \frac{1}{2}\right) \div \frac{3}{2}$ (B) $\frac{3}{4} \div \left(\frac{1}{2} \div \frac{3}{2}\right)$

(C) $\left(\frac{a}{b} \div \frac{c}{d}\right) \div \frac{e}{f}$ (D) $\frac{a}{b} \div \left(\frac{c}{d} \div \frac{e}{f}\right)$

CONCLUSION: Division is not associative.

In problems 25 through 36 solve and check each of the equations assuming that the replacement set for each variable is the set of rational numbers.

25. $5x = 7$ **26.** $3x = 8$

27. $-4x = 6$ **28.** $15x = -21$

29. $\frac{x}{3} = 4$ **30.** $\frac{x}{7} = -2$

31. $\frac{x}{6} = -\frac{1}{4}$ **32.** $-\frac{x}{3} = \frac{2}{9}$

33. $\frac{2}{3}x = \frac{4}{9}$ **34.** $\frac{1}{5}x = -\frac{3}{5}$

35. $\frac{2x}{3} = \frac{1}{3}$ **36.** $\frac{5x}{-7} = -\frac{15}{28}$

37. If you walk at 5 mph, how long will it take you to walk 3 miles?

38. An electronic card sorter sorts IBM cards at 320 cards per min. How long will it take the sorter to sort 2,800 cards? Leave the answer as the quotient of two integers reduced to lowest terms.

39. One-third of what number is one-fifth?

40. Two-thirds of what number is $-\frac{8}{9}$?

41. About $\frac{1}{9}$ of an iceberg is above water. If 50 ft are observed above water, approximately how many feet are below the surface?

42. An arrow is shot vertically upward with an initial velocity of 200 fps. Neglecting air resistance, its velocity at time t is given by the formula $v = 200 - 32t$. In how many seconds will the arrow reach its highest point? Leave the answer as a quotient of two integers reduced to lowest terms. HINT: At the highest point what is v?

43. Which of the following statements are true for all rational numbers (division by zero excluded)? For each statement that is false find replacements for the variables to show that it is false.

(A) ab is a rational number.

(B) a/b is a rational number.

(C) $ab = ba$

(D) $a/b = b/a$

(E) $(ab)c = a(bc)$

(F) $(a/b)/c = a/(b/c)$

26   ADDITION AND SUBTRACTION OF RATIONAL NUMBERS

THE LEAST COMMON MULTIPLE (LCM)

The least-common-multiple concept is useful in many places in mathematics; we will use it in this section to help us in adding and subtracting rational numbers. The concept is not difficult to understand if you start with the word "multiple."

A *multiple* of a natural number is obtained by multiplying the natural number by a natural number. Listed below are the first 14 multiples of 2, 3, and 4, respectively.

2, 4, 6, 8, 10, (12), 14, 16, 18, 20, 22, (24), 26, 28, . . .

3, 6, 9, (12), 15, 18, 21, (24), 27, 30, 33, (36), 39, 42, . . .

4, 8, (12), 16, 20, (24), 28, 32, (36), 40, 44, 48, 52, 56, . . .

The first three *common multiples* of 2, 3, and 4 are 12, 24, and 36, respectively. (We note that 12, 24, and 36 are each exactly divisible by 2, 3, and 4.) The *least common multiple* of 2, 3, and 4 is 12.

In general, the **least common multiple** (LCM) of two or more natural numbers is defined to be the smallest natural number exactly divisible by each of the numbers.

EXAMPLE 9

▶ The LCM of 4, 6, and 8 is 24.

▶ The LCM of 5, 9, and 15 is 45.

The LCM is not always easy to find by inspection; consider the numbers 8, 15, 20, and 24. The following procedure provides a systematic approach to the problem. Since the LCM of two or more natural numbers must be exactly divisible by each number, *it must contain each different prime factor present in each of the numbers to the highest power it occurs in any one number.*

EXAMPLE 10.   Find the LCM for 8, 15, 20, and 24.

SOLUTION

Step 1. Write each number as a product of prime factors:

$$8 = 2^3 \qquad 15 = 3 \cdot 5 \qquad 20 = 2^2 \cdot 5 \qquad 24 = 2^3 \cdot 3$$

Step 2. Find the LCM as directed above:

$$\text{LCM} = 2^3 \cdot 3 \cdot 5 = 120$$

We can extend the idea of LCM to algebraic expressions by defining the LCM of two or more expressions to be the "simplest" algebraic expression that is "exactly divisible" by each of the expressions. We will have to accept your intuitive knowledge of what is meant by "simplest" and "exactly divisible" for now.

EXAMPLE 11

▶ The LCM of $4x^2y$, $6xy^2$, and xy is $12x^2y^2$.

▶ The LCM of $5s^3t$, $9t^2$, and $15t$ is $45s^3t^2$.

EXERCISE 29

Find the LCM for each of the set of numbers or algebraic expressions.

1. 3, 2
2. 5, 3
3. 6, 4, 2
4. 3, 10, 15
5. 3, 8, 12
6. 4, 6, 9
7. 6, 10, 15, 18
8. 3, 7, 9, 21
9. 6, 8, 15, 20
10. 18, 28, 42
11. $2x^2$, $3x$
12. xy, $2x^2$, $3y$
13. $4y^2$, $3x^2$, 6
14. $3xy$, $8xz$, $4yz$
15. $4s^2$, $6t$, $9st^2$
16. $6u$, $8v^3$, 4

ADDITION AND SUBTRACTION

To get an idea of how we might define addition for rational numbers, let us assume for the moment that the distributive law holds. Then we would be able to write

$$\frac{a}{b} + \frac{c}{b} = \frac{1}{b} \cdot a + \frac{1}{b} \cdot c = \frac{1}{b}(a + c) = \frac{a + c}{b}$$

We find that if we use this result as the definition of addition, we will be able to continue to manipulate symbols that represent rational numbers in essentially the same way that we manipulated symbols that represented integers. This follows from the fact that we will have defined addition of rational numbers (with the same denominators) in terms of addition of their numerators, which are integers. The case where the denominators are not the same will easily be taken care of in a moment.

If a/b and c/b are two rational numbers with a, b, and c integers, then their **sum** is defined by the equation

$$\frac{a}{b} + \frac{c}{b} = \frac{a+c}{b}$$

EXAMPLE 12

▶ $\dfrac{2}{3} + \dfrac{-1}{3} = \dfrac{2 + (-1)}{3} = \dfrac{1}{3}$

▶ $\dfrac{3x}{5} + \dfrac{7x}{5} = \dfrac{3x + 7x}{5} = \dfrac{10x}{5} = 2x$

▶ $\dfrac{-8}{2x} + \dfrac{-3}{2x} = \dfrac{(-8) + (-3)}{2x} = \dfrac{-11}{2x} = -\dfrac{11}{2x}$

Now that we have defined addition of rational numbers (with like denominators) we can define **subtraction of rational numbers** (with like denominators) just as we defined subtraction for the integers. That is, $M - S = D$ *if and only if* $M = S + D$. As with the integers, we immediately have the following theorem: $M - S = M + (-S)$ (that is, *to subtract a quantity, add its negative*). From this definition and theorem we can easily prove the following useful theorem on subtraction of rational numbers.

THEOREM 5   *If a, b, and c are integers with* $b \neq 0$, *then*

$$\frac{a}{b} - \frac{c}{b} = \frac{a-c}{b}$$

PROOF

$$\frac{a}{b} - \frac{c}{b} = \frac{a}{b} + \left(-\frac{c}{b}\right) = \frac{a}{b} + \frac{-c}{b} = \frac{a + (-c)}{b} = \frac{a-c}{b}$$

(You should be able to supply the reasons for each step.)

EXAMPLE 13. $\dfrac{3}{7} - \dfrac{-5}{7} = \dfrac{3 - (-5)}{7} = \dfrac{3+5}{7} = \dfrac{8}{7}$

To add or subtract rational numbers with unlike denominators, we simply use Theorem 2 in Sec. 24 (that is, $a/b = ak/bk$) to transform the rational numbers into equivalent forms with common denominators. We then use the definition of addition above or Theorem 5 on subtraction. Even though any common denominator will do, the **least common denominator** (i.e., the least common multiple of the denominators) will generally minimize the complexity of the result. The following example should make the process clear.

EXAMPLE 14

▶ $\dfrac{-5}{6} + \dfrac{3}{4} = \dfrac{(-5)(2)}{6 \cdot 2} + \dfrac{3 \cdot 3}{4 \cdot 3} = \dfrac{-10}{12} + \dfrac{9}{12}$

$= \dfrac{(-10) + 9}{12} = \dfrac{-1}{12} = -\dfrac{1}{12}$

▶ $\dfrac{5x}{6} - \dfrac{-3x}{2} = \dfrac{5x}{6} - \dfrac{(-3x)(3)}{2 \cdot 3} = \dfrac{5x}{6} - \dfrac{-9x}{6} = \dfrac{5x - (-9x)}{6}$

$= \dfrac{5x + 9x}{6} = \dfrac{14x}{6} = \dfrac{7x}{3}$

▶ $\dfrac{a}{b} - 1 = \dfrac{a}{b} - \dfrac{b}{b} = \dfrac{a - b}{b}$

▶ $\dfrac{7x}{4y} - \dfrac{-2y}{6x} = \dfrac{(7x)(3x)}{(4y)(3x)} - \dfrac{(-2y)(2y)}{(6x)(2y)} = \dfrac{21x^2}{12xy} - \dfrac{(-4y^2)}{12xy}$

$= \dfrac{21x^2 - (-4y^2)}{12xy} = \dfrac{21x^2 + 4y^2}{12xy}$

As we noted above, the rational numbers enjoy many of the same properties as the integers. We will summarize some of these properties in the form of a theorem which we will not prove.[*]

THEOREM 6   *The set of rational numbers is closed relative to the operations of addition, subtraction, multiplication, and division (except for division by zero); the rational numbers are associative and commutative relative to addition and multiplication; and multiplication in the rational numbers distributes over addition.*

[*] Henkin, *op. cit.*, chap. 12.

To combine three or more rational numbers or terms representing rational numbers, we use the preceding results combined with the techniques discussed in Sec. 19.

EXAMPLE 15

▶ $\dfrac{-3}{4} - \dfrac{-1}{3} + \dfrac{5}{6} = \dfrac{(-3)(3)}{4 \cdot 3} - \dfrac{(-1)(4)}{3 \cdot 4} + \dfrac{5 \cdot 2}{6 \cdot 2}$

$= \dfrac{-9}{12} - \dfrac{-4}{12} + \dfrac{10}{12}$

$= \dfrac{(-9) - (-4) + 10}{12} = \dfrac{-9 + 4 + 10}{12} = \dfrac{5}{12}$

▶ $\dfrac{3}{2x^2} - \dfrac{-5}{x} + 1 = \dfrac{3}{2x^2} - \dfrac{(-5)(2x)}{2x^2} + \dfrac{2x^2}{2x^2}$

$= \dfrac{3 - (-10x) + 2x^2}{2x^2} = \dfrac{2x^2 + 10x + 3}{2x^2}$

▶ $40\left(\dfrac{x}{8} - \dfrac{1}{5} + \dfrac{x}{20} + \dfrac{3}{4}\right) = 5x - 8 + 2x + 30 = 7x + 22$

EXERCISE 30

Combine into single fractions (problems 1 through 12).

1. (A) $\dfrac{-3}{5} + \dfrac{7}{5}$ (B) $\dfrac{2y}{7} + \dfrac{y}{7}$ (C) $\dfrac{3}{5xy} + \dfrac{-6}{5xy}$

    (D) $\dfrac{3}{5} - \dfrac{7}{5}$ (E) $\dfrac{2}{7} - \dfrac{-5}{7}$ (F) $\dfrac{x}{y} - \dfrac{z}{y}$

2. (A) $\dfrac{7}{11} + \dfrac{-3}{11}$ (B) $\dfrac{2}{3} - \dfrac{5}{3}$ (C) $\dfrac{x}{5} - \dfrac{2x}{5}$

    (D) $\dfrac{3y}{x} + \dfrac{2y}{x}$ (E) $\dfrac{-3}{7y} - \dfrac{-3}{7y}$ (F) $\dfrac{3}{7y} - \dfrac{-3}{7y}$

3. (A) $\dfrac{3}{4} + \dfrac{-2}{3}$ (B) $\dfrac{-2}{5} - \dfrac{1}{2}$ (C) $\dfrac{3x}{2} + \dfrac{2x}{3}$

    (D) $\dfrac{x}{y} - \dfrac{y}{x}$ (E) $\dfrac{x}{y} - 2$ (F) $1 - \dfrac{-1}{x}$

4. (A) $\dfrac{1}{3} + \dfrac{-1}{2}$ (B) $\dfrac{1}{3} - \dfrac{-1}{2}$ (C) $\dfrac{x}{4} - \dfrac{1}{8}$.

(D) $\dfrac{1}{xy} - \dfrac{3}{y}$ (E) $\dfrac{2a}{b} + \dfrac{-1}{a}$ (F) $4 - \dfrac{1}{3x}$

5. $\dfrac{1}{3} - \dfrac{-1}{2} + \dfrac{5}{6}$ 6. $\dfrac{-3}{4} + \dfrac{2}{5} - \dfrac{-3}{2}$

7. $\dfrac{x^2}{4} - \dfrac{x}{3} + \dfrac{-1}{2}$ 8. $\dfrac{2}{5} - \dfrac{x}{2} - \dfrac{-x^2}{3}$

9. $\dfrac{1}{xy} - \dfrac{1}{yz} + \dfrac{-1}{xz}$ 10. $\dfrac{3}{y^3} - \dfrac{-2}{y^2} + \dfrac{1}{y} - 2$

11. $\dfrac{3}{4x} - \dfrac{2}{3y} + \dfrac{1}{8xy}$ 12. $\dfrac{1}{5x^3} + \dfrac{-3}{2x^2} - \dfrac{-2}{3x}$

13. Simplify.   HINT: Use distributive law.

(A) $12\left(\dfrac{x}{4} + \dfrac{1}{3}\right)$ (B) $15\left(\dfrac{2x}{3} - \dfrac{3}{5}\right)$ (C) $20\left[\dfrac{1}{5}(x - 3) + \dfrac{2x}{4}\right]$

14. Simplify.   HINT: Use distributive law.

(A) $18\left(\dfrac{x}{2} - \dfrac{2}{9}\right)$ (B) $30\left(\dfrac{5x}{6} + \dfrac{4}{15}\right)$ (C) $24\left[\dfrac{x}{3} - \dfrac{3}{8}(x - 2)\right]$

Use the prime-factor method to help you find the least common denominator, and then combine into a single fraction.

15. $\dfrac{2y}{18} - \dfrac{-1}{28} - \dfrac{y}{42}$ 16. $\dfrac{5x}{6} - \dfrac{3}{8} + \dfrac{x}{15} - \dfrac{3}{20}$

17. $\dfrac{x^2}{12} + \dfrac{x}{18} - \dfrac{1}{30}$ 18. $\dfrac{3x}{50} - \dfrac{x}{15} - \dfrac{-2}{6}$

27   EQUATIONS AND APPLICATIONS

Except for a few problems in Sec. 25 we have avoided equations with rational-number coefficients. In practical applications rational-number coefficients occur more frequently than integers. We are now at the place where we can easily convert an equation with rational coefficients into one with integral coefficients, thus placing it in a position to be solved by previously known methods.

EXAMPLE 16.   What operation can we perform on the equation

$$\frac{x + 1}{3} - \frac{x}{4} = \frac{1}{2}$$

to eliminate the denominators? If we could find a number that was exactly divisible by each denominator, then we would be able to use the multiplication property of equality and the distributive property of the rational numbers to "clear the denominators." The least common multiple of the denominators is precisely the number we are looking for! The LCM of 3, 4, and 2 is 12. Thus

$$12\left(\frac{x+1}{3}\right) - 12\left(\frac{x}{4}\right) = 12\left(\frac{1}{2}\right)$$

$$4(x + 1) - 3x = 6$$

$$4x + 4 - 3x = 6$$

$$x = 2$$

EXAMPLE 17.   Equations will often have rational coefficients written as decimal fractions.   Some equations of this type are more easily solved if the equation is first "cleared of decimals."   The following is a case in point:

$$0.2x + 0.3(x - 5) = 13$$

$$(10)(0.2)x + (10)(0.3)(x - 5) = 10 \cdot 13$$

$$2x + 3(x - 5) = 130$$

$$5x - 15 = 130$$

$$5x = 145$$

$$x = 29$$

EXAMPLE 18.   Five individuals formed a glider club and decided to share the cost of a glider equally.   They found, however, that if they let three more join the club, the share for each of the original five would be reduced by $120.   What was the total cost of the glider?

SOLUTION

Let $C =$ the total cost of the glider.

$$\begin{array}{ccc} \text{cost per share} & \text{cost per share} & \text{reduction in cost} \\ \text{for 5 members} & \text{for 8 members} & \text{for each of} \\ & & \text{the original five} \end{array}$$

$$\frac{C}{5} \quad - \quad \frac{C}{8} \quad = \quad 120$$

$$40 \cdot \frac{C}{5} - 40 \cdot \frac{C}{8} = 40 \cdot 120$$

$$8C - 5C = 4,800$$

$$3C = 4,800$$

$$C = \$1,600$$

total cost of glider

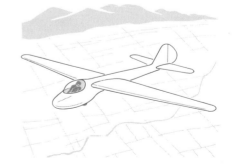

EXERCISE 31

Solve each equation in problems 1 through 14.

1. $\dfrac{3x}{5} = \dfrac{2}{3}$

2. $\dfrac{x}{7} - 1 = \dfrac{1}{7}$

3. $\dfrac{n}{5} - \dfrac{n}{6} = \dfrac{6}{5}$

4. $\dfrac{x}{3} - \dfrac{1}{4} = \dfrac{3x}{8}$

5. $0.8x = 160$

6. $x + 0.3x = 26$

7. $\dfrac{4x + 3}{9} = \dfrac{3x + 5}{7}$

8. $\dfrac{x - 2}{3} + 1 = \dfrac{x}{7}$

9. $3 - \dfrac{2x - 3}{3} = \dfrac{5 - x}{2}$

10. $\dfrac{2x - 3}{9} - \dfrac{x + 5}{6} = \dfrac{3 - x}{2} + 1$

11. $0.1(x - 7) + 0.05x = 0.8$

12. $0.4(x + 5) - 0.3x = 17$

13. $\dfrac{x}{12} - \dfrac{x + 1}{18} = \dfrac{3}{2}$

14. $\dfrac{3x}{24} - \dfrac{2 - x}{10} = \dfrac{5 + x}{40} - \dfrac{1}{15}$

15. A pole is located in a pond.   One-fifth of the pole is in the sand, 10 ft of it is in the water, and two-thirds of it is in the air.   How long is the pole?

16. Two-thirds of a bar of silver balances exactly with one-half of a bar of silver and a $\frac{1}{4}$-lb weight (Fig. 1).   How much does one whole bar of silver weigh?

17. A taxi company charges a flat fee of 50 cents and then 40 cents per mile traveled.   (A) Write a formula relating cost c and m, the number of miles traveled, using a decimal representation for cents.   (B) How long a ride can you get for $1.90 (not including tip)?

18. The retail price of a record is $2.80.   The markup on the cost is 40 percent. What did the store pay for the record?   HINT: Cost + markup = retail.

19. It is known that a carton contains 100 packages and that some of the packages weigh $\frac{1}{2}$ lb each and the rest weigh $\frac{1}{3}$ lb each.   To save time counting each type of package in the carton, you can weigh the whole contents of the box (45 lb) and determine the number of each kind of package by use of algebra. How many are there of each kind?

20. A skydiver free falls (because of air resistance) at about 176 fps or 120 mph (Fig. 2); with his parachute open he falls at about 22 fps or 15 mph.   If the sky-

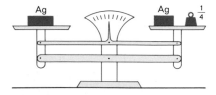

Figure 1

Figure 2

diver opened his chute halfway down and the total time for the descent was 6 min, how high was the plane when he jumped?

21. A travel agent, arranging a round-trip charter flight from New York to Europe, tells 100 signed-up members of a group that they can save $120 each if they can get 50 more people to sign up for the trip to fill the plane. What is the total round-trip charter cost of the jet transport? What is the cost per person if 100 go? What is the cost per person if 150 go?

22. Diophantus, an early Greek algebraist (A.D. 280), was the subject for a famous ancient puzzle. See if you can find Diophantus' age at death from the following information: Diophantus was a boy for one-sixth of his life; after one-twelfth more he grew a beard; after one-seventh more he married, and after 5 years of marriage he was granted a son; the son lived half as long as his father; and Diophantus died 4 years after his son's death.

28   RATIO AND PROPORTION

The comparison of quantities by use of ratios is very common. You have no doubt been using this device for many years. You will recall that the **ratio** of two quantities is simply the quotient of the two quantities—the first divided by the second. In a class of 30 students if there are ten girls and twenty boys, then the ratio of girls to boys would be 10/20 or 1 to 2 (sometimes written 1:2).

We have already encountered ratios in a number of places in this book; see, for example, Exercise 4, problems 11 and 13, where musical chords and Mendel's laws of heredity are discussed. There are few areas in life where ratios are not to be found. As a matter of fact, Pythagoras (569 B.C.?) practically founded a whole religion on the ratios of whole numbers. The following will give you an idea of their extensive use:

Psychologists talk about the *Intelligence Quotient* (*IQ*).

Anthropologists talk about the *cephalic index.*

Photographers talk about *true intensity ratios* (*f stops*).

Security analysts talk about *price-earning ratios.*

Political scientists talk about the *Shapley-Shubik index of voting power.*

Economists talk about the *cost-of-living index.*

Astronomers talk about the *order of magnitude* of a star.

Biologists talk about the *ratio of gene mutations to radiation.*

This list could be extended almost indefinitely. In the problem set we will discuss some of these ratios (as well as others) in more detail.

In addition to comparing known quantities, another reason why we want to know something about ratios is that they often lead to a simple way of finding unknown quantities.

EXAMPLE 19.   Suppose you are told that in your school the ratio of girls to boys is $3:5$, and that there are 1,450 boys. How many girls are in the school?

SOLUTION

Let $x =$ the number of girls in the school.

$$\frac{x}{1,450} = \frac{3}{5}$$

$$x = \frac{3}{5} \cdot 1,450$$

$$x = 870 \qquad \text{girls}$$

The statement of equality between two ratios is called a **proportion.** Knowing that various pairs of quantities are proportional leads to simple solutions of many types of problems.

EXAMPLE 20.   To measure the height of a tree, the distance across a lake, or many other inaccessible distances, one can use the proportional property of similar triangles*: *If two triangles are similar, their corresponding sides are proportional* (i.e., their corresponding sides have equal ratios).

To measure the height of a tree, you and a friend could place two stakes vertically in the ground in line with the tree at any convenient distance apart and distance from the tree as in the Fig. 3. You place your eye on any point on the farthest stake from the tree; your friend then marks points A and B as indicated. Triangles EAB and ECD are similar. Measure EA, AB, and EC, and determine the height CD from the proportion

$$\frac{AB}{CD} = \frac{EA}{EC}$$

---

*Two triangles are similar if their corresponding angles are equal.

Figure 3

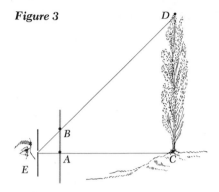

If we let h equal the height and measure AB, EC, and EA as 1.5 ft, 200 ft, and 5 ft, respectively, then

$$\frac{1.5}{h} = \frac{5}{200}$$

$$(200h)\frac{1.5}{h} = (200h)\frac{5}{200}$$

$$200(1.5) = 5h$$

$$5h = 300$$

$$h = 60 \text{ ft} \qquad \text{height of tree}$$

NOTE: We could just as well have written $h/1.5 = 200/5$, which is a little easier to solve.

EXERCISE 32

In problems 1 through 4 solve for the indicated variable.

1. $\dfrac{d}{12} = \dfrac{27}{18}$

2. $\dfrac{21}{39} = \dfrac{y}{13}$

3. $\dfrac{27}{18} = \dfrac{6}{h}$

4. $\dfrac{32}{x} = \dfrac{56}{35}$

5. PHOTOGRAPHY. If you enlarge a 6-by-3-in. picture so that the longer side is 8 in., how wide will the enlargement be?

6. SCALE DRAWINGS. An architect wishes to make a scale drawing of a 48-by-30-ft rectangular building. If his drawing of the building is 6 in. long, how wide is it?

7. COMMISSIONS. If you were charged a commission of $57 on the purchase of 300 shares of stock, what would be the proportionate commission on 500 shares?

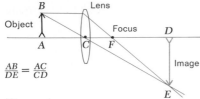

$$\frac{AB}{DE} = \frac{AC}{CD}$$

Figure 4

8. COMPUTERS. If an IBM electronic card sorter can sort 1,250 cards in 5 min, how long will it take the sorter to sort 11,250 cards?

9. OPTICS (MAGNIFICATION). In Fig. 4 triangles ABC and EDC are similar; hence, corresponding parts are proportional. If the object is 0.4 in., $AC = 1.4$ in., and $CD = 4.9$ in., what is the size of the image?

10. MUSIC. The three major chords in music are composed of notes whose frequencies are in the ratio of $4:5:6$. If the first note of the chord has a frequency of 264 cps (middle C on the piano), find the frequencies of the other two notes.   HINT: Set up two proportions using $4:5$ and $4:6$, respectively.

11. HYDRAULIC LIFTS. If in Fig. 5 the diameter of the smaller pipe is $\frac{1}{2}$ in. and the diameter of the larger pipe is 10 in., how much force would be required to lift a 3,000-lb car?   (Neglect weight of lift equipment.)

12. POPULATION SAMPLING. We stated the following problem in Sec. 1. The problem is to estimate the total population of a given species in a given region. A technique that is very widely used because of its simplicity is the "capture-mark-recapture" technique.   A group of specimens (such as deer, fish, or birds) is collected from the population in such a way as to avoid any injury to them, and these are marked in some distinctive way.   The marked specimens are then released into the total population.   After a time period adequate for thorough

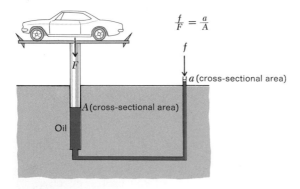

Figure 5

mixing, a new sample is captured, and the proportion of the marked specimens is determined.

Let n = the number of specimens marked first

    N = the total size of the population (unknown)

    M = the total number recaptured

    m = the number of marked specimens out of the M recaptured

(A) Write a proportion relating the four quantities above.

(B) Zoologists Green and Evans (1940) worked with snowshoe hares in the Lake Alexander area of Minnesota. They initially captured and banded 948 hares. After an appropriate mixing period they recaptured 167 marked and 254 unmarked rabbits. Estimate the total snowshoe hare population in the area.

13. MONEY EXCHANGE. If one United States dollar can be exchanged for $1.08 in Canadian money, how many United States cents would a Canadian receive for each Canadian dollar? Find the answer correct to four decimal places. (Solve by writing an appropriate proportion.)

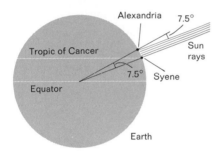

Figure 6

14. ASTRONOMY. Do you have any idea how one might measure the circumference of the earth? In 240 B.C. Eratosthenes measured the size of the earth from its curvature. At Syene, Egypt (lying on the Tropic of Cancer) the sun was directly overhead at noon on June 21. At the same time in Alexandria, a town 500 miles directly north, the sun's rays fell at an angle of 7.5° to the vertical. Using this information and a little knowledge of geometry (see Fig. 6), Eratosthenes was able to approximate the circumference of the earth using the following proportion: 7.5 is to 360 as 500 is to the circumference of the earth. Compute Eratosthenes' estimate.

15. INTELLIGENCE. The IQ (Intelligence Quotient) is found by dividing the mental age, as indicated by standard tests, by the chronological age and multiplying by 100. For example, if a child has a mental age of 12 and a chronological age of 10, his IQ is 120. If an 11-year-old has an IQ of 132 (superior intelligence), compute his mental age.

16. GENETIC GROUPINGS. Anthropologists, in their study of race and human genetic groupings use ratios called indexes. One widely used index is the cephalic index, the ratio of the breadth of the head to its length (looking down from the top) is expressed as a percent. Thus

$$\text{Cephalic index} = \frac{(\text{breadth})(100)}{\text{length}}$$

Some Indian tribes in Baja, California (Mexico) had a cephalic index of 66, and some in California (United States) had an index of 88. Assuming the lengths of the heads of each tribe averaged 9 in., what was the average width of the heads of each tribe?

29   THE SET OF REAL NUMBERS

By extending the integers to the rational numbers, we significantly increased our ability to perform certain operations, to solve equations, and to attack practical problems. From a certain point of view it may appear that the rational numbers are capable of satisfying all of our number needs because (1) the set is closed with respect to the four basic arithmetical operations of addition, subtraction, multiplication, and division (except division by zero); (2) equations of the type $ax + b = 0$ with $a \neq 0$, where a and b are rational numbers, always have a solution in the rational numbers; and (3) it may even appear that the rational numbers meet all of our requirements for measuring line segments—a first requirement would be that every point on the number line is named by a distinct rational number, and every rational number names a distinct point on the number line. One might wonder if it is necessary to go further; that is, can we get by with the rational numbers, or do we need to extend this system?

RATIONAL NUMBERS AND THE NUMBER LINE

Let us take a closer look at the relationship between the rational numbers and the points on the number line. If we take any two points on the number line with rational numbers as labels (coordinates), add the rational numbers, and divide by 2, the result (because of closure properties) will be a rational number. In addition, because of order properties to be discussed in the next section, it will name a point between the other two (see Fig. 7).

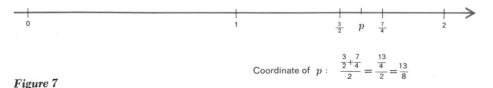

Coordinate of p : $\dfrac{\frac{3}{2} + \frac{7}{4}}{2} = \dfrac{\frac{13}{4}}{2} = \dfrac{13}{8}$

Figure 7

In general, it can be shown that *between any two points with rational numbers as coordinates there always exists another point with a rational number as a coordinate.* It would appear that points with rational numbers as coordinates are very "close" together, and that if we used all of the rational numbers to label points on the number line, all of the points would be used up. It may startle you to know that in a certain sense there are more points that have not been named by rational numbers than have been named. The line is like a sieve!

It is not difficult to find a point that cannot be named by a rational number. As a matter of fact, Pythagoras (569? B.C.) managed on the basis of this discovery (which, incidently, he made himself) to destroy the very foundations of the Pythagorean sect which he had founded. This group of religious zealots believed that all nature, natural and supernatural, was built on whole-number relationships.

Using his famous Pythagorean theorem,[*] he found that he could find a point that must be named by a number whose square is 2 (Fig. 8).

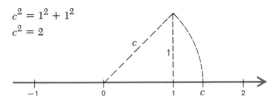

$$c^2 = 1^2 + 1^2$$
$$c^2 = 2$$

Figure 8

Now one naturally asks if there is a rational number whose square is 2. Stated in another way (since any rational number can be expressed as the quotient of two integers), is it possible to find two nonzero integers such that the square of one is twice the square of the other? Pythagoras found that if one answered either of these two questions in the affirmative, then one could show that certain odd numbers are even (see Appendix D), which, of course, is absurd. The original assumption must be false! That is, if the point is to be named by a number, it must be a number other than a rational number. This discovery, though devastating to Pythagoras at the time, is of utmost importance to modern-day mathematics and has assured Pythagoras a permanent position in the "mathematics hall of fame."

---

[*]The square of the hypotenuse of a right triangle is equal to the sum of the squares of the other two sides.

$$c^2 = a^2 + b^2$$

There are infinitely many other points on the number line that do not have rational-number coordinates. All of these points can be associated with line segments of given lengths, and many can be associated with solutions to simple equations of the form $x^2 - b = 0$, where b is a positive integer that is not the square of some integer (for example, $x^2 - 7 = 0$). We see that once again we must extend our number system. We will discuss this extension informally at this time; in later chapters and future courses the extension will be treated in greater detail.

REAL NUMBERS

To make a long story short, we will form a new set of numbers called the **real numbers** by adding the set of numbers called the **irrational numbers** to the rational numbers. The irrational numbers include numbers such as

$\sqrt{2}$ and $-\sqrt{2}$ numbers whose squares are 2

$\sqrt[3]{7}$ a number whose cube is 7

π the ratio of the circumference of any circle to its diameter

In fact, irrational numbers include such numbers as the square root of any positive integer that is not the square of an integer and the cube root of any integer that is not the cube of an integer.

You may be tempted to argue that $\sqrt{2}$ is a rational number since the square-root table in Appendix B lists its decimal value as 1.414, and 1.414 is a rational number since it can be written as $\frac{1414}{1000}$. Try squaring 1.414 and see what you get. The rational number 1.414 is an approximation of $\sqrt{2}$. Similarly $\frac{22}{7}$, 3.14, 3.14159 are all rational-number approximations of the irrational number π. It is not easy to prove that some real numbers are irrational. The proof that π, for example, is not rational is quite difficult. All that is expected of the reader at this time is that he be aware of the existence of irrational numbers and that he is able to give a few simple examples of these numbers.

The following is a summary of the number systems we have discussed so far in this book:

The set of real numbers

The set of rational numbers

The set of integers

The set of natural numbers

It should be noted that each set is a proper subset* of each set above it. For any set above the lowest the reader should be able to give examples of numbers

---

*A is a **proper subset** of B if every element in A is an element of B, but B has at least one element that is not in A.

that belong to that set and not to the lower ones.   For example, can you give an example of a rational number that is not an integer?

We will end this incomplete and informal discussion of the real numbers by stating without proof (1) a very important theorem, sometimes called "the fundamental theorem of analytic geometry," and (2) a theorem summarizing some of the fundamental properties of the real numbers.

THEOREM 7   *There exists a one-to-one correspondence between the set of real numbers and the set of points on the number line; that is, each real number names a distinct point on the number line, and each point is named by a distinct real number.*

This is a remarkable theorem with far-reaching consequences, only a few of which will be revealed in this course.

We will not attempt to give general definitions of addition and multiplication of real numbers.   This is a fairly difficult task for irrational numbers.   Actually, this will not cause us any trouble since we will mainly be interested in manipulating symbols that name real numbers.   We will find that we will be able to continue to manipulate symbols that name real numbers in essentially the same way that we manipulate symbols that represent rational numbers; the sign properties, definition of absolute value, etc., all carry over from the previous number systems.   When we want a decimal value of an irrational number, we will settle for a rational-number approximation of it.

For completeness and for convenient reference, some of the important properties of the real numbers are summarized in the following theorem (which is stated without proof):

THEOREM 8:   IMPORTANT PROPERTIES OF THE SET OF REAL NUMBERS.

(A) *The real numbers are closed with respect to addition, subtraction, multiplication, and division (division by zero excluded).*

(B) *The real numbers are associative and commutative relative to the operations of addition and multiplication.*

(C) *The real numbers have a unique additive identity called zero; i.e., for each real number a, $a + 0 = a$, and 0 is the only real number with this property.*

(D) *The real numbers have a unique multiplicative identity called 1; i.e., for each real number a, $a \cdot 1 = a$, and 1 is the only real number with this property.*

(E) *Each real number has a unique additive inverse; that is, for each real number a there exists a unique real number, denoted by $-a$, such that $a + (-a) = 0$.*

(F) *Each real number, except zero, has a unique multiplicative inverse; that is, for each real number a, with $a \neq 0$, there exists a unique real number, denoted by $1/a$, such that $a \cdot (1/a) = 1$.*

(G) *For all real numbers a, b, and c, a(b + c) = ab + ac and a(b − c) = ab − ac.*
(H) *For all real numbers a and b, (−1)a = −a, a(−b) = (−a)b = −ab, (−a)(−b) = ab, (−a)/b = a/(−b) = −(a/b), (−a)/(−b) = a/b.*

EXERCISE 33

1. Indicate which of the following statements are true:
(A) The set of integers is a subset of the set of natural numbers.
(B) The set of rational numbers is a subset of the set of real numbers.
(C) The set of integers is a subset of the set of real numbers.
(D) The set of natural numbers is a subset of the set of rational numbers.

2. (A) Give an example of a real number that is not a rational number.
(B) Give an example of an integer that is not a natural number.
(C) Give an example of a rational number that is not an integer.

3. Indicate which of the following statements are true:
(A) 5 is a real number and an integer.
(B) −3 is a natural number and a rational number.
(C) −3 is a rational number.
(D) $\frac{2}{3}$ is a real number.
(E) $\sqrt{2}$ is a rational number.

4. Indicate which of the following statements are true:
(A) $\frac{3}{5}$ is a rational number and a real number.
(B) 7 is an integer.
(C) $\sqrt{7}$ is an irrational number and a real number.
(D) $\frac{22}{7}$ is an irrational number.
(E) π is a rational number.

5. Given the sets A = the set of real numbers
$\qquad\qquad\quad B$ = the set of rational numbers
$\qquad\qquad\quad C$ = the set of integers
$\qquad\qquad\quad D$ = the set of natural numbers
Each of the following numbers belongs to which of the above sets?
(A) −3 $\qquad\qquad$ (B) 3.14 $\qquad\qquad$ (C) 1.414 $\qquad\qquad$ (D) $\sqrt[3]{5}$

6. Using the sets A, B, C, and D described in problem 5, indicate to which each of the following numbers belongs:
(A) $3\frac{1}{7}$ $\qquad\qquad$ (B) 1.73 $\qquad\qquad$ (C) $\sqrt{3}$ $\qquad\qquad$ (D) −8

7. *Every rational number has an infinite repeating-decimal representation.*
For example,

$$\tfrac{1}{4} = 0.25\overline{00}$$
$$\tfrac{1}{3} = 0.3\overline{33}$$
$$\tfrac{15}{7} = 2.142857\overline{142857}$$

(The bar indicates the block of numbers which continues to repeat indefinitely.)
Express each of the following rational numbers in repeating-decimal form:

(A) $\frac{3}{8}$ (B) $\frac{23}{9}$ (C) $\frac{7}{13}$

8. Repeat the preceding problem for (A) $\frac{37}{6}$ and (B) $\frac{15}{21}$.

9. *Every infinitely repeating decimal is a rational number.*   To find two integers
whose quotient is a repeating decimal, say $2.13\overline{535}$, proceed as follows:

$$n = 2.13\overline{535}$$

$$10n = 21.3\overline{535}$$

$$1{,}000n = 2135.3\overline{535}$$

$$1{,}000n - 10n = 2135.3\overline{535} - 21.3\overline{535}$$

$$990n = 2{,}114$$

$$n = \frac{2{,}114}{990} = \frac{1{,}057}{495}$$

Convert each of the following repeating decimals to a quotient of two integer
forms:

(A) $0.27\overline{27}$ (B) $3.21\overline{21}$

10. Proceed as in the preceding problem to convert each of the following
repeating decimals to a quotient of two integer forms:

(A) $2.17\overline{17}$ (B) $0.472\overline{72}$

COMMENT: *In general it can be shown that irrational numbers are characterized by infinite
nonrepeating decimals, and rational numbers are characterized by repeating decimals.
Hence any decimal fraction that we write must necessarily be a rational number; we cannot write an infinite nonrepeating decimal.*

30   ORDER RELATIONS AND LINE GRAPHS

To define order relations for the set of real numbers, we will use essentially the
same definition of "greater than" and "less than" that we used for the integers
in Sec. 21.   In order to make this definition meaningful, however, we will have
to accept your intuitive or common-sense knowledge of what positive and
negative real numbers are.   (Also, it is important to remember that since the set
of real numbers include the rational numbers, integers, and the natural numbers,
as well as the irrational numbers, any definition for the real numbers necessarily
applies to any of these subclasses of numbers.)

DEFINITION 1:   ORDER RELATIONS.   *If a and b are real numbers, then we write
a < b if and only if there exists a positive real number p such that a + p = b.
We write a > b if and only if b < a.*

Intuitively (as we said with the integers), one would expect that if a positive real number were added to *any* real number, the sum would be larger than the original number; that is essentially what the definition states.

The same simple geometric interpretation of Definition 1 exists for real numbers as existed for integers; that is, any real number on the number line to the right of another is larger than that number, and any real number to the left of another is less than that number.

EXAMPLE 21

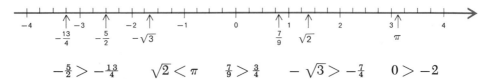

$$-\tfrac{5}{2} > -\tfrac{13}{4} \qquad \sqrt{2} < \pi \qquad \tfrac{7}{9} > \tfrac{3}{4} \qquad -\sqrt{3} > -\tfrac{7}{4} \qquad 0 > -2$$

As a consequence of Definition 1 it can be shown that the real numbers form an **ordered set.** Given any two real numbers a and b, then either $a < b$, $a = b$, or $a > b$; given any three real numbers a, b, and c, if $a < b$ and $b < c$, then $a < c$. More will be said about this property later.

We ended the last section with the important theorem that stated that there is a one-to-one correspondence between the set of real numbers and the points on the number line. Because of this theorem, graphs of inequalities (using real numbers as replacement sets) may take on a different form from the graphs of the inequalities considered earlier. The graphs we considered earlier were distinct points; the following graphs involve solid lines.

EXAMPLE 22.   The graph of the set $\{x \mid -2 < x \le 5, x \text{ a real number}\}$ is

EXAMPLE 23.   The graph of the set $\{x \mid -\pi \le x < \sqrt{2}, x \text{ a real number}\}$ is

EXAMPLE 24.   The graph of the set $\{x \mid x > -\tfrac{3}{2}, x \text{ a real number}\}$ is

We note that these graphs involve infinitely many points "packed solidly together" and are consequently represented with a solid line. End-point behavior is indicated with either solid or hollow dots depending whether the point is to be included or not.

EXERCISE 34

1. Graph (approximately) each of the following numbers on the same number line: $\frac{2}{3}$, $-\frac{3}{2}$, $\sqrt{5}$, and $-\sqrt{8}$.

2. Graph (approximately) each of the following numbers on the same number line: $\frac{5}{2}$, $-\sqrt{2}$, π, $-\frac{11}{4}$, $\sqrt{3}$.

3. Replace each question mark with an appropriate inequality symbol:
(A) $\frac{2}{3}$? 0　　　　　(B) -2 ? $-\frac{3}{2}$　　　　(C) $\sqrt{5}$? 3　　　　(D) -3 ? $-\sqrt{8}$
HINT: See problem 1.

4. Replace each question mark with an appropriate inequality symbol:
(A) $-\frac{11}{4}$? $-\sqrt{2}$　　(B) π ? 3　　　　　(C) $\sqrt{3}$? 2　　　　(D) 0 ? $-\frac{11}{4}$
HINT: See problem 2.

5. Given the set-builder description $\{x \mid -\frac{5}{2}\ ?\ x\ ?\ \frac{3}{2}$, x a real number$\}$, replace the question marks with appropriate inequality symbols to describe the following figure:

6. Given the set-builder description $\{x \mid x\ ?-\frac{11}{3}$, x a real number$\}$, replace the question mark with an appropriate inequality symbol to describe the following figure:

Graph each of the sets in problems 7 through 14 using the following approximations where necessary: $\sqrt{5} \doteq 2.2$, $\pi \doteq 3.14$, *and* $\sqrt[3]{9} \doteq 2.1$.

7. $\{x \mid -\frac{5}{4} < x < \frac{3}{4}$, x a real number$\}$

8. $\{x \mid -3 \leq x < \frac{3}{2}$, x a real number$\}$

9. $\{x \mid -\frac{15}{8} < x \leq -\frac{1}{8}$, x a real number$\}$

10. $\{x \mid x > -\frac{7}{4}$, x a real number$\}$

11. $\{x \mid -\sqrt{5} \leq x < \pi$, x a real number$\}$

12. $\{x \mid -\pi \leq x \leq \sqrt[3]{9}$, x a real number$\}$

13. $\{x \mid -\sqrt{5} \leq x \leq \pi$, x an integer$\}$

14. $\{x \mid -\pi \leq x \leq \sqrt[3]{9}$, x an integer$\}$

15. If both a and b are positive numbers and b/a is greater than 1, then is $a - b$ positive or negative?

16. If both a and b are negative numbers and b/a is greater than 1, then is $a - b$ positive or negative?

31   CHAPTER SUMMARY

GENERAL

We have arrived at one of the important objectives for this course: the real-number system. This enlarged set of numbers will take care of most of your number needs for some time to come. Even though our introduction to the irrational numbers has been informal and incomplete, it is sufficient for our purposes at this time.

We have discussed, in varying degrees of detail, the natural numbers, the integers, the rational numbers, and now the real numbers. You should be able to give examples of numbers that are included in each of these sets and numbers that are not. You should have some idea, in terms of operations that can be performed and equations that can be solved, of some of the strengths and limitations of each of these number systems. You will recall that it was considerations of this kind that motivated the enlargement of each number system.

You now have enough algebra at hand to study natural and social science courses (as well as others) with increased understanding. In addition, in these first three chapters we have laid a substantial foundation for the rest of this course and many mathematics courses to follow.

Even though we have already considered some applications, an even wider variety of applications will be presented in the next chapter.

SPECIFIC

Describe, define, or give examples of each of the following:

1. **The set of rational numbers.**

positive and negative rational numbers

"absolute value" and "negative of"

graphing rational numbers

2. **Operations and properties of rational numbers.**

multiplication, division, addition, and subtraction

sign properties: $\dfrac{-a}{-b} = \dfrac{a}{b}, \dfrac{-a}{b} = \dfrac{a}{-b} = -\dfrac{a}{b}, (-1)\dfrac{a}{b} = -\dfrac{a}{b}, -\left(-\dfrac{a}{b}\right) = \dfrac{a}{b}$

reciprocal

closure, associative, commutative, and distributive properties

3. **Equations involving rational-number coefficients or rational-number solutions.**

4. **Ratio and proportion.**

5. The set of real numbers.

irrationals, rationals, integers, and natural numbers

real numbers and the number line

6. Order relations for the real numbers.

"less than" and "greater than"

line graphs

EXERCISE 35   CHAPTER REVIEW

1. Graph (approximately) each of the following real numbers (approximate $\sqrt{8}$ with 2.8):

$$\tfrac{9}{4} \qquad -\tfrac{9}{4} \qquad \sqrt{8} \qquad -\sqrt{8}$$

2. Indicate which of the following statements are true:
(A) The set of natural numbers is a subset of the set of real numbers.
(B) π is a rational number.
(C) 0.3333 is an irrational number.
(D) $\tfrac{1}{3}$ is an irrational number.

3. Replace each question mark with an appropriate inequality symbol:
(A) $-\tfrac{2}{3}\,?\,-\tfrac{1}{3}$ \qquad (B) $-\sqrt{2}\,?\,-\sqrt{3}$ \qquad (C) $\tfrac{2}{3}\,?\,\tfrac{2}{4}$

4. Graph (approximately): $\{x \mid -\tfrac{2}{3} < x \le \pi,\, x \text{ a real number}\}$.

5. Reduce to lowest terms:
(A) $\dfrac{-9y^3}{-30y^2}$ \qquad\qquad (B) $\dfrac{15xy}{-25(xy)^2}$

6. Replace the question marks with appropriate expressions:
(A) $-\dfrac{3}{5} = \dfrac{?}{15}$ \qquad\qquad (B) $\dfrac{2x}{3} = \dfrac{-8x^2}{?}$

7. Perform the indicated operations and reduce to lowest terms:
(A) $\dfrac{10}{21} \cdot \dfrac{-15}{14}$ \quad (B) $\dfrac{10}{21} \div \dfrac{-15}{14}$ \quad (C) $\dfrac{10}{21} + \dfrac{-15}{14}$ \quad (D) $\dfrac{10}{21} - \dfrac{-15}{14}$

8. Perform the indicated operations and reduce to lowest terms:
(A) $\dfrac{-4}{9} \div \left(\dfrac{35}{18} \div \dfrac{-10}{3}\right)$ \qquad\qquad (B) $\dfrac{-4}{9} - \dfrac{35}{18} - \dfrac{-10}{3}$

9. Perform the indicated operations and reduce to lowest terms:
(A) $\dfrac{-3y}{5xz} \cdot \dfrac{-10z}{15xy}$ \quad (B) $\dfrac{-3y}{5xz} \div \dfrac{-10z}{15xy}$ \quad (C) $\dfrac{-3y}{5xz} + \dfrac{-10z}{15xy}$ \quad (D) $\dfrac{-3y}{5xz} - \dfrac{-10z}{15xy}$

10. Perform the indicated operations and reduce to lowest terms:

(A) $\dfrac{10x}{9y} \div \left(\dfrac{15xy}{2z} \cdot \dfrac{-z}{3y^2} \right)$
 (B) $\dfrac{10x}{9y} + \dfrac{15xy}{2z} - \dfrac{-z}{3y^2}$

11. Solve for x: $-3x = 7$.

12. One-eighth of what number is $\frac{3}{2}$?

13. Solve for y: $-\frac{3}{8}y = \frac{2}{3}$.

14. If you ride a bicycle at 9 mph, how long will it take you to ride $\frac{3}{5}$ of a mile?

15. Solve for x: $\dfrac{x}{5} - 2 = \dfrac{x}{7}$.

16. Solve for x: $\dfrac{3x - 5}{2} - \dfrac{x}{3} = 8$.

17. Solve for x: $0.2(x + 5) - 0.3x = 12$.

18. A store has a camera on sale at 20 percent off list price. If the sale price is $64, what is the list price?

Use appropriate proportions to solve problems 19 through 21.

19. To make a soufflé for four people, you should use a 1.5-qt baking dish. What size soufflé pan should you buy to accommodate six people?

20. In 1963, 14 out of every 100 youths not in school in the 16–21 age group were unemployed (contrasted to approximately 5 out of every 100 for the total labor force). If, in 1963, there were approximately 8 million youths between 16 and 21 not in school, how many were out of work?

21. If there are 180 Fahrenheit degrees and 100 Centigrade degrees between freezing and boiling for water, how many Centigrade degrees correspond to 9 Fahrenheit degrees? How many Fahrenheit degrees correspond to 20 Centigrade degrees?

CHAPTER FOUR
first-degree polynomial equations in one and two variables

32 FIRST-DEGREE POLYNOMIAL EQUATIONS IN ONE VARIABLE

In the fairly large variety of applications we have already considered you might have noticed that all of them gave rise to essentially the same type of equation. The equation contained no more than one variable, used perhaps more than once, and this variable never appeared to a power other than 1. The constants were all real numbers, generally integers or rational numbers. In fact, if all of the terms in any one of these equations had been transferred to the left of the equal sign (leaving zero on the right) and like terms combined, the equation would have been of the form $ax + b = 0$. Any algebraic expression of the type

$$ax + b$$

where a and b are real numbers and x is a variable, is called a **first-degree polynomial in one variable.** The associated equation

$$ax + b = 0$$

is called a **first-degree polynomial equation in one variable.**

Rather than considering all types of equations, hit or miss, it is far more efficient to identify certain types and study each in detail. Higher-degree polynomial forms will be considered in later chapters and future courses.

EXAMPLE 1:   **FIRST-DEGREE POLYNOMIALS IN ONE VARIABLE.**

$$2x + 3 \qquad 3x - \frac{1}{2} \qquad \frac{t}{2} - 3$$

EXAMPLE 2:   **FIRST-DEGREE POLYNOMIAL EQUATIONS IN ONE VARIABLE.**

$$5x - 7 = 0 \qquad \frac{x}{3} - \frac{2}{5} = 0 \qquad 3y - \frac{1}{3} = 0$$

EXAMPLE 3.   The following are not first degree polynomials in one variable.

$$3x^2 + 5x - 2 \qquad \frac{5}{x} - 3 \qquad 3x - 5y + 7 \qquad \frac{x^3}{4} - 3x + 5$$

We, of course, have already solved many first-degree polynomial equations in one variable so we will not go into the matter again here other than to say that any equation of the form $ax + b = 0$ with $a \neq 0$ always has a unique solution, namely $-b/a$. Showing that $-b/a$ is a solution is left as an exercise. To show that this solution is unique, we proceed as follows: assume p and q are both solutions of $ax + b = 0$, then

$$ap + b = aq + b \qquad \qquad \text{Why?}$$

$$ap = aq \qquad \qquad \text{Why?}$$

$$p = q \qquad \qquad \text{Why?}$$

In general, it is important to know under what conditions an equation has a solution and how many solutions are possible. We have now answered both of these questions for equations of the type $ax + b = 0$ with $a \neq 0$. Other types of equations will be studied later which have more than one solution; for example, -2 and $+2$ are both solutions of $x^2 - 4 = 0$.

EXERCISE 36

1. Which of the following are first-degree polynomial expressions in one variable?

(A) $3x - 2y + 5$ (B) $\dfrac{x}{7} - \dfrac{1}{8}$ (C) $3x^3 + 2x - 5$ (D) $\dfrac{5}{x} - \dfrac{6}{y} + 7$

2. Which of the following are first-degree polynomial expressions in one variable?

(A) $3x - \dfrac{2}{3}$ (B) $2x^2 - 3x$ (C) $\dfrac{5}{x} - \dfrac{2}{3}$ (D) $\dfrac{x}{5} - \dfrac{2}{3}$

3. Which of the following are first-degree polynomial equations in one variable (i.e., can be put into the form $ax + b = 0$)?

(A) $5x - 3 = 0$ (B) $x^2 - 9 = 0$

(C) $3x - 5 = 7 + x$ (D) $\dfrac{x}{3} - \dfrac{1}{2} = 5$

4. Which of the following are first-degree polynomial equations in one variable (i.e., can be put in the form $ax + b = 0$)?

(A) $\frac{2}{3}x - 7 = 0$ (B) $7x - 3(x - 5) = x$

(C) $3x^3 = 2(x - 3)$ (D) $\dfrac{7}{x} - 3 = x$

5. Show that $-b/a$ is solution of the first-degree polynomial equation $ax + b = 0$ with $a \neq 0$.

33   ADDITIONAL APPLICATIONS

This section contains a wide variety of applications that lead to first-degree polynomial equations. The problems are grouped by subject area, and, in addition, many are cross referenced below by problem types for added convenience.

Rate-time problems: 1, 6, 12, 28, 29, 39, 50, 51.

Mixture problems: 7, 8, 10.

Percent problems: 3, 4, 5, 10, 26.

Ratio and proportion problems: 8, 9, 15, 16, 23, 24, 31, 33, 34, 35, 36, 37.

Since many applications of first-degree polynomial equations have already been presented, this section may be treated briefly or returned to if time is of concern. In any case, every reader should spend some time scanning the problems to gain an appreciation of the number and variety of applications he now has within his command. Any time that is spent in this section will be amply rewarded. Algebra will be of limited value to you if you do not gain experience in applying it to a variety of different types of significant problems.

EXERCISE 37

The problems in this exercise are grouped in several subject areas: business, chemistry, earth sciences, economics, geometry, domestic, life science, music, physics–engineering, psychology, and puzzles.

No attempt has been made to arrange the problems in order of difficulty or to match them in pairs as in preceding exercises.

BUSINESS

1. A research chemist charges $20 per hr for his services and $8 per hr for his assistant. On a given job a customer received a bill for $1,040. If the chemist worked 10 hr more on the job than his assistant, how much time did each spend?

2. It costs a book publisher $9,000 to prepare a book for publishing (art work, plates, reviews, etc.); printing costs are $2 per book. If the book is sold to book-stores for $5 a copy, how many copies must be sold to break even?

3. A variety store sells a particular item costing $4 for $7. If this markup represents the store's pricing policy for all items, what percent markup (on cost) is used? HINT: cost + markup = retail.

4. A man borrowed a sum of money from a bank at 6 percent simple interest. At the end of $2\frac{1}{2}$ years he repaid the bank $575. How much did he borrow from the bank? HINT: $A = P + Prt$.

5. A man has $\frac{1}{2}$ of his money invested at 6 percent, $\frac{1}{4}$ at 5 percent, and the rest at 3 percent. If his total annual income from all investments is $4,000, how much money has he used for investing purposes?

6. In a soft-drink bottling plant one machine can fill and cap 20 bottles per min; another newer machine can do 30 per min. What will be the total time required to complete a 30,000-bottle order if the older machine is brought on the job 3 hr earlier than the newer machine, and then both machines are used together until the job is finished?

7. A grocer wishes to blend 84-cents-per-lb coffee with 24 lb of 60-cents-per-lb coffee so that the resulting mixture will sell for 68 cents per lb. How much 84-cents-per-pound coffee is needed?

CHEMISTRY

8. If there are 8 grams of sulfuric acid in 70 grams of solution, how many grams of sulfuric acid are there in 21 grams of the same solution?

9. A chemist wishing to produce hydrogen gas may pour hydrochloric acid (HCl) over zinc (Zn). If so, a chemical reaction takes place so as to produce two atoms of hydrogen for each atom of zinc used. Thus

$$2HCl + Zn \longrightarrow H_2 + ZnCl_2$$

To find how much hydrogen gas will be produced from, say, 100 grams of zinc, he will use the atomic weights of hydrogen (1.008) and zinc (65.38) and solve the proportion

$$\frac{x}{100} = \frac{(2)(1.008)}{65.38}$$

(A) Solve this proportion to two decimal places.

(B) Find the amount (to two decimal places) of zinc needed to produce 10 grams of hydrogen gas.

10. How many gallons of pure alcohol must be added to 3 gal of a 20 percent solution to get a 40 percent solution?

11. In the study of gases there is a simple law called Boyle's law that expresses a relationship between volume and pressure. It states that the product of the pressure and volume, as these quantities change and all other variables are held fixed, remains constant. Stated as a formula, $P_1 V_1 = P_2 V_2$. If 500 cc of air at 70-cm pressure were converted to 100 cm pressure, what volume would it have?

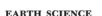

EARTH SCIENCE

12. An earthquake emits a primary wave and a secondary wave. Near the surface of the earth the primary wave travels at about 5 miles per sec, and the secondary wave at about 3 miles per sec. From the time lag between the two waves arriving at a given seismic station, it is possible to estimate the distance to the quake. (The "epicenter" can be located by getting distance bearings at three or more stations.) Suppose a station measured a time difference of 12 sec between the arrival of the two waves. How far would the earthquake be from the station?

13. As dry air moves upward, it expands and in so doing cools at the rate of about 5.5° F for each 1,000 ft in rise. This ascent is known as the "adiabatic process." If the ground temperature is 80° F, write an equation that relates temperature T with altitude h (in thousands of feet). How high is an airplane if the pilot observes that the temperature is 25° F?

14. Pressure in sea water increases by 1 atmosphere (15 lb per sq ft) for each 33 ft of depth; it is 15 lb per sq ft at the surface. Thus, $p = 15 + 15(d/33)$ where p is the pressure in pounds per square foot at a depth of d ft below the surface. How deep is a diver if he observes that the pressure is 165 lb per sq ft?

15. In a science class a scale model of the earth-sun part of the solar system is to be constructed. (A fairly large field, such as a football field or a baseball diamond is recommended.) The diameter of the sun is approximately 866,000 miles, the diameter of the earth is approximately 8,000 miles, and the distance between the sun and earth is approximately 93 million miles. If we use a 12-in.-diameter ball for the sun, what diameter sphere should we use for the earth, and

how many feet should it be placed away from the ball? Express the answers to one decimal place.

ECONOMICS

16. (A) What would a net monthly salary have to be in 1940 to have the same purchasing power of a net monthly salary of $550 in 1965? HINT: Use an appropriate proportion.
(B) Answer the same question for 1950 and 1960.

Year	Cost-of-living index
1940	48
1945	62
1950	82
1955	93
1960	103
1965	110

17. Gross national product (GNP) and net national product (NNP) are both measures of national income and are related as follows:

$$\text{GNP} = \text{NNP} + \text{depreciation}$$

A good estimate for depreciation is $\frac{1}{11}$ of GNP or $\frac{1}{10}$ of NNP.
(A) Write a formula for GNP in terms of NNP only.
(B) Use part (A) to replace the question marks in the table.

Date	NNP (billions of dollars)	GNP (billions of dollars)
1929	96	?
1933	48	?

18. Henry Schultz, an economist, formulated a price-demand equation for sugar in the United States as follows: $q = 70.62 - 2.26p$, where p = wholesale price in cents of 1 lb of sugar, and q = per capita consumption in pounds of sugar in the United States in any year. At what price per pound would the per capita consumption per year be 25.42 lb?

GEOMETRY

19. The perimeter of a tennis court for singles is 210 ft. Find the dimensions of the court if its length is 3 ft less than three times its width.

20. Find the dimensions of a rectangle with perimeter 72 in. if its length is 25 percent longer than its width.

21. What is the size of each angle of a triangle if the smallest is $\frac{1}{3}$ the size of the third, and the second is $\frac{2}{3}$ the size of the third?

22. A water reed sticks 1 ft out of the water. If it were pulled over to the side until the top just reached the surface, it would be at a point 3 ft from where it originally protruded.   How deep is the water?

HINT: Recall the Pythagorean theorem in Sec. 29.

DOMESTIC

23. If $1\frac{1}{2}$ cups of milk and 2 cups of flour are needed in a recipe for four people, how much of each is needed in a recipe for six people?

24. If on a trip your car goes 391 miles on 23 gal of gas, how many gallons of gas would be required for a 850-mile trip?

25. A father, in order to encourage his daughter to do better in algebra, agrees to pay her 25 cents for each problem she gets right on a test and to fine her 10 cents for each problem she misses.   On a test with 20 problems she received $3.60.   How many problems did she get right?

26. A friend of yours paid $72 for a pair of skis after receiving a discount of 20 percent.   What was the list price for the skis?

27. A car rental company charges $5 per day and 5 cents per mile.   If a car was rented for two days, how far was it driven if the total rental bill was $30?

28. A contractor has just finished constructing a swimming pool in your back yard, and you have turned on the large water valve to fill it.   The large valve lets water into the pool at a rate of 60 gal per min.   After 2 hr you get impatient and turn on the garden hose which lets water in at 15 gal per min.   If the swimming pool holds 30,000 gal of water, what will be the total time required to fill it?

29. The cruising speed of an airplane is 150 mph (relative to ground).   You wish to hire the plane for a 3-hr sightseeing trip.   You instruct the pilot to fly north as far as he can and still return to the airport at the end of the allotted time.

(A) How far north should the pilot fly if there is a 30-mph wind blowing from the north?

(B) How far north should the pilot fly if there is no wind blowing?

LIFE SCIENCE

30. A fairly good approximation for the normal weight of a person over 60 in. (5 ft) tall is given by the formula $w = 5.5h - 220$, where h is height in inches and w is weight in pounds.   How tall should a 121-lb person be?

Figure 1

31. The naturalists in Yosemite National Park decided to estimate the number of bears in the most popular part of the park, Yosemite Valley. They used live traps (Fig. 1) to capture 50 bears; these bears were marked and released. A week later 50 more were captured, and it was observed that 10 of these were marked. Use this information to estimate the total number of bears in the valley.

32. In biology there is an approximate rule, called the bioclimatic rule for temperate climates, that states that in spring and early summer, periodic phenomena, such as blossoming for a given species, appearance of certain insects, and ripening of fruit, usually come about 4 days later for each 500 ft of altitude increase or 1° latitude increase from any given base. In terms of formulas we have

$$d = 4\left(\frac{h}{500}\right) \qquad \text{and} \qquad d = 4L$$

where d = change in days, h = change in altitude in feet, and L = change in latitude in degrees.

What change in altitude would delay pear trees from blossoming for 16 days? What change in latitude would accomplish the same thing?

33. Gregor Mendel (1822), a Bavarian monk and biologist whose name is known to almost everyone today, made discoveries which revolutionized the science of heredity. Out of many experiments in which he crossed peas of one characteristic with those of another, Mendel evolved his now famous laws of heredity. In one experiment he crossed dihybrid yellow round peas (which contained green and wrinkled as recessive genes) and obtained 560 peas of the following types: 319 yellow round, 101 yellow wrinkled, 108 green round, and 32 green wrinkled. From his laws of heredity he predicted the ratio $9:3:3:1$. Using the ratio, calculate the theoretical expected number of each type of pea from this cross, and compare it with the experimental results.

MUSIC

34. Starting with a string tuned to a given note, one can move up and down the scale simply by decreasing or increasing its length (while maintaining the same

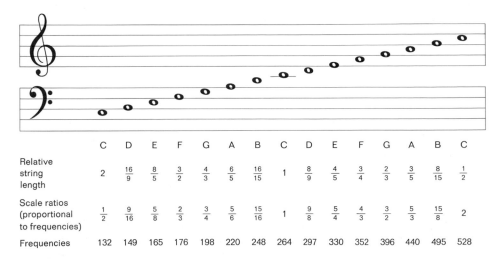

	C	D	E	F	G	A	B	C	D	E	F	G	A	B	C
Relative string length	2	$\frac{16}{9}$	$\frac{8}{5}$	$\frac{3}{2}$	$\frac{4}{3}$	$\frac{6}{5}$	$\frac{16}{15}$	1	$\frac{8}{9}$	$\frac{4}{5}$	$\frac{3}{4}$	$\frac{2}{3}$	$\frac{3}{5}$	$\frac{8}{15}$	$\frac{1}{2}$
Scale ratios (proportional to frequencies)	$\frac{1}{2}$	$\frac{9}{16}$	$\frac{5}{8}$	$\frac{2}{3}$	$\frac{3}{4}$	$\frac{5}{6}$	$\frac{15}{16}$	1	$\frac{9}{8}$	$\frac{5}{4}$	$\frac{4}{3}$	$\frac{3}{2}$	$\frac{5}{3}$	$\frac{15}{8}$	2
Frequencies	132	149	165	176	198	220	248	264	297	330	352	396	440	495	528

Figure 2 *Diatonic scale.*

tension) according to simple whole-number ratios (see Fig. 2). For example, $\frac{8}{9}$ of the C string gives the next higher note D, $\frac{2}{3}$ of the C string gives G, and $\frac{1}{2}$ of the C string gives C one octave higher. (The reciprocals of these fractions, $\frac{9}{8}$, $\frac{3}{2}$, and 2, respectively, are proportional to the frequencies of these notes.) Find the lengths of seven strings (each less than 30 in.) that will produce the following seven chords when paired with a 30-in. string:

(A) Octave   1:2   (B) Fifth   2:3
(C) Fourth   3:4   (D) Major third   4:5
(E) Minor third   5:6   (F) Major sixth   3:5
(G) Minor sixth   5:8

35. The three minor chords are composed of notes whose frequencies are in the ratio $10:12:15$. If the first note of the minor chord is A with a frequency of 220, what are the frequencies of the other two notes? Compute, then compare results with figure.

PHYSICS—ENGINEERING

36. An engineer knows that a $3\frac{1}{2}$-ft piece of steel rod weighs 25 lb. How much would a 14-ft piece of this rod weigh?

37. The magnifying power M of a telescope is the ratio of the focal length F of the objective lens to the focal length f of the eyepiece. If the focal length of the objective lens is 36 in. what must the focal length of the eyepiece be to produce a magnification of 108?

38. If a small solid object is thrown downward with an initial velocity of 50 fps, its velocity after time t is given approximately by

$$v = 50 + 32t$$

How many seconds are required for the object to attain a velocity of 306 fps?

Figure 3

39. In 1849, during a celebrated experiment, the Frenchman Fizeau made the first accurate approximation of the speed of light. By using a rotating disc with notches equally spaced on the circumference and a reflecting mirror 5 miles away (Fig. 3), he was able to measure the elapsed time for the light traveling to the mirror and back. Calculate his estimate for the speed of light (in miles per second) if his measurement for the elapsed time was $\frac{1}{20,000}$ sec?

40. A type of physics problem with wide applications is the **lever problem.** For a lever, relative to a fulcrum, to be in static equilibrium (balanced) the sum of the downward forces times their respective distances on one side of the fulcrum must equal the sum of the downward forces times their respective distances on the other side of the fulcrum (Fig. 4).

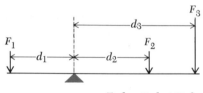

$$F_1 d_1 = F_2 d_2 + F_3 d_3$$

Figure 4

If a person has a 3-ft wrecking bar and places a fulcrum 3 in. from one end, how much can he lift if he applies a force of 50 lb to the long end?

41. Where would a fulcrum have to be placed to balance an 8-ft bar with a 6-lb weight on one end and an 7-lb weight on the other?

42. Two men decided to move a 1,920-lb rock by use of a 9-ft steel bar (Fig. 5). If they place the fulcrum 1 ft from the rock and one of the men applies a force of 150 lb on the other end, how much force will the second man have to apply 2 ft from that end to lift the rock?

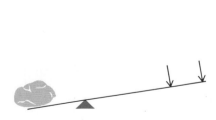

Figure 5

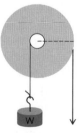

Figure 6

43. If two pulleys are fastened together as in the diagram (Fig. 6), and the radius of the larger pulley is 10 in. and the smaller one 2 in., how heavy a weight can one lift by exerting an 80-lb pull on the free rope?

44. In engineering and physics it is often necessary to measure the work done by a machine or a force.   Work done is defined to be the product of the force f and the distance d that the object is moved; that is,

$$w = fd$$

If you lift 50 lb a distance of 3 ft you will have done 150 ft-lb of work.

(A) How much work is done by a horse lifting 112 lb a distance of 196 ft?

(B) If in a vertical mine shaft an engine does 1,600,000 ft-lb of work in lifting 1 ton of ore, how far is the ore lifted?   (1 ton = 2,000 lb.)

45. In a simple electric circut, such as that found in a flashlight, the voltage provided by the batteries is related to the resistance and current in the circuit by Ohm's law,

$$E = IR$$

where E = electromotive force, volts
    I = current, amperes
    R = resistance, ohms

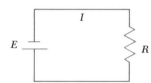

(A) If a two cell battery puts out 3 volts and a current of 0.2 ampere flows through the circuit, what is the total resistance in the circuit?

(B) How much current will flow through a five-cell flashlight circuit (putting out 1.5 volts per cell), if the total resistance in the circuit is 25 ohms?

PSYCHOLOGY

46. Phychologists define IQ (Intelligence Quotient) as

$$IQ = \frac{\text{mental age}}{\text{chronological age}} \times 100$$

$$= \frac{MA}{CA} \times 100$$

If a person has an IQ of 120 and a mental age of 18, what is his chronological age (actual age)?

47. In 1948 Professor Brown, a psychologist, trained a group of rats (in an experiment on motivation) to run down a narrow passage in a cage to receive food in a goal box.   He then put a harness on each rat and connected it to an overhead wire that was attached to a scale (Fig. 7).   In this way he could place the rat at different distances from the food and measure the pull (in grams) of the rat

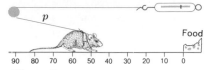

Figure 7

toward the food.   He found that a relation between motivation (pull) and position was given approximately by the equation

$$p = -\tfrac{1}{5}d + 70 \qquad 30 \le d \le 175$$

where pull p is measured in grams and distance d is measured in centimeters. If the pull registered was 40 grams, how far was the rat from the goal box?

48. Professor Brown performed the same kind of experiment as described in the preceding problem except that he replaced the food in the goal box with a mild electric shock.   With the same kind of apparatus, he was able to measure the avoidance strength relative to the distance from the object to be avoided.   He found that the avoidance strength a (measured in grams) was related to the distance d that the rat was from the shock (measured in centimeters) approximately by the equation

$$a = -\tfrac{4}{3}d + 230 \qquad 30 \le d \le 175$$

If the same rat was trained as described in this and the last problem, at what distance (to one decimal place) from the goal box would the approach and avoidance strength be the same?   (What do you think that the rat would do at this point?)

PUZZLES

49. A friend of yours came out of a post office having spent $1.32 on thirty 4-cent and 5-cent stamps.   How many of each type did he buy?

50. A classic problem is the courier problem.   If a column of men 3 miles long is marching at 5 mph, how long will it take a courier on a motorcycle traveling at 25 mph to deliver a message from the end of the column to the front and then return?

51. After twelve o'clock noon exactly, what time will the hands of a clock be together again?

34   CARTESIAN COORDINATE SYSTEM; GRAPHS

In preceding chapters we graphed many different sets of numbers using number lines; many of these sets of numbers were solution sets of equations or inequalities in one variable. Scientists and others are frequently involved with problems where two variables are needed; for example, distances that objects fall at different times, pressures of an enclosed gas at different temperatures, temperatures at a given place in a rocket engine at different times after firing, the approach drive of a rat at different distances from the goal box, the pitch of musical notes and lengths of strings, and the demand for a given commodity at different prices. Each of these examples involves two variable quantities.

It might be useful to have a picture (a graph) to visually show how two variables are related. How do we form such a graph? Frequently, one is able to start with an equation relating the two variables; the equations

$$d = 40t \qquad F = \tfrac{9}{5}C + 32 \qquad s = 16t^2$$

are well-known examples. Other times we must start with a table of values obtained from experimental work. For example, values obtained from wind-tunnel tests showing how the pressure on a lowered landing gear is related to air speed.

In any case, when we are working with problems involving two variables, we are actually interested in pairing numbers. Consider the matched Centigrade and Fahrenheit temperature readings in Table 1.

TABLE 1

C	−30	−20	−10	0	10	20	30
F	−22	−4	14	32	50	68	86

We might convert this table of paired numbers into a set of elements by taking each associated pair of numbers as a unit, called an **ordered pair,** with the first number in the pair representing Centigrade degrees and the second number representing Fahrenheit degrees. Table 1 converted to a set of ordered pairs of numbers would look like this:

$$\{(-30, -22), (-20, -4), (-10, 14), (0, 32), (10, 50), (20, 68), (30, 86)\}$$

How can we graph this set? Our one-dimensional coordinate system, the number line, is inadequate for this purpose. We must design a new coordinate system! This new system, a two-dimensional coordinate system called the "Cartesian coordinate system," will allow us to graph sets of pairs of numbers, including solution sets of equations and inequalities in two variables.

CARTESIAN COORDINATE SYSTEM

Our task now is to construct a system by which we can associate ordered pairs of numbers with points and points with ordered pairs of numbers. The number line, a familiar tool from the preceding chapters, will form an important part of this new system.

We will start with two sets, the set of all points in a plane (a set of geometric

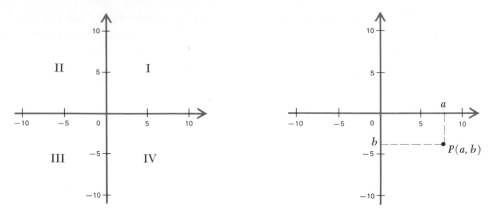

Figure 8   **Figure 9**

objects and the set of all ordered pairs of real numbers. We would like to match the elements of these two sets.

We start with the set of points in an extended plane (think of this page as extending indefinitely, left and right, up and down). In the plane we will select two number lines, one vertical and one horizontal. Let them cross at their respective origins as indicated in Fig. 8. Up and to the right are the usual choices for the positive directions (but there are exceptions). These two number lines are called the **horizontal axis** and the **vertical axis** or (together) the **coordinate axes.** The coordinate axes divide the plane into four parts called **quadrants;** the quadrants are numbered counterclockwise from I to IV.

Pick a point P in the plane at random (see Fig. 9). Pass horizontal and vertical lines through the point. The vertical line will intersect the horizontal axis at a point with coordinate a, and the horizontal line will intersect the vertical axis at a point with coordinate b. The coordinate of each point of intersection, a and b, respectively, form the **coordinates** (a, b) of the point P in the plane.

The first number a (called the **abscissa**) in the ordered pair (a, b) is the directed distance of the point P from the vertical axis (measured on the horizontal scale); the second number b (called the **ordinate**) is the directed distance of the point from the horizontal axis (measured on the vertical scale).

From the fundamental theorem of analytic geometry (Theorem 7, Sec. 29) we know that a and b exist for each point in the plane since every point on each axis has a real number associated with it. Hence, by the procedure described, every point in the plane can be labeled with a pair of real numbers; conversely, by reversing the process, every pair of real numbers can be associated with a point in the extended plane. Thus we have the following theorem.

THEOREM 1   *There exists a one-to-one correspondence between the set of points in an extended plane and the set of all ordered pairs of real numbers.*

The system that we have just defined to produce this correspondence is called the **Cartesian coordinate system** (sometimes referred to as the *rectangular coordinate system* or the *rectangular Cartesian coordinate system*).

EXAMPLE 4.   Find the coordinates of each of the points A, B, C, and D.

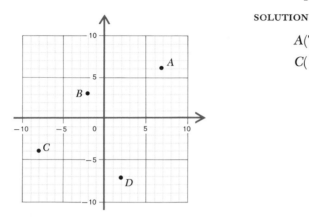

SOLUTION

$$A(7, 6) \qquad B(-2, 3)$$
$$C(-8, -4) \qquad D(2, -7)$$

EXAMPLE 5.   Graph (associate each ordered pair of numbers with a point in the Cartesian coordinate system):

$$(2, 7) \qquad (7, 2)$$
$$(-8, 4) \qquad (4, -8)$$
$$(-8, 4) \qquad (-4, -8)$$

SOLUTION

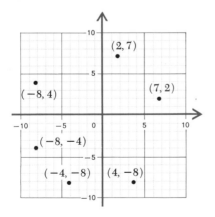

It is very important to note that the ordered pair $(2, 7)$ and the set $\{2, 7\}$ are not the same thing; $\{2, 7\} = \{7, 2\}$, but $(2, 7) \neq (7, 2)$.

EXERCISE 38

1. Write down the coordinates of each labeled point:

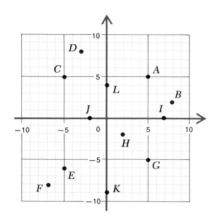

2. Write down the coordinates of each labeled point:

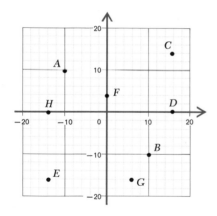

3. Graph the following ordered pairs of numbers on the same coordinate system:
$(2, 7)$, $(7, 2)$, $(-6, 3)$, $(-4, -7)$, $(2, 3)$, $(0, -8)$, and $(9, 0)$.

4. Graph the following ordered pairs of numbers on the same coordinate system:
$(-9, 8)$, $(8, -9)$, $(0, 5)$, $(4, -8)$, $(-3, 0)$, $(7, 7)$, and $(-6, -6)$.

5. Write down the coordinates of each labeled point to the nearest quarter of a unit:

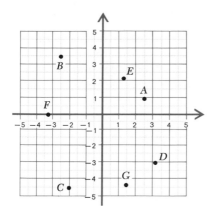

6. Write down the coordinates of each labeled point to the nearest quarter of a unit:

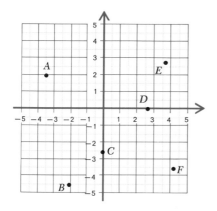

7. Graph the following ordered pairs of numbers on the same coordinate system: $A(3\frac{1}{2}, 2\frac{1}{2})$, $B(-4\frac{1}{2}, 3)$, $C(0, -3\frac{3}{4})$, $D(-2\frac{3}{4}, -3\frac{3}{4})$, and $E(4\frac{1}{4}, -3\frac{3}{4})$.

8. Graph the following ordered pairs of numbers on the same coordinate system: $A(1\frac{1}{2}, 3\frac{1}{2})$, $B(-3\frac{1}{4}, 0)$, $C(3, -2\frac{1}{2})$, $D(-4\frac{1}{2}, 1\frac{3}{4})$, and $E(-2\frac{1}{2}, -4\frac{1}{4})$.

9. Without graphing, tell which quadrants contain the graph of each of the following ordered pairs (see Fig. 8):
(A) $(-23, 403)$ (B) $(32\frac{1}{2}, -430)$ (C) $(2001, 25)$ (D) $(-0.008, -3.2)$

10. Without graphing, tell which quadrants contain the graph of each of the following ordered pairs:
(A) $(-20, -4)$ (B) $(-3, 22\frac{3}{4})$ (C) $(4, 35{,}000)$ (D) $(\sqrt{2}, -3)$

GRAPHS

We are now able to graph any ordered pair of real numbers (at least approximately); hence we are in a position to graph a set of ordered pairs of real numbers. In the remaining part of this section we will consider graphs of small finite sets. In the next section we will take up the problem of graphing infinite sets.

The **graph of a set of ordered pairs of real numbers** in a Cartesian coordinate system is the set of points in the system having the set of ordered pairs as coordinates.

EXAMPLE 6. Graph the set of ordered pairs of numbers taken from the Centigrade-Fahrenheit table in the first part of this section.

SOLUTION

We first look over the range of values for C and F so that we can establish an appropriate scale for each axis. We then plot each pair of numbers, letting the first number in each ordered pair represent Centigrade degrees and letting the second number represent Fahrenheit degrees. We call the horizontal axis the Centigrade axis and the vertical axis the Fahrenheit axis.

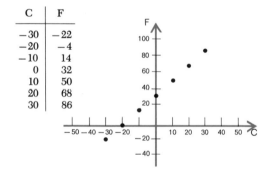

C	F
−30	−22
−20	−4
−10	14
0	32
10	50
20	68
30	86

The graph in example 6 shows a relationship between Centigrade and Fahrenheit degrees of which you probably were not aware: Centigrade and Fahrenheit degrees seem to be linearly related; that is, all of the plotted points seem to lie along a straight line. You might even be tempted to draw a straight line through the points and say that the coordinates of every point on the line represent matched temperatures, i.e., temperatures that are solutions to the equation $F = \frac{9}{5}C + 32$. (We will not yield to this temptation now but will consider it in detail in the next section.)

EXAMPLE 7. Given the set $A = \{(t, I) \mid I = 4t, t \text{ an integer}, 0 \leq t \leq 6\}$,
(A) List the elements of set A within braces.
(B) Graph the set A.

SOLUTION

(A) We are looking for the set of all ordered pairs (t, I) such that $I = 4t$ and t is an integer between 0 and 6, inclusive. Substituting the integers from 0 to 6 into $I = 4t$ for t we obtain the corresponding values for I. Thus

$$A = \{(0, 0), (1, 4), (2, 8), (3, 12), (4, 16), (5, 20), (6, 24)\}$$

(B)

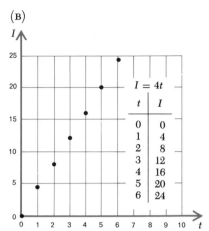

EXERCISE 39

Graph each of the following sets. Choose appropriate scales for each problem, and remember that the scale on the vertical axis need not be the same as the scale on the horizontal axis. It is recommended that you use graph paper; an inexpensive variety is all that is necessary.

1. $\{(1, 1), (1, 2), (1, 3), (2, 2), (2, 3), (3, 3)\}$
2. $\{(-1, 1), (-1, 0), (-1, -1), (0, 0), (0, -1), (1, -1)\}$
3. Graph the table by considering it a set of ordered pairs of numbers.

t	0	1	2	3	4	5
I	0	6	12	18	24	30

4. Graph the table by considering it a set of ordered pairs of numbers.

t	0	1	2	3	4	5
d	0	60	120	180	240	300

5. $\{(t, I) \mid I = 6t, t \text{ an integer}, 0 \leq t \leq 5\}$
HINT: Write as a table and graph.

6. $\{(t, d) \mid d = 60t, t \text{ an integer}, 0 \leq t \leq 5\}$

7. $\{(x, y) \mid y = 2x + 8, x \text{ an even number}, -10 \leq x \leq 10\}$.

HINT: Complete the following table and graph.

x	-10	-8	-6	-4	-2	0	2	4	6	8	10
y	-12	-8									

8. $\{(x, y) \mid y = 8 - 2x, x \text{ an even number}, -10 \leq x \leq 10\}$

9. $\{(x, y) \mid 2x + 3y = 6, x \, \varepsilon \, \{-9, -6, -3, 0, 3, 6, 9\}\}$

10. $\{(x, y) \mid 3x + 4y = 12, x \, \varepsilon \, \{-8, -4, 0, 4, 8\}\}$

11. $\{(C, F) \mid F = \frac{9}{5}C + 32, C \text{ an integer divisible by } 5, -30 \leq C \leq 30\}$

HINT: Complete the following table and graph.

C	-30	-25	-20	-15	-10	-5	0	5	10	15	20	25	30
F													

Compare with the graph in example 6.

12. $\{(t, I) \mid I = 4t, t \, \varepsilon \, \{0, \frac{1}{2}, 1, \frac{3}{2}, 2, \frac{5}{2}, 3, \frac{7}{2}, 4\}\}$

(HINT: Make a table and graph as in the preceding problems.)   Compare with graph in example 7.

13. $\{(V, P) \mid PV = 12, V \, \varepsilon \, \{\frac{1}{3}, \frac{1}{2}, 1, 2, 3, 4, 6, 12, 24, 36\}\}$

14. $\{(t, s) \mid s = 16t^2, t \, \varepsilon \, \{0, \frac{1}{4}, \frac{1}{2}, \frac{3}{4}, 1, \frac{3}{2}, 2\}\}$.   Choose horizontal and vertical scales carefully.

15. $\{(x, y) \mid x \text{ and } y \text{ are integers}, -4 \leq x \leq 6, 1 \leq y \leq 3\}$

16. $\{(x, y) \mid x \text{ and } y \text{ are odd numbers}, 0 < x \leq 3, -5 \leq y < 4\}$

35   FIRST-DEGREE POLYNOMIAL EQUATIONS IN TWO VARIABLES; STRAIGHT LINES

The invention of the Cartesian coordinate system represented a very important advance in mathematics. It was through the use of this system that Rene Descartes (1596–1650), a French philosopher-mathematician, was able to transform geometric problems requiring long tedious reasoning into algebraic problems which could be solved quite mechanically. This joining of algebra and geometry has now become known as *analytic geometry.*

Two fundamental problems of analytic geometry are the following: (1) given an equation (or inequality), find its graph; and (2) given a geometric figure, such as a straight line, circle, or ellipse, find its equation. In this course we will be mainly interested in the first problem, with particular emphasis on equations whose graphs are straight lines.

The graphs in most of the examples and exercises in the last section appeared to be linear; that is, the points seemed to lie along straight lines. Was this an accident? Suppose in problem 7, Exercise 39, you had been asked to graph the set

$$A = \{(x, y) \mid y = 2x + 8, x \text{ and } y \text{ are } \textit{any} \text{ real numbers}\}$$

instead of

$$B = \{(x, y) \mid y = 2x + 8, x \text{ an even number}, -10 \le x \le 10\}$$

Certainly set B is a subset of A. Is the straight line that passes through all of the points of the graph of set B the graph of set A? (See Fig. 10.)

Set A is an infinite set, the solution set of the equation $y = 2x + 8$ (that is, all ordered pairs of real numbers (x, y) that satisfy the equation $y = 2x + 8$). Obviously we cannot graph an infinite set point by point. By this time most of us are probably ready to speculate that the graph of set B lies on a straight line and that the graph of set A is the extended straight line passing through the graph of set B. Theorem 2 below tells us that we have speculated correctly.

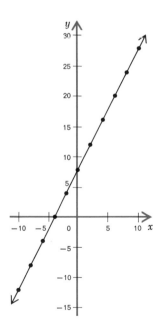

Figure 10

THE EQUATION OF A STRAIGHT LINE

The equation $y = 2x + 8$ is an example of a first-degree polynomial equation in two variables. In general, any equation that can be put into the form

$$Ax + By = C$$

where A, B, and C are constants (A and B not both zero) and x and y are variables, is called a **first-degree polynomial equation in two variables.** The equations

$$2x + 3y = 5 \qquad u = \tfrac{1}{3}v - 5 \qquad s = 7 - 8t$$

are all first-degree polynomial equations in two variables, whereas

$$PV = 17 \qquad s = 16t^2 \qquad \frac{3}{x} + \frac{2}{y} = 5$$

are not.

We will state without proof the following important theorem on graphs of first-degree equations in two variables.

THEOREM 2   *The graph of the equation $Ax + By = C$ where A, B, and C are constants (A and B not both zero) and x and y are variables, is a straight line. Every straight line in a Cartesian coordinate system is the graph of an equation of this form.*

If we know that the graph of $Ax + By = C$ is a straight line, then its graph is easily found by plotting two points of the solution set (since two points determine a line) and using a straight edge to draw a line through these two points. It is sometimes wise to find a third point as a check point. It should be obvious that we cannot draw a straight line extending indefinitely in either direction; we will settle for the part of the line in which we are interested—usually the part around the origin unless otherwise stated.

EXAMPLE 8
Graph of $y = 2x + 8$:   Graph of $I = 4t$:

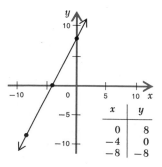

x	y
0	8
-4	0
-8	-8

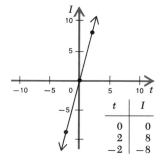

t	I
0	0
2	8
-2	-8

Graph of $x + 3y = 6$:

Graph of $y = 4$ (that is, $0x + y = 4$):

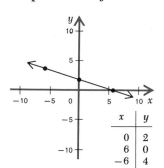

x	y
0	2
6	0
-6	4

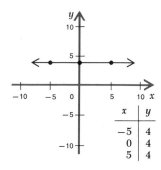

x	y
-5	4
0	4
5	4

EXAMPLE 9. Graph $F = \frac{9}{5}C + 32$:

C	F
0	32
10	50
-10	14

It should now be clear why first-degree polynomial equations in two variables are often called **linear equations.**

Finally, it is important to remember that when it is stated that a line is the graph of an equation two conditions must be met:

1. Every pair of real numbers that satisfies the equation are coordinates of a point on the line.

2. Every point on the line has coordinates that satisfy the equation.

EXERCISE 40

Graph each of the following equations.

1. $y = 2x$

2. $y = 4x$

3. $y = \frac{1}{2}x$

4. $y = \frac{1}{4}x$

5. $d = 60t,\ t \geq 0$

6. $I = 6t,\ t \geq 0$

7. $y = 4x - 3$ 8. $y = 2x + 4$ 9. $y = 9 - 3x$

10. $y = 6 - 2x$ 11. $x + y = 6$ 12. $x + y = -4$

13. $x - y = 6$ 14. $y - x = 4$ 15. $2x + 3y = 6$

16. $3x + 4y = 12$ 17. $2x - 3y = 15$ 18. $2y - 3x = 15$

19. $y = 7$ 20. $y = -3$ 21. $x = -4$

22. $x = 5$ 23. $y = 0$ 24. $x = 0$

25. $A = 100 + 10t, 0 \leq t \leq 10$ 26. $v = 10 + 32t, 0 \leq t \leq 5$

Write problems 27 and 28 in the form ax + by = c and graph.

27. $6x - 3 + y = 2y + 4x + 5$ 28. $y + 8 = 2 - x - y$

Write problems 29 and 30 in the form y = mx + b and graph.

29. $y - x - 2 = x + 1$ 30. $x + 6 = 3x + 2 - y$

31. Graph each equation that is linear (that is, a first-degree polynomial equation in two variables):

(A) $y = x^2$ (B) $y = \dfrac{1}{x}$ (C) $y = \frac{1}{3}x - 7$ (D) $2x^2 - 3y = 6$

32. Graph each equation that is linear:

(A) $xy = 9$ (B) $2x = \frac{1}{3}y$ (C) $x - \dfrac{9}{y} = 0$ (D) $x^2 + y^2 = 25$

33. Graph $y = |x|$.   HINT: Graph $y = x$ for $x \geq 0$ and $y = -x$ for $x < 0$.

34. Graph $y = |2x|$ and $y = |\frac{1}{2}x|$ on the same coordinate system.

35. Graph $x + y = 3$ and $2x - y = 0$ on the same coordinate system. Determine by inspection the coordinates of the point where the two graphs cross. Show that the coordinates of the point of intersection satisfies both equations.

36. Repeat the preceding problem with the equations

$$2x - 3y = -6 \quad \text{and} \quad x + 2y = 11$$

In the following problems, choose horizontal and vertical scales to produce maximum clarity in graphs. Remember that one of the purposes of a graph is to provide maximum information (with minimum effort on the part of the individual looking at the graph).

37. In biology there is an approximate rule, called the bioclimatic rule, for temperate climates that states that in spring and early summer periodic phenomena such as blossoming for a given species, appearance of certain insects, and ripening of fruit usually come about 4 days later for each 500 ft of altitude. Stated as a formula,

$$d = 4\left(\frac{h}{500}\right)$$

where d = change in days and h = change in altitude in feet. Graph the equation for $0 \leq h \leq 4{,}000$.

38. In a simple electric circuit, such as found in a flashlight, if the resistance is 30 ohms, the current in the circuit I (in amperes) and the electromotive force E (in volts) are related by the equation $E = 30\,I$. Graph this equation for $0 \leq I \leq 1$.

39. In 1948 Professor Brown, a psychologist, trained a group of rats (in an experiment on motivation) to run down a narrow passage in a cage to receive food in a goal box. He then put a harness on each rat and connected it to an overhead wire that was attached to a scale. In this way he could place the rat at different distances (in centimeters) from the food and measure the pull (in grams) of the rat toward the food. He found that a relation between motivation (pull) and position was given approximately by the equation $p = -\frac{1}{5}d + 70$, $30 \leq d \leq 175$. Graph this equation for the indicated values of d.

40. A man, with a wife and three children, earns I dollars per year. He is allowed to deduct \$600 per dependent (including himself) from his income; in addition, he may deduct a straight 10 percent of his income. His tax is then 20 percent of his income after deductions are subtracted. The relationship between income and tax is linear and is given by the equation

$$T = 0.2[I - 5(600) - 0.1\,I] = 0.18\,I - 600$$

Graph this equation for $5{,}000 \leq I \leq 15{,}000$.

36   SLOPE-INTERCEPT FORM OF LINEAR EQUATIONS

The equation $Ax + By = C$, $B \neq 0$, can always be written in the form $y = mx + b$, where m and b are constants. For example,

$$2x - 3y = 6$$
$$-3y = -2x + 6$$
$$y = \tfrac{2}{3}x - 2$$

The form $y = mx + b$ has several interesting and useful properties. In particular, the constants m and b have special geometric significance. In this section we will investigate these properties, and, in addition, we will consider the second fundamental problem of analytic geometry to which we referred earlier; that is, given a figure (in our case a straight line), find its equation.

THE FORM $y = mx + b$

To understand the geometric significance of b, we will assign m a particular value, say $m = \frac{1}{2}$, and graph $y = mx + b$ for various values of b (Fig. 11).

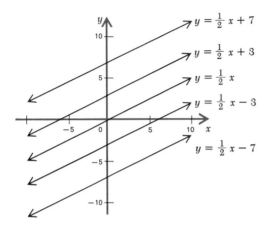

Figure 11

In each case we see that b is the point where the graph crosses the y axis. In general, if we let $x = 0$ in $y = mx + b$, then $y = b$. Thus $(0, b)$, the point where the graph crosses the y axis, is called the **y intercept.**

EXAMPLE 10.   The y intercepts for $y = \frac{1}{2}x + 7$, $y = \frac{1}{2}x$, and $y = \frac{1}{2}x - 3$ are 7, 0, and -3, respectively.   (See Fig. 11.)

EXAMPLE 11.   The y intercept for an equation of the form $3y - x = 9$ may be found by first writing the equation in the form $y = mx + b$ or simply by substituting $x = 0$ into the original equation and solving for y.   In either case the y intercept of $3y - x = 9$ is 3.

What happens when we hold b fixed, say $b = 3$, and assign m different values? The graphs (Fig. 12) all have the same y intercept (3), but as m is assigned different values, the steepness of the lines changes.   To give a definite geometric meaning to m, let us choose two points (x_1, y_1) and (x_2, y_2) on the line $y = mx + b$ (Fig. 13).   Since these two points lie on the line, their coordinates must satisfy $y = mx + b$; that is,

$$y_1 = mx_1 + b \qquad \text{and} \qquad y_2 = mx_2 + b$$

or $\qquad\qquad\quad y_1 - mx_1 = b \qquad \text{and} \qquad y_2 - mx_2 = b$

Since $y_1 - mx_1$ and $y_2 - mx_2$ are both equal to b, we set them equal to each other and solve for m.   Thus

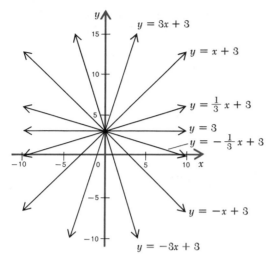

Figure 12

$$y_1 - mx_1 = y_2 - mx_2$$

$$mx_2 - mx_1 = y_2 - y_1$$

$$m(x_2 - x_1) = y_2 - y_1$$

$$m = \frac{y_2 - y_1}{x_2 - x_1} = \frac{\text{vertical change}}{\text{horizontal change}}$$

Interpreting this last equation in terms of Fig. 13, it is seen that m is the ratio of the change in y to the corresponding change in x between any two distinct points on the line. The number m is called the **slope** of the line. Thus, if an equation of a line is written in the form $y = mx + b$, the constant m is the

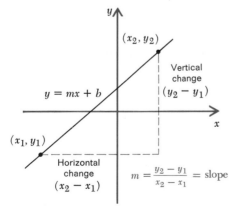

Figure 13

slope of the line. If we are given the coordinates of two points (x_1, y_1) and (x_2, y_2) and want to find the slope of the line joining the two points, we use the formula $m = (y_2 - y_1)/(x_2 - x_1)$.

EXAMPLE 12.   The slope and y intercept of the graph of $y = \frac{1}{3}x + 2$ are $\frac{1}{3}$ and 2, respectively.

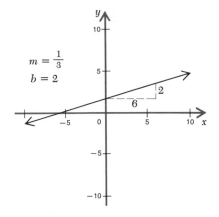

EXAMPLE 13.   Find the slope of the line passing through $(1, 5)$ and $(6, -7)$.

SOLUTION

$$m = \frac{y_2 - y_1}{x_2 - x_1}$$

$$m = \frac{-7 - 5}{6 - 1} = \frac{-12}{5} = -\frac{12}{5}$$

or $m = \dfrac{5 - (-7)}{1 - 6} = \dfrac{12}{-5} = -\dfrac{12}{5}$

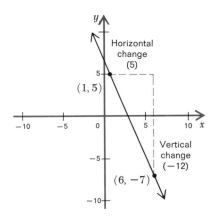

The slope of the line may be positive, negative, zero, or not defined. What is the slope of a vertical line? It should now be clear why $y = mx + b$ is called the **slope-intercept form** of the equation of a line.

FINDING THE EQUATION OF A GIVEN LINE

With the information developed in this section so far, we can easily find the equation of a nonvertical line if we know (1) the y intercept and slope of the line, (2) the y intercept and the coordinates of a point on the line, or (3) the coordinates of two points on the line. The following three examples will illustrate the process.

EXAMPLE 14. Find the equation of a line with slope -2 and y intercept 3. Graph the equation.

SOLUTION

$$y = mx + b$$

$$m = -2 \text{ and } b = 3$$

$$y = -2x + 3$$

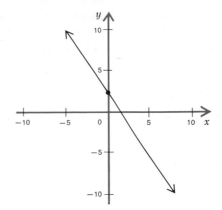

EXAMPLE 15. Find the equation of a line that passes through $(6, 4)$ and has y intercept -4. Graph the equation.

SOLUTION

$$y = mx + b$$

$$y \text{ intercept} = -4 = b$$

and hence $y = mx - 4$. To find m, we note that $(6, 4)$ must satisfy the equation $y = mx - 4$. Solving for m after substitution, we obtain $m = \frac{4}{3}$. The equation of the line is

$$y = \tfrac{4}{3}x - 4$$

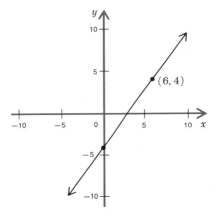

EXAMPLE 16. Find the equation of a line that passes through $(-4, -7)$ and $(4, 1)$. Graph the equation.

SOLUTION

First find m.

$$m = \frac{1 - (-7)}{4 - (-4)} = \frac{8}{8} = 1$$

Thus $y = x + b$

Since $(-4, -7)$ and $(4, 1)$ must satisfy the equation (since they are both on the line), use either to find b. Using $(4, 1)$, we see that $1 = 4 + b$ and $b = -3$. Therefore, $y = x - 3$ is the equation of the line through $(-4, -7)$ and $(4, 1)$. (You should check that both points satisfy the equation.)

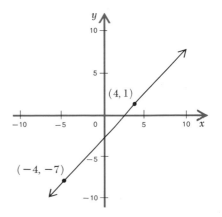

What do we do about vertical lines? If a line is vertical, its slope is not defined. Since points on a vertical line have constant abscissas and arbitrary ordinates, the **equation of a vertical line** will be of the form

$$x + 0y = c$$

or simply
$$x = c$$

where c is the abscissa of every point on the line.

EXAMPLE 17.   Find the equation of the vertical line that passes through $(-3, 5)$.

SOLUTION

$$x = -3$$

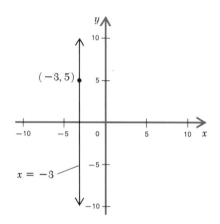

EXERCISE 41

1. (A) Graph $y = -2x + b$ for $b = -5$, $b = 0$, and $b = 5$ all on the same coordinate system.
(B) Graph $y = mx$ for $m = 6$, $m = 1$, $m = 0$, $m = -1$, and $m = -6$, all on the same coordinate system.
2. (A) Graph $y = -\frac{1}{2}x + b$ for $b = -6$, $b = 0$, and $b = 6$ all on the same coordinate system.
(B) Graph $y = mx - 2$ for $m = 2$, $m = \frac{1}{2}$, $m = 0$, $m = -\frac{1}{2}$, and $m = -2$, all on the same coordinate system.

Find the slope, y intercept, and graph each equation.

3. $y = 2x - 3$ 　　　　　　　　　4. $y = 4x - 6$
5. $y = \frac{1}{4}x + 1$ 　　　　　　　　6. $y = -\frac{2}{3}x + 2$
7. $y - x = -3$ 　　　　　　　　　8. $2y - x = 4$
9. $2x + 3y = 6$ 　　　　　　　　10. $3x + 4y = 12$

Write the equation of the line with slope and y intercept as indicated.

11. slope $= -1$, y intercept $= -1$ 12. slope $= \frac{1}{2}$, y intercept $= -3$

13. slope $= \frac{2}{3}$, y intercept $= \frac{3}{2}$ 14. slope $= -\frac{3}{2}$, y intercept $= 2$

Write the equation of the line that passes through the given point with the indicated slope.

15. $m = 1$, $(5, 5)$ 16. $m = 2$, $(2, 0)$

17. $m = -\frac{1}{3}$, $(3, -3)$ 18. $m = -\frac{2}{5}$, $(-5, 4)$

In problems 19 through 22 find the slope of the line that contains the given points.

19. $(2, 1)$ and $(10, 5)$ 20. $(1, 2)$ and $(3, 4)$

21. $(-6, 4)$ and $(3, 7)$ 22. $(-5, -2)$ and $(5, -4)$

23. Find the equation of the line that contains the given points in (A) problem 19 and (B) problem 21.

24. Find the equation of the line that contains the given points in (A) problem 20 and (B) problem 22.

In problems 25 through 28 write the equations of the lines through the given pair of points.

25. $(-6, 4)$ and $(3, 4)$ 26. $(-2, -3)$ and $(7, -3)$

27. $(2, 5)$ and $(2, -1)$ 28. $(-4, 2)$ and $(-4, -9)$

29. It is known from physics that the relationship between the stretch of a spring S and the weight W causing the stretch is linear (a principle upon which all spring scales are constructed). (A) If a 10-lb weight stretches a spring 1 in., write a linear equation relating the two variables. (HINT: With no weight the stretch of the spring is zero.) (B) Graph the equation for $0 \leq W \leq 40$ (associate W with the horizontal axis). (C) From the equation find the stretch of the spring for a 23-lb weight.

NOTE: From the information in this problem you can easily construct a spring scale from a spring purchased at a hardware store. The size of the spring will depend on the weight range of objects you wish to weigh.

30. It is known that water freezes at $32°\,\mathrm{F}$ and $0°\,\mathrm{C}$ and boils at $212°\,\mathrm{F}$ and $100°\,\mathrm{C}$. It is also known that Centigrade and Fahrenheit degrees are linearly related. (A) Using this information, write an equation relating Fahrenheit and Centigrade temperature readings. (B) Graph the equation for $-100 \leq C \leq 100$. (Associate C with the horizontal axis.)

31. The management of a company manufacturing ball-point pens estimates costs for running the company to be $200 per day at zero output (fixed costs) and $700 per day at an output of 1,000 pens.   (A) Assuming total cost per day, c, is linearly related to total output per day, x, write an equation relating these two quantities.   (B) Graph the equation for $0 \leq x \leq 2,000$.

32. A photography store sells a camera costing $20 for $33 and an enlarger costing $60 for $93.   (A) If the markup policy of the store for items costing over $10 is assumed to be linear and is reflected in the pricing of these two items, write an equation that relates retail price R with cost C.   (B) Graph this equation for $10 \leq C \leq 400$.   (C) Use the equation to find the cost of a camera retailing for $300.

37   SYSTEMS OF LINEAR EQUATIONS

Two companies have offered you a sales position.   Both jobs are essentially the same, but one company pays a straight 10 percent commission and the other pays $100 per week plus 5 percent commission.   After a little investigating you find that the best salesmen with either company rarely have sales greater than $4,000 in any one week, usually less. If we let E represent weekly earnings and S weekly sales, then

$$E = 0.1\ S \qquad \text{straight-commission company}$$

and

$$E = 100 + 0.05\ S \qquad \text{salary-plus-commission company}$$

where

$$0 \leq S \leq 4000$$

Before accepting either offer, it would be helpful to know at what point both companies pay the same and which of the companies pays more on either side of this point.   How do you find this point; that is, how do you find a single pair of numbers that will make both equations true?

The problem we have presented is one of a very large number of problems from many different fields that give rise to essentially the same mathematical form, a **system of two linear equations in two variables:**

$$\begin{aligned} ax + by &= c \\ dx + ey &= f \end{aligned} \qquad (1)$$

A pair of numbers is said to be a **solution** of this system if it is a solution of the first equation *and* a solution of the second equation.   In terms of set notation, the **solution set** of the system of Eq. (1) is defined as

$$\{(x,\ y)\ |\ ax + by = c \ and \ dx + ey = f\ \}$$

In this section we will consider three methods of finding the solution set to systems of type (1).

SOLVING SYSTEMS OF EQUATIONS BY GRAPHING

The method of solving a system of equations by graphing is perhaps the easiest of the three methods to understand.   For this reason it will be considered first.

We proceed by graphing both equations on the same coordinate system.   Then *the coordinates of any points that the graphs have in common must be solutions to the system since they must satisfy both equations.*   (Why?)

EXAMPLE 18.   Solve the commission problem above by graphing.

SOLUTION

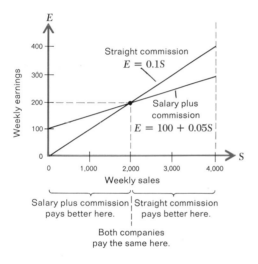

Figure 14

The amount of sales for which earnings are the same at both companies is found at the point of intersection of the two graphs (Fig. 14).   Since this point is on both lines, its coordinates must satisfy both equations; the coordinate pair at the point of intersection is called the *simultaneous solution* of the system

$$E = 0.1 \ S$$
$$E = 100 + 0.05 \ S$$

A weekly sales figure of $2,000 would earn $200 at each company; below $2,000 the salary-plus-commission choice would net you more; above $2,000 the straight commission would be a better choice.

EXAMPLE 19. Solve the following three systems by graphing.

(A) $2x - 3y = 2$
   $\quad x + 2y = 8$

(B) $4x + 6y = 12$
   $\quad 2x + 3y = -6$

(C) $2x - 3y = -6$
   $\quad -x + \frac{3}{2}y = 3$

SOLUTIONS

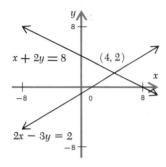

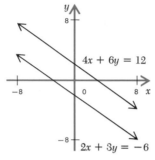

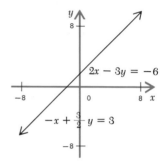

Lines intersect at one point only:
Exactly one solution

$\quad x = 4, y = 2$

Lines are parallel:

No solution

Lines coincide:

Infinite number of solutions

In general, two lines in the same coordinate system must be related to each other in one of the three ways indicated in example 19. They intersect in one and only one point, they are parallel, or they coincide. Now we know exactly what to expect when solving a system of two linear equations in two unknowns: *exactly one pair of numbers as a solution, no solutions, or an infinite number of solutions.* In most applications the first case prevails. If we find a pair of numbers that satisfy the system of equations and the graphs of the equations meet at only one point, then that pair of numbers is the only solution of the system, and we need not look further for others.

EXERCISE 42

In problems 1 through 10 solve each system by graphing.

1. $x + y = 5$
   $\quad 2x - y = 4$

2. $2x + y = 6$
   $\quad y = x + 3$

3. $\quad 3y = 2x + 12$
   $\quad 2x - y = 4$

4. $3x - 2y = 12$ 5. $y = 3x + 9$ 6. $x + 5y = -10$

$\quad\;\; 7x + 2y = 8$ $3x + 4y = -24$ $\quad\quad\; y = 5x + 24$

7. $\;\; x + 2y = 4$ 8. $3x + \;\; 5y = 15$ 9. $\quad \frac{1}{2}x - \;\; y = -3$

$\quad\;\; 2x + 4y = -9$ $\;\; 6x + 10y = -5$ $\quad\quad -x + 2y = 6$

10. $3x - 5y = 15$

$\quad\;\; x - \frac{5}{3}y = 5$

11. Solve the commission problem in example 18 graphically if the straight-commission company pays 7 percent and the salary-plus-commission company pay \$75 per week plus 4 percent commission. Assume $0 \leq S \leq 4,000$.

12. Solve the commission problem in example 18 graphically if the straight-commission company pays 8 percent and the salary-plus-commission company pays \$51 per week plus 5 percent commission. Assume $0 \leq S \leq 4,000$.

13. Prove that if two lines have the same slope they are parallel. HINT: Assume the contrary, and show that this leads to a contradiction.

SOLVING SYSTEMS OF EQUATIONS BY ADDITION OR SUBTRACTION

The graphical method of solving systems of equations yielded considerable information as to what to expect in the way of solutions to a system of two linear equations in two unknowns. In addition, graphs frequently reveal relationships in problems that would otherwise be hidden. On the other hand, if one is interested in solutions with several-decimal-place accuracy, the graphical method is often not practical. The problems considered so far avoided fractional or decimal solutions; most practical problems of any consequence usually do not fall into this category.

The method of solving a system of equations we are now going to discuss has to do with the replacement of systems of equations with simpler equivalent systems (by performing appropriate operations) until we get a system whose solution is obvious. **Equivalent systems** are, as you would expect, systems with the same solution set. What operations on a system produce equivalent systems? The following theorem, stated but not proved, answers this question.

THEOREM 3   *Equivalent systems result* (A) *if the operations that were used on first-degree equations to produce equivalent equations (see theorem 10, Sec. 20) are used on either equation in the system, or* (B) *if the equation that is obtained by combining the two equations of the system into one using the addition property of equality is paired with either of the two original equations.*

Solving a system of equations by use of this theorem is best illustrated by examples. So that the fundamental principles will be clear, we will go through one example in detail writing in more steps than are generally included in practice. We will then reduce the process to a relatively few key operational steps.

EXAMPLE 3.   Solve the system

$$3x + 2y = 13$$
$$2x - y = 4$$

SOLUTION

1. We note that if we combine these two equations by either addition or subtraction we obtain

addition	subtraction
$3x + 2y = 13$	$3x + 2y = 13$
$2x - y = 4$	$2x - y = 4$
$5x + y = 17$	$x + 3y = 9$

If we pair either of these two resulting equations with one of the original ones, we obtain an equivalent system, but certainly not a "simpler" system. However, if we multiply the second original equation through by 2 first, we obtain the following equivalent system:

$$3x + 2y = 13$$
$$4x - 2y = 8$$

Now if we combine these two equations by addition, one of the variables drops out. Thus

$$3x + 2y = 13$$
$$4x - 2y = 8$$
$$\overline{\quad 7x \qquad = 21}$$

This last equation may be combined with either of the two original equations to form a simpler equivalent system (in practice we choose one or the other, but not both; here we will proceed with both for purposes of illustration).

$$
\begin{array}{ccc}
3x + 2y = 13 & & 2x - y = 4 \\
7x \quad\;\; = 21 & \text{or} & 7x \quad\;\; = 21
\end{array}
$$

Dividing $7x = 21$ through by 7, we obtain the simpler equivalent system

$$
\begin{array}{ccc}
3x + 2y = 13 & & 2x - y = 4 \\
x \quad\;\; = 3 & \text{or} & x \quad\;\; = 3
\end{array}
$$

We now know what x is; we find y by substituting $x = 3$ into the top equation. Thus

$$3 \cdot 3 + 2y = 13 \qquad\qquad 2 \cdot 3 - y = 4$$
$$2y = 4 \qquad \text{or} \qquad -y = -2$$
$$y = 2 \qquad\qquad\qquad y = 2$$

The solution to the original system is therefore $x = 3$ and $y = 2$.

CHECK

$$3x + \quad 2y = 13 \qquad\qquad 2x - y = 4$$
$$3 \cdot 3 + 2 \cdot 2 \overset{?}{=} 13 \qquad\qquad 2 \cdot 3 - 2 \overset{?}{=} 4$$
$$9 + \quad 4 \overset{\vee}{=} 13 \qquad\qquad 6 - 2 \overset{\vee}{=} 4$$

NOTE: The solution must check in both equations.

2. We now repeat the solution including only the key operational steps.

(A) $3x + 2y = 13$

(B) $2x - \quad y = 4$

(A) $3x + 2y = 13$

2(B) $\underline{4x - 2y = 8}$

(A) + 2(B) $7x \qquad = 21$ Eliminate y by addition.

$$\boxed{x = 3}$$

$2 \cdot 3 - y = 4$ Substitute $x = 3$ back into either (A)

$-y = -2$ or (B), the simpler of the two, and solve for y.

$$\boxed{y = 2}$$

CHECK   (A)   (B)

$$3x + 2y = 13 \qquad\qquad\qquad 2x - y = 4$$
$$3 \cdot 3 + 2 \cdot 2 \overset{?}{=} 13 \qquad\qquad 2 \cdot 3 - 2 \overset{?}{=} 4$$
$$9 + 4 \overset{\vee}{=} 13 \qquad\qquad\qquad 6 - 2 \overset{\vee}{=} 4$$

EXAMPLE 4.   Solve the system

$$2x + 3y = 1$$
$$5x - 2y = 12$$

SOLUTION

(A) $\qquad$ $2x + 3y = 1$

(B) $\qquad$ $5x - 2y = 12$

If we multiply (A) by 2 and (B) by 3 and add we can eliminate y.

$$4x + 6y = 2$$
$$\underline{15x - 6y = 36}$$
$$19x \qquad = 38$$

$$\boxed{x = 2}$$

$$2 \cdot 2 + 3y = 1$$
$$3y = -3$$

$$\boxed{y = -1}$$

Substitute $x = 2$ back into either (A) or (B).

CHECK $\qquad$ (A) $\qquad\qquad\qquad\qquad\qquad$ (B)

$$2x + 3y = 1 \qquad\qquad\qquad\qquad 5x - 2y = 12$$
$$2 \cdot 2 + 3(-1) \overset{?}{=} 1 \qquad\qquad\qquad 5 \cdot 2 - 2(-1) \overset{?}{=} 12$$
$$4 - 3 \overset{\vee}{=} 1 \qquad\qquad\qquad\qquad 10 + 2 \overset{\vee}{=} 12$$

EXAMPLE 5.   Solve the system

$$x + 3y = 2$$
$$2x + 6y = -3$$

SOLUTION

(A) $\qquad$ $x + 3y = 2$

(B) $\qquad$ $2x + 6y = -3$

$$2x + 6y = 4$$
$$\underline{2x + 6y = -3}$$
$$0 = 7 \qquad\qquad\qquad \text{A contradiction!}$$

Our assumption that there are values for x and y that satisfy (A) and (B) simultaneously must be false (otherwise, we have proved that $0 = 7$). If you check the slope of each line, you will find them the same; hence, the lines are parallel, and the system has no solution. Systems of this type are called **inconsistent**—conditions have been placed on the unknowns x and y that are impossible to meet.

EXAMPLE 6. Solve the system

$$-2x + y = -8$$
$$x - \tfrac{1}{2}y = 4$$

SOLUTION

(A) $\qquad -2x + y = -8$

(B) $\qquad x - \tfrac{1}{2}y = 4$

$$-2x + y = -8$$
$$\underline{2x - y = 8}$$
$$0 = 0$$

Both unknowns have been eliminated! Actually, if we had multiplied (B) by -2, we would have obtained (A). When one equation is a constant multiple of the other, the system is said to be **dependent,** and their graphs will coincide. There are infinitely many solutions to the system—any solution of one equation will be a solution to the other.

EXERCISE 43

Solve problems 1 through 24 by method of addition or subtraction; check the solutions.

1. $x + y = 5$
   $x - y = 1$

2. $x + 3y = 13$
   $-x + y = 3$

3. $2c + d = 0$
   $3c + d = 2$

4. $a + 5b = 16$
   $a - 2b = 2$

5. $2x - 3y = 9$
   $x + 2y = -13$

6. $3x - y = -3$
   $5x + 3y = -19$

7. $5m - 3n = 7$
   $7m + 12n = -1$

8. $3p + 8q = 4$
   $15p + 10q = -10$

9. $11x + 2y = 1$
   $9x - 3y = 24$

10. $3x - 11y = -7$
    $4x + 3y = 26$

11. $5a - 4b = 1$
    $3a - 6b = 6$

12. $4m + 6n = 2$
    $6m - 9n = 15$

13. $x + 2y = 4$

 $2x + 4y = -9$

14. $3x + 5y = 15$

 $6x + 10y = -5$

15. $3x = 2y$

 $y = -7 - 2x$

16. $y = 3x - 3$

 $6x = 8 + 3y$

17. $2x - 3y = 1 - 3x$

 $4y = 7x - 2$

18. $3m + 2n = 2m + 2$

 $2m + 3n = 2n - 2$

19. $0.3x - 0.6y = 0.18$

 $0.5x + 0.2y = 0.54$

20. $0.8x - 0.3y = 0.79$

 $0.2x - 0.5y = 0.07$

21. $\frac{1}{2}x + \frac{1}{3}y = 1$

 $\frac{2}{3}x + \frac{1}{2}y = 2$

22. $\dfrac{a}{4} - \dfrac{2b}{3} = -2$

 $\dfrac{a}{2} - b = -2$

23. $\frac{1}{2}x - y = -3$

 $-x + 2y = 6$

24. $3x - 5y = 15$

 $x - \frac{5}{3}y = 5$

25. Solve problem 11 (on commissions) in Exercise 42 by the addition or subtraction method.

26. Solve problem 12 (on commissions) in Exercise 42 by the addition or subtraction method.

27. *Any ordered pair of numbers* (a, b) *that satisfies the system*

$$Ax + By + C = 0$$
$$Dx + Ey + F = 0$$

will also satisfy the equation

$$m(Ax + By + C) + n(Dx + Ey + F) = 0$$

where m and n are any real numbers.
Prove this theorem.

SOLVING SYSTEMS OF EQUATIONS BY SUBSTITUTION

The substitution principle (a quantity may be substituted for its equal in any expression without changing the truth or falsity of the expression) is often used in mathematics. We will show how this important principle is used to solve systems of equations.

EXAMPLE 19.   Solve the system $2x - 3y = 7$, $-3x + y = -7$ by the substitution method.

SOLUTION

Briefly the method is this: we solve either one of the equations for one of the variables in terms of the other.   We then substitute the result into the other equation to produce one equation with one variable and solve for the one variable.   Then we substitute that value back into either one of the original equations (as with the method of addition or subtraction) and solve for the other variable.

(A) $\qquad 2x - 3y = 7$

(B) $\qquad -3x + y = -7$

$$y = 3x - 7 \qquad$$ Solve (B), the simplest choice, for y in terms of x.

$$2x - 3(3x - 7) = 7 \qquad$$ Replace y in (A) with $3x - 7$.

$$2x - 9x + 21 = 7 \qquad$$ Solve for x.

$$-7x = -14$$

$$\boxed{x = 2}$$

$$(-3)(2) + y = -7 \qquad$$ Substitute $x = 2$ into either (A) or (B) and solve for y.

$$-6 + y = -7$$

$$\boxed{y = -1}$$

CHECK $\qquad$ (A) $\qquad\qquad\qquad\qquad\qquad\qquad$ (B)

$$2x - 3y = 7 \qquad\qquad\qquad -3x + y = -7$$

$$2 \cdot 2 - 3(-1) \overset{?}{=} 7 \qquad\qquad (-3)(2) + (-1) \overset{?}{=} -7$$

$$4 + 3 \overset{\vee}{=} 7 \qquad\qquad\qquad -6 - 1 \overset{\vee}{=} -7$$

When solving either one of the original equations for one of the variables in terms of the other, try to make a choice that will involve the minimum number of fractional forms.   The substitution method is particularly fast when the original system contains an equation where one of the variables is already stated in terms of the other.   The following example is a case in point.

EXAMPLE 20.   Two cars traveling the same route to New York leave different towns 98 miles apart at the same time.   The car furthest away from New York averages 57 mph, while the other car averages 43 mph.   How long will it take the faster car to overtake the slower car, and how far will it have traveled?

SOLUTION

Let d = distance that the car is from furthest town at time t.

(A) $d = 57t$ faster car

(B) $d = 98 + 43t$ slower car with a head start

$57t = 98 + 43t$ Replace d in (B) with $57t$ and solve for t.

$14t = 98$

$t = 7 \text{ hr}$

$d = 57 \cdot 7$ Substitute $t = 7$ back into either (A) or

$d = 399 \text{ miles}$ (B) and solve for d.

CHECK   (A)   (B)

$d = 57t$ $d = 98 + 43t$

$399 \overset{?}{=} (57)(7)$ $399 \overset{?}{=} 98 + (43)(7)$

$399 \overset{\vee}{=} 399$ $399 \overset{\vee}{=} 399$

EXERCISE 44

Solve problems 1 through 8 by the substitution method and check.

1. $y = 5 - x$ 2. $2x + y = 6$
    $2x - y = 4$ $y = x + 3$

3. $3y - 2x = 12$ 4. $3x - y = -3$
    $2x - y = 4$ $5x + 3y = -19$

5. $y - 3x = 9$ 6. $2m - 3n = 9$
    $3x + 24 = -4y$ $m + 2n = -13$

7. $a = 4 - 2b$ 8. $x - 2y = 0$
    $2a + 4b = -9$ $-3x + 6y = 8$

9. Solve problem 11 (on commissions) in Exercise 42 by the substitution method.
10. Solve problem 12 (on commissions) in Exercise 42 by the substitution method.

Solve problems 11 and 12 by all three methods discussed in this section.

11. $5x + y = 4$ 12. $x - 3y = -11$
    $x - 2y = 3$ $2x + 5y = 11$

13. If three limes and 12 lemons cost 81 cents, and two limes and five lemons cost 42 cents, what is the cost of one lime and of one lemon?

14. Find the capacity of each of two trucks if three trips of the larger and four trips of the smaller results in a total haul of 41 tons and if four trips of the larger and three trips of the smaller results in a total haul of 43 tons.

15. Two secretaries are typing the same form letter for a personalized mailing. Mary can type seven per hour, while Nancy can do five. Nancy started on the job an hour before Mary; hence Nancy has a head start of five letters. How long will it take Mary to catch up with Nancy, and how many letters will both girls have typed by then? Solve the problem graphically and algebraically using two equations and two unknowns.

16. The population of a town is 30,000, and it is decreasing at the rate of 550 per year. Another town has a population of 18,000 which is increasing at the rate of 1,450 per year. In how many years will both towns be the same size, and what will their population be at that time? Solve the problem graphically and algebraically.

38   ADDITIONAL APPLICATIONS

This section contains a wide variety of applications grouped by subject areas similar to those found in Sec. 33. All of these problems should be solved using a two-equation–two-unknown method discussed in the preceding section. Choose the method or methods from the last section that are best suited for each problem.

You will find that the two-equation–two-unknown methods and one-equation–one-unknown methods can often be used interchangeably. For this reason a number of the problems stated in Sec. 33 are restated here, some in a slightly modified form.

EXERCISE 45

The problems in this exercise are grouped in the following subject areas: business, chemistry, earth sciences, economics, geometry, domestic, life science, music, physics–engineering, psychology, and puzzles.

No attempt has been made to arrange the problems in order of difficulty nor to match them in pairs as in preceding exercises.

BUSINESS

1. A packing carton contains 144 small packages, some weighing $\frac{1}{4}$ lb each and the others $\frac{1}{2}$ lb each. How many of each type are in the carton if the total contents of the carton weighs 51 lb?

2. Two architects contract to do the design and detail drawings for a building and agree to share the fee in the ratio of 3:5. If the total fee to the client is $3,600, how much should each receive? HINT: Use the proportion $x/y = 3/5$ as one of the two equations.

3. A secretarial service charges $4 per hr for a stenographer and $2.50 per hr for a typist. On a particular job the bill from the service was $44. If the typist worked 2 more hours than the stenographer, how much time did each spend on the job, and how much did each earn?

4. BREAKEVEN ANALYSIS. It costs a book publisher $12,000 to prepare a book for publication (art work, plates, reviews, etc.); printing costs are $3 per book.

(A) If the book is sold to bookstores for $7 a copy, how many copies must be sold to break even, and what are the cost and revenue for this number. HINT: Solve the system

$$C = 12,000 + 3n$$
$$R = 7n$$
$$R = C$$

(B) Graph the first two equations on the same coordinate system for $0 \le n \le$ 20,000. Interpret the regions between the lines to the left and to the right of the break-even point.

CHEMISTRY

5. A chemist has two concentrations of hydrochloric acid in stock, a 50 percent solution and an 80 percent solution. How much of each should he take to get 100 grams of a 68 percent solution?

6. A farmer placed an order with a chemical company for a fertilizer that would contain, among other things, 120 lb of nitrogen and 90 lb of phosphoric acid. The company had two mixtures on hand with the following compositions:

	Nitrogen	Phosphoric acid
Mixture A	20%	10%
Mixture B	6%	6%

How many pounds of each mixture should the chemist mix to fill the order?

EARTH SCIENCES

7. An earthquake emits a primary wave and a secondary wave. Near the surface of the earth the primary wave travels at about 5 miles per sec and the secondary wave at about 3 miles per sec. From the time lag between the two waves arriv-

ing at a given station, it is possible to estimate the distance to the quake.   (The "epicenter" can be located by getting distance bearings at three or more stations.) Suppose a station measured a time difference of 16 sec between the arrival of the two waves.   How long did each wave travel, and how far would the earthquake be from the station?

ECONOMICS

8. SUPPLY AND DEMAND. An important problem in economic studies has to do with supply and demand.   The quantity of a product that people are willing to buy on a given day generally depends on its price; similarly, the quantity of a product that a supplier is willing to sell on a given day also depends on the price he is able to get for his product.

Let us assume that in a small town on a particular day the demand (in pounds) for sirloin steak is given by

$$d = 2,400 - 1,200p \qquad \$0.50 \le p \le \$1.75$$

and the supply by

$$s = -900 + 1,800p \qquad \$0.50 \le p \le \$1.75$$

Using these equations, we see that at \$1.50 per lb the people in the town would only be willing to buy 600 lb of steak on that day, whereas the suppliers would be willing to supply 1,800 lb.   Hence, the supply would exceed the demand and force prices down.   On the other hand, if the price were 75 cents per pound, the people would then be willing to buy 1,500 lb of steak on that day, but the supplier would only be willing to sell 450 lb.   Thus the demand would exceed the supply, and prices would go up.   At what price would sirloin steak stabilize for the day; that is, at what price would the supply actually equal the demand?
(A) Solve graphically by graphing the supply and demand equations on the same coordinate system.   (The point of intersection of the two graphs is called the *equilibrium point.*)
(B) Solve algebraically.
(C) Interpret the graph to the left and to the right of the equilibrium point.

GEOMETRY

9. An 18-ft board is cut into two pieces so that one piece is 4 ft longer than the other piece.   How long is each piece?

10. Find the dimensions of a rectangle with perimeter 72 in. if its length is 25 percent longer than its width.

11. If the sum of two angles in a right triangle is 90° and their difference is 14°, find the two angles.

DOMESTIC

12. A family wishes to invest its savings of $15,000. They decide to put part of it in the bank at 4 percent and the rest in a riskier real estate investment at 6 percent. How much should they invest in each if they want the annual return from each to be the same?

13. A school put on a musical comedy and sold 1,000 tickets for a total of $650. If tickets were sold to students for 50 cents and to adults for $1, how many of each type were sold?

14. Wishing to log some flying time, you have rented an airplane for 2 hr. You decide to fly due east until you have to turn around in order to be back at the airport at the end of the 2 hr. The cruising speed of the plane is 120 mph in still air.

(A) If there is a 30-mph wind blowing from the east, how long should you head east before you turn around, and how long will it take you to get back?

(B) How far from the airport were you when you turned back?

(C) Answer parts (A) and (B) with the assumption that no wind is blowing.

LIFE SCIENCE

15. Twelve hundred thirty-six offspring have brown-eyed parents who carry the recessive gene for blue eyes. According to Mendel's laws of heredity, the expected ratio of offspring with brown eyes to those with blue eyes is $3:1$. How many offspring with each eye color would you expect in the 1,236 sample? HINT: For one of the equations use the proportion $x/y = 3/1$.

16. A biologist, in a nutrition experiment, wants to prepare a special diet for his experimental animals. He requires a food mixture that contains, among other things, 20 oz of protein and 6 oz of fat. He is able to purchase food mixes of the following compositions:

	Protein	Fat
Mix A	20%	2%
Mix B	10%	6%

How many ounces of each mix should he use to get the diet mix? Solve graphically and algebraically.

MUSIC

17. If a guitar string is divided in the ratio of $4:5$, a major third will result. What will be the length of each part if a 36-in. string is used? HINT: Use the proportion $x/y = 4/5$ for one of the equations.

18. If a guitar string is divided in the ratio of 5:8, a minor sixth will result. How would you divide a 39-in. string to produce a minor sixth?

PHYSICS–ENGINEERING

19. Where should the fulcrum be placed on a 12-ft bar if it is to balance with a 14-lb weight on one end and a 42-lb weight on the other end?

20. In a Gemini-Agena rendezvous flight preparatory to placing man on the moon, the Agena passed over a tracking station in Carnoarvon, Australia, 6 min (0.1 hr) before the pursuing, astronaut-carrying Gemini. If the Agena was traveling at 17,000 mph and the Gemini at 18,700 mph, how long did it take the Gemini (after passing the tracking station) to rendezvous with the Agena, and how far from the tracking station, in the direction of motion, did this take place?

PSYCHOLOGY

21. Professor Brown, a psychologist, trained a group of rats (in an experiment on motivation and avoidance) to run down a narrow passage in a cage to receive food in a goal box. He put a harness on each rat and connected the harness to an overhead wire that was attached to a scale. In this way he could place the rat at different distances from the food and measure the pull (in grams) of the rat toward the food. He found that a relation between motivation and distance was given approximately by the equation $p = -\frac{1}{5}d + 70$ with $30 \leq d \leq 175$, where p is the pull in grams and d is the distance from the goal box in centimeters.

Professor Brown then replaced the food with a mild electric shock, and with the same apparatus he was able to measure the avoidance strength relative to the distance from the object to be avoided. He found that the avoidance strength was given approximately by $a = -\frac{4}{3}d + 230$ with $30 \leq d \leq 175$, where a is the avoidance measured in grams and d is the distance from the goal box in centimeters.

If the rat were trained in both experiments, at what distance from the goal box should the approach and avoidance strength be the same? Solve algebraically and graphically. If the goal box is on the right, what would you predict that the rat will do if he is placed to the right of this point? To the left of this point?

PUZZLES

22. A friend of yours came out of a post office having spent $1.32 on thirty 4-cent and 5-cent stamps. How many of each type did he buy?

23. A bank gave you $1.50 in change consisting of only nickels and dimes. If there were 22 coins in all, how many of each type of coin did they give you?

24. If one flask and four mixing dishes balance 14 test tubes and two mixing dishes, and if two flasks balance two test tubes and 6 mixing dishes, how many test tubes will balance one flask, and how many test tubes will balance one mixing dish?

39   CHAPTER SUMMARY

GENERAL

First-degree polynomial forms in one or more variables appear with great frequency in mathematics and applications of mathematics. We have restricted our attention to one- and two-variable forms; in future courses forms with three or more variables will be considered. It is interesting to note that in some areas of applications, notably an area called *linear programming,* it is not unusual for people to work with systems of first-degree equations numbering in the thousands with as many or more variables.

In this chapter we have also had our first introduction to the branch of mathematics called *analytic geometry*—a joining of geometry and algebra. From its beginning with the discussion of Cartesian coordinate system and the straight line, this branch of mathematics will continue to be developed in this and future courses.

Many applications from many different fields were included in this chapter; it is hoped that each person found problems that interested him. The often-raised question "What is algebra used for?" should now be partly answered.

SPECIFIC

Describe, define, or give examples of each of the following:

1. First-degree polynomial and polynomial equations
first-degree polynomial in one variable $\qquad\qquad\qquad\qquad ax + b$
first-degree polynomial equation in one variable $\qquad\quad ax + b = 0, a \neq 0$

2. Cartesian coordinate system
number line
coordinate axes (horizontal and vertical)
coordinates of a point
ordered pair of real numbers $\qquad\qquad\qquad\qquad\qquad\qquad (a, b)$
abscissa, ordinate
graph of an ordered pair of real numbers
graph of a set of ordered pairs of real numbers

3. First-degree polynomial equation in two variables
$ax + by = c$, not both $a = 0$ and $b = 0$

graph of $ax + by = c$, $x = c$, and $y = c$
the equation of a straight line
linear equation
slope
x intercept, y intercept
slope-intercept form $y = mx + b$
the equation of a line given:
    the slope and y intercept
    the slope and coordinates of one point on the line
    the coordinates of two points on the line

4. **Systems of linear equations**
solutions by $ax + by = c$
    graphing $dx + ey = f$
    addition or subtraction
    substitution

EXERCISE 46   CHAPTER REVIEW

1. Identify each of the following in the list below: (A) first-degree polynomials in one variable, (B) first-degree polynomials in two variables, (C) first-degree polynomial equations in one variable, (D) first-degree polynomial equations in two variables.

(1) $2x - 3 = 5$ (2) $x - 3y = 8$

(3) $3x + 5y - 7$ (4) $\dfrac{1}{x} - \dfrac{2}{y} = 3$

(5) $2x - 3$ (6) $xy = 5$

2. Graph the set

$$\{(x, y) \mid y = \frac{x}{2} - 3,\ x \text{ an even number, } -8 \le x \le 8\}$$

3. Graph on the same coordinate system:

(A) $y = \dfrac{x}{3} - 2$ (B) $y = 3x - 2$

4. Graph on the same coordinate system:
(A) $3x - 2y = 6$ (B) $3x - 2y = -6$

5. Graph on the same coordinate system:
(A) $4x + 2y = 7$ (B) $y = -2x + \frac{7}{2}$

6. (A) Graph $3x - 2 + y = x + 5$.
   (B) What is the slope of the line?
   (C) What is the y intercept?

7. Graph each equation that is linear:

(A) $2y = \frac{4}{3}x$ (B) $xy = 1$ (C) $y = -3$ (D) $y + \dfrac{1}{x} = 0$

8. Write the equation of the line with slope -2 and y intercept -4.

9. Write the equation of a line with slope $-\frac{1}{2}$ that contains the point $(4, 3)$.

10. Write the equation of the line that passes through the points $(-3, 2)$ and $(6, 5)$.

11. Solve the following system by three different methods:

$$-x + 3y = 12$$
$$7x + 3y = -12$$

12. Solve and check:

$$4a + 12b = 2$$
$$12a + 3b = -16$$

13. Solve and check:

$$0.3x - 0.02y = 0.38$$
$$0.2x - 0.05y = 0.4$$

14. Solve and check:

$$\frac{x}{3} - \frac{y}{2} = -6$$

$$\frac{x}{2} + \frac{y}{4} = -1$$

15. If a recipe for five people calls for 1.5 cups of milk and 1.75 cups of flour, how many cups of each would be required for eight people?

16. Write the equation of a line with the property (A) the ordinate of each point is one-half the abscissa, and (B) the ordinate of each point is five less than the abscissa.

17. A fairly good approximation for the normal weight of a person over 60 in. (5 ft) tall is given by the linear formula $w = 5.5h - 220$. Graph this equation for $60 \leq h \leq 75$.

18. You are considering a job with a company as a salesman. You are offered $50 per week plus 4 percent commission on sales. If E represents total weekly earnings and S represents weekly sales, (A) write an equation relating these two quantities, and (B) graph the equation for $0 \leq S \leq 5,000$.

19. Without graphing, tell which of the following have graphs that are parallel to each other:

(A) $y = -\frac{3}{2}x + 2$ (B) $2y - 3x = 4$

(C) $6x + 4y = 2$ (D) $12x + 8y = -1$

20. Find a and b so that the graph of $ax + by = 1$ passes through $(2, -3)$ and $(1, 3)$.

21. If the fulcrum on an 11-ft bar is placed 6 ft from one end, how should 132 lb be divided between the two ends to balance the system? (A) Solve using two equations and two unknowns. (B) Solve using one equation and one unknown.

22. The perimeter of a tennis court for singles is 210 ft. Find the dimensions of the court if its length is 3 ft less than three times its width.
(A) Solve using one equation and one unknown.
(B) Solve using two equations and two unknowns.

23. An airplane made a 240-mile trip with the wind in 1 hr and 20 min. Returning against the wind required an hour and a half. Find the cruising speed of the plane in still air and the speed of the wind.
(A) Solve using one equation and one unknown.
(B) Solve using two equations and two unknowns.

24. A manufacturer of ball-point pens makes two models, an economy model and a deluxe model. Each pen requires the following work (in hours):

	Fabricating	Assembling and packaging
Economy model	0.25	0.03
Deluxe model	0.25	0.05

The plant has 650 man-machine hours available for fabricating and 110 man-machine hours available for assembling and packaging. How many pens of each type should be produced to exactly use the number of man-machine hours available? Solve graphically and algebraically.

25. "From the fact that $2x + y = 3$ and $2x + y = 8$ we can conclude that $3 = 8$." What is wrong with this argument?

first-degree polynomial inequalities in one and two variables

40 LINEAR INEQUALITIES IN ONE VARIABLE

In the preceding chapters we worked with simple inequalities whose solutions were obvious; for example, $x < 5$, $-3 \leq t < 4$, and $m \geq -7$. In this chapter we will consider inequalities whose solutions are not always obvious. Can you guess the solution set for

$$2x - 3 < 4x + 5$$

if the replacement set for x is the set of real numbers? The answer is very likely "No." By the end of this section you will be able to solve this type of inequality almost as easily as you solved equations of the same type.

The familiar ideas and procedures which apply to equations also apply to inequalities, but with modification in certain cases. As with equations, we are interested in performing operations on inequalities that will produce simpler **equivalent inequalities** (inequalities that have the same solution set), leading eventually to an inequality whose solution is obvious. The following operations on inequalities produce equivalent inequalities.

THEOREM 1:   PROPERTIES OF THE INEQUALITY RELATION.

(A) *The inequality sign remains unchanged if*

(1) *The same number is added to both sides of the inequality.*
For example, if $a > b$ and c is any real number, then $a + c > b + c$.

(2) *The same number is subtracted from both sides of the inequality.*
For example, if $a \leq b$ and c is any real number, then $a - c \leq b - c$.

(3) *Each side of the inequality is multiplied by the same positive number.*
For example, if $a > b$ and p is any positive real number, then $pa > pb$.

(4) *Each side of the inequality is divided by the same positive number.*
For example, if $a \leq b$ and p is any positive real number, then $a/p \leq b/p$.

(B) *The inequality sign reverses if*

(1) *The left and right members of the inequality are interchanged.*
For example, if $a < b$, then $b > a$.

(2) *Each side of the inequality is multiplied by the same negative number.*
For example, if $a > b$ and n is any negative real number, then $na < nb$.

(3) *Each side of the inequality is divided by the same negative number.*
For example, if $a \leq b$ and n is any negative real number, then $a/n \geq b/n$.

These properties follow from the formal definition of "$<$" and "$>$" and from the properties of equality.° To illustrate the technique that is used to prove the various parts of the theorem, we will prove the following: *If $a > b$ and p is any positive real number and n is any negative real number, then $pa > pb$ and $na < nb$.*

PROOF

$$a > b$$
$$a - b = \text{positive number}$$

Part 1: Multiply by p.

$$p(a - b) = p(\text{positive number})$$
$$pa - pb = (\text{positive number})$$
$$pa > pb$$

Part 2: Multiply by n.

$$n(a - b) = n(\text{positive number})$$
$$na - nb = (\text{negative number})$$
$$na < nb$$

Can you supply the reasons for each step?

° Recall that we write $a > b$ if and only if $a - b = $ a positive number, and we write $a < b$ if and only if $a - b = $ a negative number.

EXAMPLE 1

$$-2 < 5$$

Add -3 to both sides:

$$(-2) + (-3) < 5 + (-3)$$

$$-5 < 2$$

The inequality sign remains unchanged.

$$-2 < 5$$

Multiply both sides by -3:

$$(-3)(-2) > (-3)(5)$$

$$6 > -15$$

The inequality sign reverses.

EXAMPLE 2.   Solve (using Theorem 1) and graph $2x - 3 \leq 4x + 5$.

SOLUTION

$$2x - 3 \leq 4x + 5$$

$$2x - 3 + 3 \leq 4x + 5 + 3$$

$$2x \leq 4x + 8$$

$$2x - 4x \leq 4x + 8 - 4x$$

$$-2x \leq 8$$

$$\frac{-2x}{-2} \geq \frac{8}{-2}$$

$$x \geq -4$$

EXAMPLE 3.   Solve and graph $(3x - 2)/2 - 5 > 1 - (x/4)$.

SOLUTION

$$\frac{3x - 2}{2} - 5 > 1 - \frac{x}{4}$$

$$6x - 4 - 20 > 4 - x$$

$$7x > 28$$

$$x > 4$$

EXAMPLE 4.   If the temperature for a 24-hr period in the Antarctica ranged between $-49°F$ and $14°F$ (that is, $-49 \leq F \leq 14$), what was the range in Centigrade degrees?   (Recall $F = \frac{9}{5}C + 32$)

SOLUTION

Since $F = \frac{9}{5}C + 32$, we replace F in $-49 \leq F \leq 14$ with $\frac{9}{5}C + 32$ and solve the double inequality:

$$-49 \leq \tfrac{9}{5}C + 32 \leq 14$$

$$\boxed{-49 - 32 \leq \tfrac{9}{5}C + 32 - 32 \leq 14 - 32}$$

$$-81 \leq \tfrac{9}{5}C \leq -18$$

$$\boxed{(\tfrac{5}{9})(-81) \leq (\tfrac{5}{9})(\tfrac{9}{5}C) \leq (\tfrac{5}{9})(-18)}$$

$$-45 \leq C \leq -10$$

Notice that in example 4 we are actually solving an inequality pair; that is, we found values of C for which

$$-49 \leq \tfrac{9}{5}C + 32 \qquad \text{and} \qquad \tfrac{9}{5}C + 32 \leq 14$$

We could solve these two inequalities separately, but it is quite correct and more convenient to proceed as shown in the example.

EXERCISE 47

1. Replace each question mark with an appropriate inequality symbol:

(A) $\quad -2 < 7$
$$-2 + 3 \; ? \; 7 + 3$$

(B) $\quad -2 > -5$
$$-2 - 3 \; ? \; -5 - 3$$

(C) $\quad 3 > -1$
$$(-4)(3) \; ? \; (-4)(-1)$$

(D) $-9 < -3$
$$\frac{-9}{-3} \; ? \; \frac{-3}{-3}$$

2. Replace each question mark with an appropriate inequality symbol:

(A) $\quad -5 < -2$
$$-5 + 6 \; ? \; -2 + 6$$

(B) $\quad 3 > -1$
$$(2)(3) \; ? \; (2)(-1)$$

(C) $12 > 4$
$$\frac{12}{-2} \; ? \; \frac{4}{-2}$$

(D) $\quad 3 > 2$
$$3 - 8 \; ? \; 2 - 8$$

3. Replace each question mark with an appropriate inequality symbol:

(A) $x \geq y$

$x + 3 \ ? \ y + 3$

(B) $x < y + 3$

$x - 3 \ ? \ y$

(C) $m > n$

$-3m \ ? \ -3n$

(D) $\dfrac{a}{3} \leq b$

$a \ ? \ 3b$

4. Replace each question mark with an appropriate inequality symbol:

(A) $x - 7 < y$

$x \ ? \ y + 7$

(B) $-x \geq 0$

$x \ ? \ 0$

(C) $\dfrac{x}{-2} < -3$

$x \ ? \ 6$

(D) $-3x > 9$

$-x \ ? \ -3$

In problems 5 through 32 solve and graph each inequality statement.

5. $2x - 3 > 5$

6. $3x + 7 < 13$

7. $6m + 2 \leq 4m + 6$

8. $7x - 8 < 4x + 7$

9. $4x + 8 \geq x - 1$

10. $9y + 3 < 4y - 7$

11. $2(x - 3) + 5 < 5 - x$

12. $3 - x \geq 5(3 - x)$

13. $-2x > 6$

14. $-5t < -10$

15. $\dfrac{x}{3} < -7$

16. $\dfrac{x}{-2} > 4$

17. $2x + 3 > 4x - 3$

18. $3 - x < 2x - 6$

19. $2(1 - x) \geq 5x$

20. $3 - (2 - x) > -9$

21. $\dfrac{p}{5} - 3 < \dfrac{3}{5} - p$

22. $q - \frac{1}{2} > \frac{8}{3}$

23. $\dfrac{x - 3}{2} - 1 > \dfrac{x}{4}$

24. $-2 - \dfrac{x}{4} < \dfrac{1 + x}{3}$

25. $2 < x + 3 \leq 5$

26. $-3 \leq x - 5 \leq 8$

27. $-4 \leq 2n \leq 3$

28. $4 < 6m < 12$

29. $2 < 3x - 7 < 14$

30. $-4 < 5x + 6 < 21$

31. $-1 \leq \frac{2}{3}m + 5 \leq 11$

32. $-4 \leq \frac{9}{5}C + 32 \leq 68$

33. If $x < 0$ and $y < 0$, then which of the following are true? (A) $x + y < 0$, (B) $xy < 0$, (C) $x/y < 0$.

34. If $x < 0$ and $y > 0$, then which of the following are true?   (A) $x + y > 0$, (B) $xy < 0$, (c) $x/y > 0$.

In the following problems set up appropriate inequalities and solve them using the techniques discussed in this section.

35. What numbers satisfy the condition, "Three less than twice the number is greater than or equal to -6"?

36. What numbers satisfy the condition, "If 15 is diminished by three times the number, the result is less than 6"?

37. If the perimeter of a rectangle with a length of 10 in. must be smaller than 30 in., how large may the width be?

38. If the area of a rectangle of length 10 in. must be greater than 65 sq. in., how large may the width be?

39. A doctor told a woman, "Even if you lost 30 lb you would still not weigh less than 125 lb." What can you say about the woman's weight?

40. If in driving the 420 miles between San Francisco and Los Angeles you know that your average speed is less than 50 mph, what can you say about the time it will take you to make the trip?

41. In a chemistry experiment the solution of hydrochloric acid is to be kept between 30 and 35°C. What would the range of temperature be in Fahrenheit degrees?   [$C = \frac{5}{9}(F - 32)$.]

42. A person's IQ is found by dividing his mental age, as indicated by standard tests, by his chronological age and then multiplying this ratio by 100. In terms of a formula,

$$IQ = \frac{MA \cdot 100}{CA}$$

If the IQ range of a group of 12-year-olds is $70 \leq IQ \leq 120$, what is the mental age range of this group?

43. Find the mistake: Assume that $a > b > 0$. Then

$$a > b$$
$$ab > b^2$$
$$ab - a^2 > b^2 - a^2$$
$$a(b - a) > (b + a)(b - a)$$
$$a > b + a$$
$$0 > b$$

But b was assumed to be positive!

See Sec. 42 for additional applications.

41 LINEAR INEQUALITIES IN TWO VARIABLES

We know how to graph first-degree equations such as

$$y = 2x + 3 \quad \text{or} \quad 2x - 3y = 5$$

but how do we graph first-degree inequalities such as

$$y \le 2x + 3 \quad \text{or} \quad 2x - 3y \le 5$$

In this section we will find that graphing first-degree inequalities in two variables is almost as easy as graphing first-degree equations in two variables. The following discussion leads to a simple solution to the problem.

An extended line in a Cartesian coordinate system divides the plane into two **half planes.** A **point** not on the line is said to be **above the line** if its ordinate (the second coordinate) is greater than the ordinate of a point on the line with the same abscissa. A **point** not on the line is said to be **below the line** if its ordinate is less than the ordinate of a point on the line with the same abscissa (see Fig. 1). A **set of points** is said to be **above or below the line** according to whether each point in the set is above or below the line.

EXAMPLE 5. Without graphing determine whether $P(-3, 2)$ and $Q(4, -3)$ are above or below the line $y = 2x - 3$.

SOLUTION: To find a point on the line with the same abscissa as P, substitute -3 into $y = 2x - 3$ for x and find y. Thus $y = 2(-3) - 3 = -9$. Hence, $(-3, -9)$ is a point on the line, and since $2 > -9$, P is above the line.

Similarly, $(4, 5)$ is a point on the line with the same abscissa as Q, and since $-3 < 5$, Q is below the line.

We are now in a position to compare the graphs of $y > 2x - 3$, $y = 2x - 3$, and $y < 2x - 3$. For each fixed x, say $x = x_0$, $y_0 = 2x_0 - 3$ is true if (x_0, y_0) is on the line $y = 2x - 3$; $y_0 > 2x_0 - 3$ is true if (x_0, y_0) is above the line; and $y_0 < 2x_0 - 3$ is true if (x_0, y_0) is below the line. (See Fig. 2.)

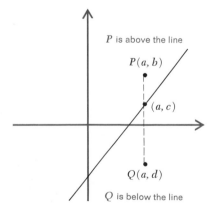

Figure 1

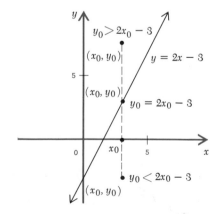

Figure 2

We conclude that the graph of $y > 2x - 3$ is the upper half plane determined by $y = 2x - 3$ and the graph of $y < 2x - 3$ is the lower half plane determined by $y = 2x - 3$.

In graphing $y \geq 2x - 3$ we show the line $y = 2x - 3$ as a solid line, indicating it is part of the graph; in graphing $y > 2x - 3$ we show the line $y = 2x - 3$ as a dotted line, indicating it is not part of the graph.

EXAMPLE 6

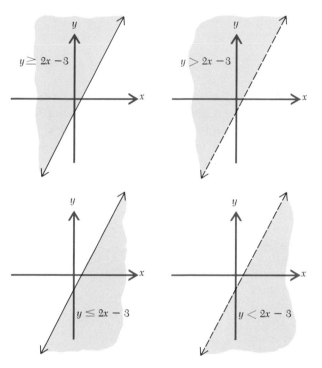

The preceding discussion leads to the following important theorem which we state without proof.

THEOREM 2   *The graph of a linear inequality $Ax + By < C$ or $Ax + By > C$, with $B \neq 0$, is either the upper half plane or the lower half plane (but not both) determined by the line $Ax + By = C$.*

To graph a linear inequality in two variables quickly, one generally proceeds as follows: graph the equation obtained by replacing the inequality symbol in the inequality with an equality symbol.   Then choose any point in the plane not on this line—the origin is usually the simplest choice if it is not on the line.   If the coordinates of the point satisfy the inequality, then the half-plane that includes that point is the graph of the inequality; if not, the other half plane is the graph. (Of course, if equality is included in the inequality statement, the line is included as a solid line; if equality is not included, the line is represented as a dotted line.)

EXAMPLE 7. Graph $3x - 4y \leq 12$.

SOLUTION: First graph the line $3x - 4y = 12$. Pick a convenient point above or below the line. The origin is the easiest choice in this case. We see that $3 \cdot 0 - 4 \cdot 0 \leq 12$ is true; hence, the graph of the inequality is the upper half plane.

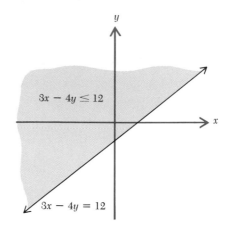

This section will be concluded by a demonstration of how graphs of linear inequalities in two variables can be used to solve certain types of practical problems. Several additional applications will be considered in the problem set for this section as well as in the next section on Additional Applications.

EXAMPLE 8. On flights within the United States, the airlines allow a passenger to carry, without extra charge, a small handbag, measuring up to 45 in. in total dimensions (length + width + height), that can be placed beneath the seat. If the space under the seat is 24 by 24 by 10 in. and one has a piece of baggage x by y by 10 in., write a system of inequalities that shows the restrictions on the x and y dimensions. Graph the system, indicating the region of permissible values of x and y.

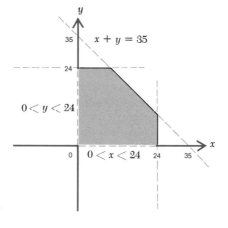

SOLUTION: The x and y dimensions must satisfy the following system of inequalities:

$$x + y + 10 \leq 45$$
$$0 < x \leq 24$$
$$0 < y \leq 24$$

Graph each of the inequalities in the same coordinate system; the set of points common to all three graphs is the graph of the system. In set notation

$$\{(x, y) \mid x + y \leq 35, 0 < x \leq 24, \text{ and } 0 < y \leq 24\}$$

EXERCISE 48

1. (A) Graph the equation $y = 3x + 4$.
   (B) Plot each of the following points and indicate whether each is above or below the line:

$$A(1, 8) \qquad B(-2, -3) \qquad C(8, 1) \qquad D(-8, -3)$$

2. (A) Graph the equation $y = -2x - 2$.
   (B) Plot each of the following points and indicate whether each is above or below the line:

$$A(-1, 1) \qquad B(1, -5) \qquad C(-6, 4) \qquad D(5, -9)$$

3. Without graphing determine whether $P(3, 2)$ and $Q(-8, -2)$ are above or below the line $y = \frac{1}{2}x + 1$.

4. Without graphing determine whether $P(4, -8)$ and $Q(-2, 1)$ are above or below the line $y = -x - 2$.

Graph the linear inequalities in two variables in problems 5 through 20.

5. $y \geq x + 1$ 6. $y \geq -x - 1$

7. $y < -x + 1$ 8. $y < \dfrac{x}{3} + 2$

9. $y \leq \frac{2}{3}x - 3$ 10. $y \leq -\frac{3}{2}x - 2$

11. $y > -2$ 12. $x < 4$

13. $x \leq 0$ 14. $y \geq 0$

15. $x + y \leq 8$ 16. $x - y \leq 5$

17. $2x - 3y > 6$ 18. $3x + 4y > 12$

19. $3x + 2y \leq 18$ 20. $2x - 3y \geq 8$

Graph each of the systems of inequalities in problems 21 through 30.

21. $x + y \leq 6$ 22. $2x + 3y \leq 12$
   $\quad x > 0$ $\quad x \geq 0$
   $\quad y > 0$ $\quad y \geq 0$

23. $2 \leq x \leq 5$ 24. $4 \leq x \leq 6$
   $\quad 3 \leq y \leq 5$ $\quad 1 \leq y \leq 8$

25. $-3 \leq x < 1$ 26. $-5 < x \leq -1$
   $\quad -1 \leq y < 4$ $\quad -4 \leq y < 6$

27. $2x + y \leq 8$
    $0 < x \leq 3$
    $0 < y \leq 5$

28. $x + 3y \leq 12$
    $0 < x \leq 8$
    $0 < y \leq 3$

29. $2x + y \leq 8$
    $x + 3y \leq 12$
    $x > 0$
    $y > 0$

30. $x + 2y \leq 10$
    $3x + y \leq 15$
    $x \geq 0$
    $y \geq 0$

31. Graph: $\{(x, y) \mid 4x + 3y \leq 24, 0 < x \leq 4, \text{ and } 0 < y \leq 5\}$.

32. Graph: $\{(x, y) \mid y \leq x + 6, 0 \leq x \leq 7, \text{ and } y \geq 0\}$.

33. If an arrow is shot straight upward with an initial velocity of 256 fps, its velocity at time t is given by $v = 256 - 32t$ with $0 \leq t \leq 8$, if air resistance is neglected. If air resistance is not neglected, then $v \leq 256 - 32t$ with $0 \leq t \leq 8$. Graph the set

$$\{(t, v) \mid v \leq 256 - 32t, v \geq 0, \text{ and } 0 \leq t \leq 8\}$$

and interpret the graph.

34. When flying in the United States, the traveler is permitted two pieces of luggage (in addition to what can be placed under the seat), one measuring up to 62 in. and the other up to 55 in. in total dimensions (length + width + height). If he would like the height of the larger piece of luggage to be 10 in. and the length to be greater than the width but no more than 10 in. more than the width, write a system of inequalities that indicates the restrictions on the x and y dimensions (see Fig. 3). Graph the system, indicating the region of permissible values for x and y.

35. Repeat the preceding problem for the smaller piece of luggage with a height of 8 in. (see Fig. 3).

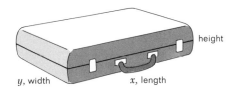

height

y, width x, length

Figure 3

42   ADDITIONAL APPLICATIONS

This section contains a variety of applications from several different fields.   The applications are divided into two parts: those involving first-degree inequalities in one variable and those involving first-degree inequalities in two variables.

Even though other methods can be used to solve some of the problems, the inequality methods described in the preceding sections should be used.

EXERCISE 49

Inequality methods are to be used to solve the problems in this exercise.

FIRST-DEGREE INEQUALITIES IN ONE VARIABLE

1. How long would you have to leave $100 invested at 6 percent simple interest for it to amount to more than $133? $(A = P + Prt.)$

2. A family has between $12,000 and $18,000 to spend on a cabin.   If a contractor estimates the building costs to be around $12 per sq ft, then the number of square feet designed into the cabin should lie in what range?

3. To be eligible for a certain university, a student must have an average grade of not below 70 on three entrance examinations.   If a student received a 55 and a 73 on the first two examinations, what must he receive on the third examination to be eligible to enter the university?

4. At the same university (referred to in the preceding problem), if a student attains an average grade above 90 on the three examinations, he will be eligible for certain honors courses.   If no score above 100 is possible on any one of the tests, is it possible for the student in the preceding problem to receive a high enough score on the third test to make him eligible for an honors course?

5. In an 110-volt electrical house circuit a 30-ampere fuse is used.   In order to keep the fuse from "blowing," the total wattages in all of the appliances on that circuit must be kept below what figure? $(W = EI$, where $W =$ power in watts, $E =$ pressure in volts, and $I =$ current in amperes.)   HINT: $I = W/E$ and $I \leq 30$.

6. If the power demands in an 110-volt electrical circuit in a home range between 220 and 2,750 watts, what is the range of current flowing through the circuit? $(W = EI$, where $W =$ power in watts, $E =$ pressure in volts, and $I =$ current in amperes.)

7. It is customary in supersonic studies to specify the velocity of an object relative to the velocity of sound.   The ratio between these two velocities is called the Mach number, and it is given by the formula

$$M\text{(Mach number)} = \frac{V\text{(speed of object)}}{S\text{(speed of sound)}}$$

If a supersonic transport is designed to operate between Mach 1.7 and 2.4, what is the speed range of the transport in miles per hour?   (Assume that the speed of sound is 740 mph.)

8. It is known that the temperature has a small but measurable effect upon the velocity of sound.   For each degree Centigrade rise in temperature in the air the velocity of sound increases about 2 fps.   If at 0°C sound travels at 1,087 fps, its speed at other temperatures is given by

$$V = 1,087 + 2T$$

(A) What temperature range will correspond to a velocity range of $1,097 \leq V \leq 1,137$?

(B) What is the corresponding temperature range in Fahrenheit degrees $[C = \frac{5}{9}(F - 32)]$?

9. If in a given storm the time it takes thunder to be heard after lightning strikes varies between 5 and 10 sec, how does the distance (in miles) to the lightning vary?   ($d = 1,088t$ and 1 mile $= 5,280$ ft.)

10. For a business to make a profit it is clear that revenue R must be greater than costs C; in short, a profit will result only if $R > C$.   If a company manufactures records and its cost equation for a week is $C = 300 + 1.5x$, where x is the number of records manufactured in a week, and its revenue equation is $R = 2x$, where x is the number of records sold in a week, how many records must be sold for the company to realize a profit?

FIRST-DEGREE INEQUALITIES IN TWO VARIABLES

11. A foreign car dealer has display and storage facilities for a maximum of 30 cars.   He must decide on how many of each of two models to stock.   His company produces a standard model and a deluxe model.   He knows from past experience that he cannot sell more than 15 deluxe models and 25 standard models.   If s is the number of standard models and d is the number of deluxe models the dealer is willing to order, write a system of inequalities that indicate the restrictions on s and d.   Graph this system, showing the permissible values for s and d.

12. A manufacturer of surfboards makes a standard model and a competition model.   The pertinent manufacturing data are summarized in the table.

	Standard model (man-hours per board)	Competition model (man-hours per board)	Maximum man-hours available per week
Fabricating	6	8	120
Finishing	1	3	30

If x is the number of standard models and y is the number of competition models produced per week, write a system of inequalities that indicate the restrictions on x and y. Graph this system, showing the region of permissible values for x and y.

13. A small manufacturer makes two types of radios, a transistor model and a tube model. The relevant manufacturing data are shown in the table.

	Transistor (man-hours per radio)	Tube (man-hours per radio)	Maximum man-hours available per day
Fabricating	4	1	16
Assembling	1	3	15

If x is the number of transistor radios and y is the number of tube radios produced per week, write a system of inequalities that indicate the restrictions on x and y. Graph this system, showing the region of permissible values for x and y.

14. Post-office regulations state that packages cannot be mailed if they are oversized; the length plus the girth of the package cannot be over 72 in. Stated as an inequality, $l + 2w + 2h \leq 72$, where the length l is the longest dimension. If a person wants to mail several toys, the longest of which is 2 ft, in one box, write a system of inequalities that indicate the restrictions on w and h. Graph this system, showing the region of permissible values for w and h.

15. If in the preceding problem we add the additional restrictions that the height is to be greater than the width, but no more that 6 in. greater, modify the permissible region found in that problem so that these new constraints are accounted for.

43   CHAPTER SUMMARY

GENERAL

This chapter was included to provide you with a brief introduction to inequality methods. Even though this subject is extensive and involved, you now have enough background to enable you to solve a fairly substantial number of significant problems.

We have restricted our attention to linear inequalities in one and two variables; in future courses nonlinear inequalities in one or more variables will be considered. For example, $2x^2 - 3 \leq 5 - x$ is a nonlinear inequality in one variable.

SPECIFIC

Describe, define, or give examples of each of the following:

Linear inequality in one variable
Solution set
Equivalent inequalities
Operations on inequalities that produce equivalent inequalities
Operations on inequalities that do not affect the inequality sign
Operations on inequalities that reverse the inequality sign
Graphs of linear inequalities in one variable
Graphs of linear inequalities in two variables
Graphs of systems of linear inequalities in two variables

EXERCISE 50   CHAPTER REVIEW

1. (A) What is meant by equivalent inequalities?
(B) Which of the following inequalities are equivalent to each other?

$$2(x - 3) + 5 \leq x - 5$$
$$2x - 6 \leq x - 10$$
$$2x \leq x - 4$$
$$x \leq -2$$

Solve and graph each of the inequalities in problems 2 through 11.

2. $-x < 0$

3. $-x < -3$

4. $3x - 7 < 5$

5. $2x - 8 \geq 5x + 1$

6. $\frac{2}{3}x > -8$

7. $-\frac{9}{5}x \leq 18$

8. $\frac{5}{9}(F - 32) \leq 20$

9. $1 - \frac{2x - 1}{2} < \frac{x}{3}$

10. $-5 < 2x - 3 \leq 9$

11. $-40 \leq \frac{9}{5}C + 32 \leq 59$

12. Which of the following are true?
(A) If $x < y$ and $a > 0$, then $x + a < y + a$.
(B) If $x < y$ and $a < 0$, then $x + a < y + a$.
(C) If $x < y$ and $a > 0$, then $xa < ya$.
(D) If $x < y$ and $a < 0$, then $xa < ya$.

13. Without graphing determine whether $Q(-1, 0)$ is above or below the line $2x + y = -4$.

Graph the linear inequalities in two variables in problems 14 through 19.

14. $y \leq 2x + 3$

15. $y > \dfrac{x}{2} - 4$

16. $x + 2y \leq 4$

17. $x - 3y > -3$

18. $x > -2$

19. $y \geq 0$

Graph each of the systems of inequalities in problems 20 and 21.

20. $5x + 3y \leq 30$
    $1 < x \leq 5$
    $1 \leq y \leq 7$

21. $5x + 10y \leq 50$
    $4x + \quad y \leq 20$
    $x \geq 0$
    $y \geq 0$

22. Graph: $\{(x, y) \mid 3x + 5y \leq 60, 0 \leq x \leq 15, \text{ and } y > 0\}$.

23. What numbers satisfy the condition, "If 5 is reduced by the number, the result is greater than or equal to the number"?

24. To develop a certain roll of photographic film, the temperature of the solution must be kept between 20 and 25°C (that is, $20 \leq C \leq 25$). Find the temperature range in Fahrenheit degrees $[C = \frac{5}{9}(F - 32)]$.

See Sec. 42 for additional applications.

CHAPTER SIX polynomials

44   POLYNOMIALS IN ONE OR MORE VARIABLES

Practically all of the algebraic expressions with which we have dealt in this course so far are called polynomials.   A **polynomial** (over the real numbers) is any algebraic expression that can be built up using only the operations of addition, subtraction, and multiplication on variables and real-number constants.   We may have polynomials in one variable, two variables, and so on; the constants may be any real number, rational or irrational.

EXAMPLE 1

(A) Algebraic expressions that are polynomials:

$$2x - 1 \qquad 2x^2 - 5x + 8$$

$$a^2 - 2ab + b^2 \qquad 3t^3 + 2t^2 - 5t + 7$$

$$2x^3 - 3x^2y + xy^2 - 4y^3 \qquad \frac{x^7}{3} - \sqrt{3}x^2y^3 + 3.5y^5$$

(B) Algebraic expressions that are not polynomials:

$$3\sqrt{x} - 4y^3 \qquad \frac{3x - y}{x + y}$$

$$\frac{1}{x} - y^2 \qquad x^3 - \frac{3\sqrt{x}}{y^2} + 3y^4$$

The polynomial form, particularly in one and two variables, is encountered with great frequency at all levels in mathematics and science. As a consequence, it is a form that receives a great deal of attention in beginning and intermediate algebra.

It is convenient to identify certain types of polynomials for more efficient study. The concept of degree is used for this purpose. The **degree of a term** in a polynomial is the power of the variable present in the term; if more than one variable is present as a factor, then the sum of the powers of the variables in the term is the degree of the term.

EXAMPLE 2.

▶ $3x^5$ is of degree 5.

▶ $5x^2y^3$ is of degree 5.

▶ The degree of the third term in $4x^7 - 3x^5 + 2x^3 - 1$ is 3; the degree of the first term is 7, and the degree of the second term is 5.

▶ The degree of each of the first three terms in $x^2 - 2xy + y^2 + 2x - 3y + 2$ is 2; the fourth and fifth terms each have degree 1.

The degree of a polynomial is the degree of the term with the highest degree in the polynomial.

EXAMPLE 3. a, b, c, d, e, and f are constants.
First-degree polynomials in one variable:

$$3x - 8 \qquad \sqrt{2}t + 7 \qquad \frac{y}{3} - \frac{1}{2} \qquad ax + b$$

First-degree polynomials in two variables:

$$2x - 3y + 7 \qquad \frac{m}{2} - 8n + \frac{1}{4} \qquad ax + by + c$$

Second-degree polynomials in one variable:

$$3x^2 - 2x + 5 \qquad y^2 - \tfrac{1}{4} \qquad y^2 - 3.1y \qquad ax^2 + bx + c$$

Second-degree polynomials in two variables:

$$2x^2 - 3xy + y^2 \qquad m^2 - n^2 \qquad u^2 - 3uv + v^2 - 3u + v - 9$$

$$ax^2 + bxy + cy^2 + dx + ey + f$$

Third-degree polynomials in one variable:

$$3x^3 - x^2 - 5x + 1 \qquad t^3 - 2t - 3 \qquad ax^3 + bx^2 + cx + d$$

NOTE: A constant is often defined as a polynomial of *degree zero* for reasons that will become clear later on.

The Table of Contents should make more sense to you now. Turn to it, and see how polynomial classifications are used for chapter and section headings.

We have spent most of our time studying first-degree polynomial expressions, equations, and inequalities in one and two variables. In this and the next chapter we will study basic operations on general polynomials.

45   ADDITION, SUBTRACTION, AND MULTIPLICATION

In the preceding chapters you worked many problems involving addition, subtraction, and multiplication of polynomials. Considerable use was made of the associative and commutative properties of real numbers relative to addition and multiplication, as well as the distributive property. These procedures will be reviewed and extended in this section.

ADDITION AND SUBTRACTION

In problems involving the addition or subtraction of polynomials, such as solving equations or simplifying algebraic expressions, it is often convenient to work horizontally rather than vertically. Actually, you should be able to work either way, horizontally or vertically, letting the situation dictate the choice.

EXAMPLE 4. Simplify $(2x^2 - 3x + 1) + (x^2 - 2) - (2x - 5)$.

SOLUTION

$$
\begin{aligned}
(2x^2 - 3x + 1) + (x^2 - 2) - (2x - 5) &= 2x^2 - 3x + 1 + x^2 - 2 - 2x + 5 \\
&= 3x^2 - 5x + 4
\end{aligned}
$$

EXAMPLE 5. Subtract $(4x^2 - 3x + 5)$ from $(x^2 - 8)$.

SOLUTION

$$
\begin{array}{ll}
(x^2 - 8) - (4x^2 - 3x + 5) & \qquad \text{or} \qquad \quad x^2 \qquad\quad -8 \\
= x^2 - 8 - 4x^2 + 3x - 5 & \qquad\qquad\qquad \underline{4x^2 - 3x + 5} \\
= -3x^2 + 3x - 13 & \qquad\qquad\qquad -3x^2 + 3x - 13
\end{array}
$$

EXAMPLE 6. Add $x^4 - 3x^3 + x^2$, $-x^3 - 2x^2 + 3x$, and $3x^2 - 4x - 5$.

SOLUTION

$$x^4 - 3x^3 + x^2$$
$$ - x^3 - 2x^2 + 3x$$
$$ 3x^2 - 4x - 5$$
$$\overline{x^4 - 4x^3 + 2x^2 - x - 5}$$

like terms are lined up vertically and coefficients added

MULTIPLICATION

The distributive property is the important principle behind multiplying polynomials. It leads directly to the following mechanical procedure: *To multiply
two polynomials, multiply each term of one by each term of the other, and add
like terms.* The commutative and associative properties are, of course, also used
in the process of simplifying the result.

EXAMPLE 7. Multiply $(x - 3)(x^2 - 2x + 3)$.

SOLUTION

$(x - 3)(x^2 - 2x + 3)$ 　　　　　　　or　　　$x^2 - 2x + 3$
$= x(x^2 - 2x + 3) - 3(x^2 - 2x + 3)$ 　　　　　$\underline{x - 3}$
$= x^3 - 2x^2 + 3x - 3x^2 + 6x - 9$ 　　　　　$x^3 - 2x^2 + 3x$
$= x^3 - 5x^2 + 9x - 9$ 　　　　　　　　　$\underline{ - 3x^2 + 6x - 9}$
　　　　　　　　　　　　　　　　　　　$x^3 - 5x^2 + 9x - 9$

EXAMPLE 8. Find $(x - 2y)^3$.

SOLUTION: Multiply $(x - 2y)(x - 2y)$, and then multiply the result by $(x - 2y)$:

$x - 2y$ 　　　　　　　　　　　$x^2 - 4xy + 4y^2$
$\underline{x - 2y}$ 　　　　　　　　　　　$\underline{x - 2y}$
$x^2 - 2xy$ 　　　　　　　　　$x^3 - 4x^2y + 4xy^2$
$\underline{ - 2xy + 4y^2}$ 　　　　　　$\underline{ - 2x^2y + 8xy^2 - 8y^3}$
$x^2 - 4xy + 4y^2$ 　　　　　　$x^3 - 6x^2y + 12xy^2 - 8y^3$

EXERCISE 51

1. Which of the following algebraic expressions are polynomials?

(A) $3x^2 - 2x - 9$ (B) $x - \frac{1}{3}$

(C) $x^2 - 3\sqrt{xy} + 2y^3$ (D) $x^3 - 2xy^2 + y^3$

(E) $x^2 + \dfrac{x}{y}$ (F) $t^4 + 1$

(G) $2x - 3y + 5$ (H) $m^2 - 2mn + n^2$

2. Which of the following algebraic expressions are polynomials?

(A) $xy - 2x + 3y - 1$ (B) $\sqrt{x} + 5\sqrt{x} - 7$

(C) $3x^2 - 2x - 4$ (D) $2t^5 - \sqrt{2}t^3 + 5t - 12$

(E) $5x^2 - 3xy + 7y^2$ (F) $\dfrac{x^2 - 3x + 7}{2x^2 - 5}$

(G) $\sqrt{2x} - 3$ (H) $2x + y - \frac{1}{2}$

3. In problem 1
   (A) Identify all of the first-degree polynomials in one variable.
   (B) Identify all of the first-degree polynomials in two variables.
   (C) Identify all of the second-degree polynomials in one variable.
   (D) Identify all of the second-degree polynomials in two variables.

4. Repeat the preceding problem for problem 2.

Simplify:

5. $(2x - 1) + (3x - 5) - (x - 3) - (2x + 1)$
6. $(7t + 5) - (3t - 1) + (t + 5) - (t - 3)$
7. $[(x - y) + (x - 3y)] - [(2x - y) + (3x + y)]$
8. $[(2x - 4y) - (x - 4y)] - [(3x + y) - (3x - y)]$

Subtract:

9. $(x^2 - 3x - 5)$ from $(2x^2 - 6x - 5)$
10. $(2y^2 - 6y + 1)$ from $(y^2 - 6y - 1)$
11. $(x^2 - 3x)$ from $(2x^2 - 7x - 5)$
12. $(2m + 8)$ from $(m^2 - m - 7)$

13. Subtract the sum of the second two polynomials from the sum of the first two: $(2x^2 - 4xy + y^2)$, $(3xy - y^2)$, $(x^2 - 2xy - y^2)$, and $(-x^2 + 3xy - 2y^2)$.

14. Subtract the sum of the first two polynomials from the sum of the second two: $(3m^3 - 2m + 5)$, $(4m^2 - m)$, $(3m^2 - 3m - 2)$, and $(m^3 + m^2 + 2)$.

Add by arranging polynomials vertically:

15. $(2x - 3y + 5)$, $(x - 7y - 3)$, $(-x - 3)$, $(y + 8)$, and $(2x - 3y)$.

16. $(x^2 - 3x + 5)$, $(3x^2 + x - 3)$, $(-x^2 + 5)$, $(2x^2 - 3x)$, and $(4x - 8)$.

17. $(2x^4 - 6x^3 + 10x^2)$, $(x^3 - 3x^2 + 5x)$, and $(-2x^2 + 6x - 10)$.

18. $(6m^4 + 6m^3 - 3m^2)$, $(-4m^3 - 4m^2 + 2m)$, and $(2m^2 + 2m - 1)$.

Multiply, using a vertical arrangement:

19. $(x^2 - 3x + 5)$ by $(2x - 1)$

20. $(2y^2 + 5y - 3)$ by $(3y + 2)$

21. $(x^2 - 3xy + y^2)$ by $(x - 3y)$

22. $(m^2 - 4mn - n^2)$ by $(m + 2n)$

23. $(a^2 - ab + b^2)$ by $(a + b)$

24. $(a^2 + ab + b^2)$ by $(a - b)$

25. $(x + 2y)^3$

26. $(2m - n)^3$

27. $(x^2 - 3x + 5)$ by $(2x^2 + x - 2)$

28. $(2m^2 + 2m - 1)$ by $(3m^2 - 2m + 1)$

29. $(2x^2 - 3xy + y^2)$ by $(x^2 + 2xy - y^2)$

30. $(a^2 - 2ab + b^2)$ by $(a^2 + 2ab + b^2)$

46   FACTORING AND SPECIAL PRODUCTS

INTRODUCTION

You have now had quite a bit of experience with multiplying polynomials. In this section we will consider the reverse problem, that of expressing a polynomial as the product of two or more polynomials. This operation (called factoring) has many uses. In this course its main use will be found in working with algebraic fractions and solving second-degree equations.

For example, in the next chapter we will be working with expressions of the type

$$\frac{6x^4 - 30x^3 + 36x^2}{6x^3 - 18x^2}$$

It certainly isn't obvious that this expression and $x - 2$ name the same number for all replacements of x by real constants, except for $x = 0$ and $x = 3$. But from the distributive property and other properties of real numbers

$$\frac{6x^4 - 30x^3 + 36x^2}{6x^3 - 18x^2} = \frac{6x^2(x^2 - 5x + 6)}{6x^2(x - 3)} = \frac{6x^2}{6x^2} \cdot \frac{x^2 - 5x + 6}{x - 3} = \frac{x^2 - 5x + 6}{x - 3}$$

$$x \neq 0$$

If, in addition, we know that $x^2 - 5x + 6 = (x - 3)(x - 2)$, then

$$\frac{x^2 - 5x + 6}{x - 3} = \frac{(x - 3)(x - 2)}{x - 3} = \frac{x - 3}{x - 3} \cdot \frac{x - 2}{1} = x - 2 \qquad x \neq 3$$

and we conclude that

$$\frac{6x^4 - 30x^3 + 36x^2}{6x^3 - 18x^2} = x - 2 \qquad \text{for } x \neq 0 \text{ and } x \neq 3$$

Thus, factoring can be used to simplify complicated algebraic expressions.

In Chap. 9 we will take up the general problem of solving equations of the type $x^2 - 5x + 6 = 0$ (that is, second-degree polynomial equations in one variable). The equation-solving procedures that have been developed so far are not quite up to this type of equation (try them!). However, if we know that $x^2 - 5x + 6 = (x - 2)(x - 3)$, then we can write

$$(x - 2)(x - 3) = 0$$

and the solutions to the equation, $x = 2$ and $x = 3$, are almost obvious. Hence, factoring can be used to solve higher degree equations.

Now to return to the problem of expressing polynomials in factored forms. Recall that the distributive law may be written $ab + ac = a(b + c)$; the right side is said to be a factored form of the left side. Using the distributive law, we may write $6x^3 - 18x^2 = 3x(2x^2 - 6x)$ or $6x^3 - 18x^2 = -2x(-3x^2 + 9x)$ or $6x^3 - 18x^2 = 6x^2(x - 3)$ or $6x^3 - 18x^2 = 6x^3(1 - 3/x)$; there are an unlimited number of possibilities! Before we study methods of factoring, we must state more precisely what it is that we mean by factoring.

As with factoring integers in terms of prime factors, we wish to factor polynomials in a unique way except for the order of factors and signs. In this course we will limit our investigation to polynomials with integers as coefficients.

DEFINITION 1 *A polynomial with integral coefficients is written in a **completely factored form** if*

(A) *All factors are constants or are polynomials with integral coefficients.*
(B) *No polynomial factors, other than single term polynomials, have other polynominal factors with integral coefficients.*

Thus, out of all of the factorings we wrote for $6x^3 - 18x^2$, only $6x^2(x - 3)$ would qualify as a completely factored form under the stated conditions of the definition.

MONOMIAL FACTORS

In addition to degree classification, polynomials are often named for the number of terms they contain. A polynomial of one term is called a **monomial,** of two terms a **binomial,** and of three terms a **trinomial.** This type of classification is usually not continued beyond three terms (nor is it restricted to polynomial forms).

We will consider the easiest type of factoring problem first, that of "factoring out" common monomial factors. You have already had experience with this type of factoring in a number of places in the preceding chapters. A few examples should serve to refresh your memory.

EXAMPLE 9:   FACTORING OUT COMMON MONOMIAL FACTORS.

▶ $8x^3 - 6x^2 = 2x^2(4x - 3)$

▶ $x^2y - xy^2 = xy(x - y)$

▶ $-6a^2 - 12b^2 = -6(a^2 + 2b^2)$

▶ $-3x^2 + 9x - 12 = -3(x^2 - 3x + 4)$

▶ $2x^3y - 8x^2y^2 - 6xy^3 = 2xy(x^2 - 4xy - 3y^2)$

How can you check each of the above?

EXERCISE 52

Multiply:

1. $3x(x - 5)$
2. $4t(3t - 8)$
3. $-5x(x^2 - 3x + 2)$
4. $-4y(2y^2 + y - 3)$
5. $2xy(x^2 - 3xy - 2y^2)$
6. $-3xy(2x^2 - y^2)$
7. $-2m^2n^2(8m^3 - 3mn + 4n^3)$
8. $3a^2b(2ab^2 + b - 1)$

Replace each question mark with an appropriate polynomial:

9. $9x^2 - 6x = 3x(\ ?\ )$
10. $2y^3 + 6y^2 - 4y = 2y(\ ?\ )$
11. $3m^2n - 6mn^2 = 3mn(\ ?\ )$
12. $12ab^3 - 24b^3 = 12b^3(\ ?\ )$
13. $-2x^3y^2 + 4x^2y^3 = -2x^2y^2(\ ?\ )$
14. $-ab^2 + 3a^2b = -ab(\ ?\ )$

Factor out all common monomial factors in problems 15 *through* 26.

15. $4ac - 6bc$

16. $9bx + 12by$

17. $6x^3 - 4x^2 + 2x$

18. $3y - 6y^2 - 12y^3$

19. $-2xy + 6y$

20. $-3st - s$

21. $10x^3y - 5x^2y^2 - 15xy^3$

22. $12m^2n + 4mn^2 - 8n^3$

23. $-6x^3y - 4xy^3$

24. $-9a^5b^2 + 15a^2b^5$

25. $-8x^5 - 10x^4 - 6x^3$

26. $-27y^4 - 9y^5 - 18y^7$

27. $12t^2 - 32t$ and $4t(3t - 8)$ name the same number for (*all, two, no*) replacements of t by real numbers.

28. The solution set for $3x^2 - 15x = 3x(x - 5)$ is the set containing (*none, one, all*) of the real numbers.

29. Describe the elements in the set

$$A = \{x \mid -3x^3 - 6x = -3x(x^2 + 2), x \text{ a real number}\}$$

30. Describe the elements in the set

$$B = \{x \mid -2x^2 + 2x = -2x(x - 1), x \text{ a real number}\}$$

MULTIPLYING FACTORS OF THE FORM $(ax + b)(cx + d)$

Before proceeding with more complicated factoring problems it is necessary to first concentrate on special products involving first-degree polynomial factors in one and two variables. It is essential that you learn how to multiply these forms mentally; that is, you should be able to multiply factors such as $(2x - 3)(3x + 5)$ or $(2m - n)(3m + 5n)$ in your head. Actually it isn't difficult, and after a little practice you will be able to accomplish the task quickly and efficiently.

First, consider the following example:

EXAMPLE 10

▶ $(2x - 1)(3y + 2) = 6xy + 4x - 3y - 2$

▶ $(2x - 1)(3x + 2) = 6x^2 + 4x - 3x - 2 = 6x^2 + x - 2$

▶ $(2a - b)(c + 3d) = 2ac + 6ad - bc - 3bd$

▶ $(2a - b)(a + 3b) = 2a^2 + 6ab - ab - 3b^2 = 2a^2 + 5ab - 3b^2$

We note two things in example 10: (1) Each product is a second-degree polynomial. (This is a general property of polynomials; that is, *the product of any two first-degree polynomials is a second-degree polynomial*.) (2) The second and fourth products (involving linear factors with the same variables) have like terms that combine into one term.

In the rest of this section we will restrict our attention to the process of mentally multiplying factors of the type $(ax + b)(cx + d)$ or $(ax + by)(cx + dy)$. The following examples illustrate a systematic approach to the problem.

EXAMPLE 11

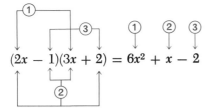

$$(2x - 1)(3x + 2) = 6x^2 + x - 2$$

The like terms are picked up in step 2 and are combined in your head.

EXAMPLE 12

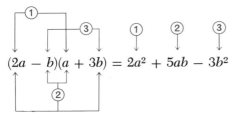

$$(2a - b)(a + 3b) = 2a^2 + 5ab - 3b^2$$

EXAMPLE 13

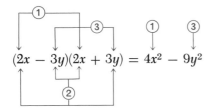

$$(2x - 3y)(2x + 3y) = 4x^2 - 9y^2$$

Notice that the middle term dropped out since its coefficient is zero.

In the next section we will consider the reverse problem: given a second-degree polynomial, such as $2x^2 - 5x - 3$ or $3m^2 - 7mn + 2n^2$, find first-degree factors with integral coefficients that will produce these second-degree polynomials as products.   To be able to factor second-degree polynomial forms with any degree of efficiency, it is important that you know how to mentally multiply first-degree factors of the types illustrated in this section quickly and accurately.

EXERCISE 53

Multiply mentally.

1. $(x + 3)(x + 2)$
2. $(y + 3)(y + 5)$
3. $(m - 2)(m - 3)$
4. $(x - 5)(x - 4)$
5. $(t - 6)(t + 4)$
6. $(s + 7)(s - 2)$
7. $(a + 4)(a - 8)$
8. $(m - 12)(m + 5)$
9. $(t - 3)(t + 3)$
10. $(u + 4)(u - 4)$
11. $(b + 10)(b - 8)$
12. $(a - 7)(a + 11)$
13. $(y + 7)(y + 9)$
14. $(c - 6)(c - 8)$
15. $(n - 3)(n - 1)$
16. $(u + 5)(u + 4)$
17. $(x - 7)(x + 7)$
18. $(m + 9)(m - 9)$
19. $(y + 10)(y - 1)$
20. $(c - 12)(c + 2)$
21. $(2x + 3)(x + 3)$
22. $(x + 2)(3x + 1)$
23. $(x - 4)(2x - 1)$
24. $(4t - 3)(t - 2)$
25. $(2t - 3)(t + 4)$
26. $(y - 3)(3y + 7)$
27. $(a - 6)(5a + 6)$
28. $(5s - 1)(s + 7)$
29. $(2x - 1)(3x - 2)$
30. $(4n - 7)(3n + 2)$
31. $(2m - 7)(2m + 7)$
32. $(3y + 2)(3y - 2)$
33. $(2x - 3)^2$
34. $(3y + 1)^2$
35. $(4x + 1)^2$
36. $(2m - 3)^2$
37. $(x + y)(x + 3y)$
38. $(m + 2n)(m + n)$
39. $(m - n)(m + n)$
40. $(a + b)(a - b)$
41. $(2x - 3y)(3x - 2y)$
42. $(2s - 3t)(3s - t)$
43. $(4m - n)(3m + 5n)$
44. $(4u - v)(2u + 3v)$
45. $(a - b)^2$
46. $(m + n)^2$
47. $(2x - 3y)^2$
48. $(4a + 3b)^2$

FACTORING SECOND-DEGREE POLYNOMIALS OF THE FORM $ax^2 + bx + c$ AND $ax^2 + bxy + cy^2$

It should now be very easy for you to obtain the products

$$(x - 3)(x + 2) = x^2 - x - 6$$

or

$$(x - 3y)(x + 2y) = x^2 - xy - 6y^2$$

but can you reverse the process?   Can you, for example, find integers a, b, c, and d so that

$$2x^2 - 5x - 3 = (ax + b)(cx + d)$$

Representing a second-degree polynomial with integral coefficients as the product of two first-degree polynomials with integral coefficients is not as easy as multiplying first-degree polynomials.   There is, however, a systematic approach to the problem that will enable you to find first-degree factors of special second-degree polynomials if they exist.

More precisely stated, we have this problem: given integers a, b, and c find integers d, e, f, and g if they exist, so that

$$ax^2 + bx + c = (dx + e)(fx + g)$$

or

$$ax^2 + bxy + cy^2 = (dx + ey)(fx + gy)$$

If we are given a second-degree polynomial to factor, say $2x^2 + 3x - 2$ or $3x^2 - 2x + 4$, it would be of great help to know ahead of time if first-degree factors with integral coefficients exist for either, thus saving us time and energy in looking for the factors if they do not exist.   Actually, it turns out that if we pick integral coefficients at random for $ax^2 + bx + c$, the chances of the resulting polynomial not being factorable are greater than the chances of it being factorable.   The following important theorem (which is partly proved in Appendix C) gives us an easy method of determining whether a given second-degree polynomial can be factored into linear factors with integral coefficients.

THEOREM 1   *Given integers a, b, and c, then there exist integers d, e, f, and g such that*

$$ax^2 + bx + c = (dx + e)(fx + g)$$

if and only if ac can be written as the product of two integers whose sum is b (that is, if and only if there exist integers m and n such that $ac = mn$ and $m + n = b$).

We are now ready to illustrate a systematic approach to factoring.   The letters used in examples 14 through 21 are identified in the following model; copy it on a piece of paper, and refer to it as you read through the examples.

Factoring Model:

$$ax^2 + bx + c = (dx + e)(fx + g) = (df)x^2 + (dg + ef)x + (eg)$$

outer product

inner product

sum of inner and outer product

$$a = df \qquad b = dg + ef \qquad c = eg$$

EXAMPLE 14. Write $2x^2 + 3x - 2$ in a completely factored form.

SOLUTION

Step 1. Use Theorem 1 to test for factorability.

$$ac = (2)(-2) = -4$$

Look for factors of -4 whose sum is 3.

Factors of -4	Factor sums
$(1)(-4)$	$(1) + (-4) = -3$
$(-1)(4) \longrightarrow$	$(-1) + (4) = 3 = b$
$(2)(-2)$	$(2) + (-2) = 0$

Since $ac = -4$ has factors whose sum is 3, $2x^2 + 3x - 2$ (by Theorem 1) can be factored.

Step 2. Find the factors of $2x^2 + 3x - 2$. Since $b = (-1) + (4)$ is the sum of the outer and inner products, we may identify -1 with the outer product and 4 with the inner product (or vice versa). We then assign combinations of factors of -1 to d and g and of 4 to e and f until we find a combination that "works." It is helpful to first write

$$(x \quad)(x \quad) = 2x^2 + 3x - 2$$

and, keeping an eye on the coefficient of x^2 and the constant term, mentally (or on scratch paper) insert the factor combinations referred to above until the right combination turns up. Thus, with a little experimentation we find that

$$(x + 2)(2x - 1) = 2x^2 + 3x - 2$$

After a little practice you will find shortcuts of your own, and the process will not be difficult.

EXAMPLE 15. Write $3x^2 - 2x + 4$ in a completely factored form.

SOLUTION

Step 1. Test for factorability.

Factors of 12

$ac = (3)(4) = 12$

$(1)(12)$	$(-1)(-12)$
$(2)(6)$	$(-2)(-6)$
$(3)(4)$	$(-3)(-4)$

None of these factors have a sum of -2; hence, the polynomial cannot be factored.

EXAMPLE 16.   Write $x^2 - 5x + 6$ in a completely factored form.

SOLUTION: $ac = 6, (-3)(-2) = 6,$ and $(-3) + (-2) = -5;$ hence, $x^2 - 5x + 6$ is factorable.

Let
$$\text{outer product} = -3$$
$$\text{inner product} = -2$$

and obtain (after perhaps a few trials)

$$(x - 2)(x - 3) = x^2 - 5x + 6$$

EXAMPLE 17.   Write $x^2 - 3x - 5$ in a completely factored form.

SOLUTION: $ac = -5$

-5 has no factors whose sum is $-3;$ hence, $x^2 - 3x - 5$ cannot be factored.

EXAMPLE 18.   Write $2x^2 - 5xy - 3y^2$ in a completely factored form.

SOLUTION: Proceed as you would with $2x^2 - 5x - 3:$

$$ac = (2)(-3) = -6 \qquad (-6)(1) = -6 \qquad (-6) + (1) = -5$$

Let
$$\text{outer product} = -6$$
$$\text{inner product} = 1$$

and obtain

$$(2x + y)(x - 3y) = 2x^2 - 5xy - 3y^2$$

EXAMPLE 19.   Write $A^2 - B^2$ in a completely factored form.

SOLUTION

$$A^2 - B^2 = A^2 + 0AB - B^2$$

$ac = (1)(-1) = -1,$ $(1)(-1) = -1,$ and $(1) + (-1) = 0;$ hence, $A^2 - B^2$ is factorable.

Let
$$\text{outer product} = 1$$
$$\text{inner product} = -1$$

and obtain

$$(A + B)(A - B) = A^2 - B^2$$

Thus the **difference of two squares,** $A^2 - B^2,$ can always be factored.   This form occurs with sufficient frequency to warrant your memorizing the formula

$$A^2 - B^2 = (A + B)(A - B)$$

and using it directly whenever a difference of two squares is encountered.   For example, $9x^2 - 4y^2 = (3x)^2 - (2y)^2 = (3x + 2y)(3x - 2y)$.

EXAMPLE 20.   Write $A^2 + B^2$ in a completely factored form.

SOLUTION

$$A^2 + B^2 = A^2 + 0AB + B^2$$
$$ac = (1)(1) = 1$$

1 has no factors whose sum is 0; hence, *the sum of two squares, $A^2 + B^2$, does not factor.*

EXAMPLE 21.   Write $3x^3y + 3x^2y - 36xy$ in a completely factored form.

SOLUTION: Remove the common factor first and proceed as above (if it is present, a common factor should always be removed first):

$$3x^3y + 3x^2y - 36xy = 3xy(x^2 + x - 12)$$
$$= 3xy(x - 3)(x + 4)$$

It must be understood that when we say that a second-degree polynomial cannot be factored, we mean that it cannot be factored in terms of first-degree polynomials with integral coefficients.   If we allow rational or real coefficients for the linear factors, then this becomes a different matter and the subject for a more advanced treatment of the subject.   In this course Definition 1 (in the beginning of this section) states exactly what we mean by factoring a polynomial.

EXERCISE 54

In problems 1 through 54 write each of the polynomials in a completely factored form.   If the polynomial cannot be factored, say so.

1. $x^2 + 5x + 6$
2. $x^2 + 6x + 8$
3. $m^2 - 7m + 12$
4. $m^2 - 7m + 10$
5. $y^2 + 3y + 3$
6. $y^2 - 2y + 6$
7. $x^2 + 9xy + 20y^2$
8. $x^2 + 8xy + 15y^2$
9. $u^2 + u + 4$
10. $u^2 - 6u + 3$
11. $t^3 - 12t^2 + 20t$
12. $t^3 - 11t^2 + 24t$
13. $2x^2 + 7x + 3$
14. $3x^2 + 7x + 2$

15. $2x^2 - 7xy + 6y^2$

16. $3x^2 - 11xy + 6y^2$

17. $3x^2 + 4x + 5$

18. $2x^2 + 3x + 6$

19. $6y^3 - 17y^2 + 12y$

20. $6y^3 - 19y^2 + 10y$

21. $2x^3 - 2x^2 + 8x$

22. $3x^3 - 6x^2 + 15x$

23. $6x^2 + 11xy + 3y^2$

24. $12x^2 + 17xy + 6y^2$

25. $n^2 + 2n - 8$

26. $n^2 - 2n - 8$

27. $x^2 - 4xy - 12y^2$

28. $x^2 + 4xy - 12y^2$

29. $x^2 - 3x - 8$

30. $x^2 + 4x - 6$

31. $2s^2 + 5s - 3$

32. $3s^2 - 5s - 2$

33. $6x^3 - 9x^2 - 15x$

34. $6x^3 + 2x^2 - 8x$

35. $6u^2 - uv - 12v^2$

36. $6u^2 + 7uv - 3v^2$

37. $2x^2 - 3xy - 4y^2$

38. $3x^2 + 2xy - 3y^2$

39. $15x^2 + 17xy - 4y^2$

40. $12x^2 - 40xy - 7y^2$

41. $x^2 - 9$

42. $x^2 - 16$

43. $2x^3 + 8x$

44. $3x^4 + 27x^2$

45. $9y^2 - 25$

46. $25y^2 - 16$

47. $4x^3y - xy^3$

48. $x^3y - 9xy^3$

49. $x^2 + y^2$

50. $9u^2 + 4v^2$

51. $4x^2 - 28x + 48$

52. $6x^2 + 48x + 72$

53. $3x^3y - 15x^2y^2 + 18xy^3$

54. $4x^3y + 14x^2y^2 + 6xy^3$

55. Find all positive integers p under 15 so that $x^2 - 7x + p$ can be factored.

56. Find all integers p such that $x^2 + px + 12$ can be factored.

47   DIVISION

QUOTIENT NOTATION

Just as with the integers, for each pair of real numbers a and b, with $b \neq 0$,

$$\frac{a}{b}, \quad a/b, \quad a \div b, \quad \text{and } b\overline{)a}$$

name the same real number.

　　If the coefficients of a polynomial are real, then because of closure properties of the real numbers, the polynomial names a real number for each real-number replacement of the variables.   Thus, one may write the quotient of two poly-nomials in any one of the four ways indicated above.   For example,

$$\frac{2x^2 + 5x - 3}{x + 3} = (2x^2 + 5x - 3)/(x + 3)$$

$$= (2x^2 + 5x - 3) \div (x + 3)$$

$$= x + 3\overline{)2x^2 + 5x - 3}$$

CANCELING COMMON FACTORS

If the numerator and denominator in a quotient of two polynomials contain a common factor, it may be "canceled out" according to the property of real numbers.

$$\frac{ak}{bk} = \frac{a}{b}$$

The right-hand member is sometimes called the quotient of ak divided by bk, since $(bk)(a/b) = ak$.   (Recall the definition of division: $A/B = Q$ if and only if $A = BQ$ and Q is unique.)

EXAMPLE 22:   ELIMINATION OF COMMON FACTORS FROM THE NUMERATOR AND THE DENOMINATOR.

▶ $\dfrac{2x^2 + 8x}{2x} = \dfrac{2x(x + 4)}{2x} = x + 4$

▶ $\dfrac{3x^3y - 6x^2y + 12xy}{6xy^2} = \dfrac{3xy(x^2 - 2x + 4)}{(3xy)(2y)} = \dfrac{x^2 - 2x + 4}{2y}$

▶ $\dfrac{x^2y - xy^2}{x^2 - xy} = \dfrac{\overset{y}{\cancel{xy}}(x - y)}{\underset{1}{\cancel{x}}(x - y)} = y$

▶ $\dfrac{2x^2 + 5x - 3}{x + 3} = \dfrac{(2x - 1)(x + 3)}{(x + 3)} = 2x - 1$

NOTE: Each of these is easily checked by multiplying the quotient by the divisor to see if the dividend is obtained.

LONG DIVISION

There are times when it is useful to find quotients of polynomials by a long-division process similar to that used in arithmetic.   Several examples will illustrate the process.

EXAMPLE 23.   Divide $2x^2 + 5x - 12$ by $x + 4$.

SOLUTION

COMMENTS

$$x + 4 \overline{) 2x^2 + 5x - 12}$$

Both polynomials are arranged in descending powers of the variable if this is not already done.

$$\begin{array}{r} 2x \\ x + 4 \overline{) 2x^2 + 5x - 12} \end{array}$$

Divide the first term of the divisor into the first term of the dividend, i.e., what must x be multiplied by so that the product is exactly $2x^2$?

$$\begin{array}{r} 2x \\ x + 4 \overline{) 2x^2 + 5x - 12} \\ \underline{2x^2 + 8x } \\ -3x - 12 \end{array}$$

Multiply the divisor by $2x$, line up like terms, subtract as in arithmetic, and bring down -12.

$$\begin{array}{r} 2x - 3 \\ x + 4 \overline{) 2x^2 + 5x - 12} \\ \underline{2x^2 + 8x } \\ -3x - 12 \\ \underline{-3x - 12} \\ 0 \end{array}$$

Repeat the process above until the degree of the remainder is less than that of the divisor.

CHECK: $(x + 4)(2x - 3) = 2x^2 + 5x - 12$.

EXAMPLE 24.   Divide $x^3 + 8$ by $x + 2$.

SOLUTION

COMMENT

$$\begin{array}{r} x^2 - 2x + 4 \\ x + 2 \overline{) x^3 + 0x^2 + 0x + 8} \\ \underline{x^3 + 2x^2 } \\ -2x^2 + 0x \\ \underline{-2x^2 - 4x } \\ 4x + 8 \\ \underline{4x + 8} \\ 0 \end{array}$$

Insert, with zero coefficients, any missing terms of lower degree than 3, and proceed as in example 23.

Can you check this problem?

EXAMPLE 25.   Divide $6x^2 - 7x + 3$ by $3x + 1$.

SOLUTION

COMMENT

$$
\begin{array}{r}
2x - 3 \\
3x + 1 \overline{\smash{)}6x^2 - 7x + 3} \\
\underline{6x^2 + 2x} \\
-9x + 3 \\
\underline{-9x - 3} \\
6 = \text{Remainder}
\end{array}
$$

Remember to continue the dividing process until the degree of the remainder is less than the degree of the divisor.

CHECK: Just as in arithmetic, when there is a remainder we check by adding the remainder to the product of the divisor and quotient. Thus

$$(3x + 1)(2x - 3) + 6 \overset{?}{=} 6x^2 - 7x + 3$$
$$6x^2 - 7x - 3 + 6 \overset{?}{=} 6x^2 - 7x + 3$$
$$6x^2 - 7x + 3 \overset{\vee}{=} 6x^2 - 7x + 3$$

EXERCISE 55

Eliminate common factors from numerator and denominator.

1. $\dfrac{2x^2 - 4x}{2x}$

2. $\dfrac{9y - 3y^2}{3y}$

3. $\dfrac{9x^2 - 3x + 6}{3}$

4. $\dfrac{2 - 6x - 4x^2}{2}$

5. $\dfrac{12t^2 + 4t - 8}{4t}$

6. $\dfrac{10 + 5m - 15m^2}{5m}$

7. $\dfrac{4m^3n - 2m^2n^2 + 6mn^3}{2mn}$

8. $\dfrac{6x^3y - 12x^2y^2 - 9xy^3}{3xy}$

9. $\dfrac{a^2b + ab^2}{ab + b^2}$

10. $\dfrac{m^2 - mn}{m^2n - mn^2}$

11. $\dfrac{x^2 - x - 6}{x - 3}$

12. $\dfrac{x^2 + 2x - 8}{x - 2}$

13. $\dfrac{3x^2 + 14x - 5}{3x - 1}$

14. $\dfrac{2x^2 - 13x - 7}{2x + 1}$

15. $\dfrac{4x^2 - 9y^2}{2x + 3y}$

16. $\dfrac{a^2 - 16b^2}{a - 4b}$

17. $\dfrac{x^2y - 8xy + 15y}{xy - 3y}$

18. $\dfrac{m^3 + 7m^2 + 10m}{m^2 + 5m}$

Divide, using the long-division process.   Check the answers.

19. $(2x^2 + x - 6)/(x + 2)$

20. $(3x^2 - 5x - 2)/(x - 2)$

21. $(2m^2 + m - 10)/(2m + 5)$

22. $(3p^2 + 5p - 12)/(3p - 4)$

23. $(8x^2 - 14x + 3)/(2x - 3)$

24. $(6x^2 + 5x - 6)/(3x - 2)$

25. $(y^2 - 9)/(y + 3)$

26. $(4m^2 - 1)/(2m - 1)$

27. $(x^3 - 1)/(x - 1)$

28. $(a^3 + 27)/(a + 3)$

29. $(2x^2 - 7x - 1)/(2x + 1)$

30. $(3x^2 + 13x - 12)/(3x - 2)$

31. $(4a^2 - 7a - 22)/(a - 3)$

32. $(5c^2 + 8c + 4)/(c + 2)$

33. $(8x^2 + 7)/(2x - 3)$

34. $(9x^2 - 8)/(3x - 2)$

35. $(x^3 - 5x^2 + x + 10)/(x - 2)$

36. $(2y^3 + 5y^2 - y - 6)/(y + 2)$

37. $(x^4 - 16)/(x + 2)$

38. $(x^5 + 32)/(x - 2)$

39. $(3 + x^3 - x)/(x - 3)$

40. $(3y - y^2 + 2y^3 - 1)/(y + 2)$

48 CHAPTER SUMMARY

GENERAL

In this chapter we have concentrated our attention on basic operations on polynomials. The polynomial is a very important and frequently encountered mathematical form; consequently, it is important that you learn the operations discussed in this chapter well. In the next chapter we will discuss the basic arithmetical operations on fractional forms involving polynomials. The discussion will parallel the discussion of the addition, subtraction, multiplication, and division of rational numbers.

SPECIFIC

Describe, define, or give examples of each of the following:

1. **Polynomials**

monomial, binomial, trinomial

degree of a term

degree of a polynomial

first-degree polynomial in one variable

first-degree polynomial in two variables
second-degree polynomial in one variable
second-degree polynomial in two variables
third-degree polynomial in one variable

2. Addition, subtraction, multiplication, and division of polynomials.

3. Special products and factoring.

mental multiplication of certain polynomial forms
completely factored form
factoring out monomials
test for factorability for second-degree polynomials
factoring second-degree polynomial forms

EXERCISE 56   CHAPTER REVIEW

1. Which of the following algebraic expressions are polynomials?

(A) $x^2 - 3x + 5$ (B) $x - \dfrac{2}{x}$

(C) $3x + 2y - 3$ (D) $x^2 - 2xy + 5$

(E) $\dfrac{x + y}{x - y}$ (F) $3x - 7$

2. In problem 1:
(A) Identify all of the first-degree polynomials in two variables.
(B) Identify all of the second-degree polynomials in one variable.

Given the polynomials $(3x - 2)$, $(2x + 5)$, $3x^2 + 7x - 6$, *and* $9x^2 - 4$:

3. Add all four.
4. Subtract the second from the first.
5. Subtract the third from the fourth.
6. Subtract the sum of the first two from the sum of the second two.
7. Multiply the first two.
8. Multiply the last two.
9. Divide the third by the first.
10. Divide the last by the first.
11. Factor the third.
12. Factor the last.

13. Simplify: $[(3x^2 - x + 1) - (x^2 - 4)] - [(2x - 5)(x + 3)]$.

14. Simplify: $[-2xy(x^2 - 4y^2)] - [-2xy(x - 2y)(x + 2y)]$.

15. Eliminate common factors from the numerator and denominator:

(A) $\dfrac{2x^3y - 4x^2y^2 + 6xy^3}{2xy}$ (B) $\dfrac{x^3 + 2x^2 - 15x}{x^3 + 5x^2}$

16. Write each in a completely factored form:

(A) $-6a^2b - 8ab^2$ (B) $25x^2 - 16y^2$

(C) $m^2 + 4n^2$ (D) $x^2 - 10x + 25$

(E) $2x^2 - 8x - 3$ (F) $4x^3 - 10x^2 - 6x$

17. Divide, using long division, and check:

(A) $(8t^2 - 2t - 5)/(2t + 1)$ (B) $(8x^3 + 1)/(2x + 1)$

18. The solution set for $3x^2 + 7x - 6 = (3x - 2)(x + 3)$ is the set containing (*none, one, all*) of the real numbers.

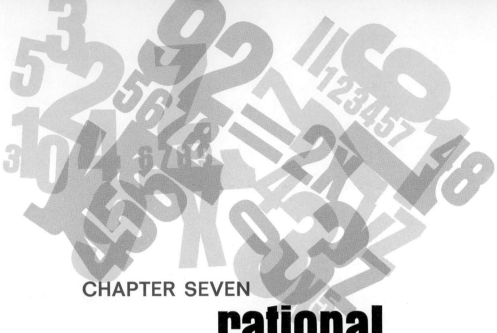

CHAPTER SEVEN
rational expressions

49 RATIONAL EXPRESSIONS

Fractional forms in which the numerator and denominator are polynomials are called **rational expressions.**

$$\frac{1}{x} \qquad \frac{1}{y-3} \qquad \frac{1}{x^2 - x - 6} \qquad \frac{t-2}{2t^2 - 2t + 5} \qquad \frac{x^2 - 3xy + y^2}{x^3 - y^3}$$

are all rational expressions. (Recall that a constant is a polynomial of zero degree.)

In the last chapter we considered the problem of canceling common factors from numerators and denominators of rational expressions and even referred to this process as reducing an expression to lowest terms. In this chapter you will, in addition, learn how to add, subtract, multiply, and divide rational expressions, as well as how to solve equations involving rational expressions. The development will very closely parallel the development found in Chap. 3 for rational numbers. Here, however, we will find it easier to start with multiplication and division rather than addition and subtraction.

Throughout this chapter we assume that we are dealing with **real polynomials,** that is, polynomials with real coefficients whose replacement set for the variable(s) is the set of real numbers. Since a polynomial names a real number for each replacement of its variables by real numbers, the properties of real numbers control operations on polynomials and, in particular, on rational expressions.

50   MULTIPLICATION AND DIVISION

MULTIPLICATION

For a, b, c, and d any real numbers with $b \neq 0$ and $d \neq 0$,

$$\frac{a}{b} \cdot \frac{c}{d} = \frac{a \cdot c}{b \cdot d}$$

This definition of **multiplication of real fractions** coupled with the property

$$\frac{ak}{bk} = \frac{a}{b} \qquad k \neq 0$$

provide the basis for multiplying and reducing rational expressions. The following examples should make the process clear.

EXAMPLE 1

▶ $\dfrac{3a^2b}{4c^2d} \cdot \dfrac{8c^2d^3}{9ab^2} = \dfrac{(3a^2b) \cdot (8c^2d^3)}{(4c^2d) \cdot (9ab^2)} = \dfrac{24a^2bc^2d^3}{36ab^2c^2d} = \dfrac{(2ad^2)(12abc^2d)}{(3b)(12abc^2d)} = \dfrac{2ad^2}{3b}$

This process is quickly shortened to the following when it is realized that, in effect, any factor in a numerator may "cancel" any like factor in a denominator. Thus,

$$\frac{\overset{1 \cdot a \cdot 1}{3a^2b}}{\underset{1 \cdot 1 \cdot 1}{4c^2d}} \cdot \frac{\overset{2 \cdot 1 \cdot d^2}{8c^2d^3}}{\underset{3 \cdot 1 \cdot b}{9ab^2}} = \frac{2ad^2}{3b}$$

▶ $(x^2 - 4) \cdot \dfrac{2x - 3}{x + 2} = \dfrac{\overset{1}{(x + 2)}(x - 2)}{1} \cdot \dfrac{2x - 3}{\underset{1}{x + 2}} = (x - 2)(2x - 3)$

$$\blacktriangleright \quad \frac{4a^2 - 9b^2}{4a^2 + 12ab + 9b^2} \cdot \frac{6a^2b}{8a^2b^2 - 12ab^3} = \frac{\overset{1}{\cancel{(2a-3b)}}\overset{1}{\cancel{(2a+3b)}}}{\underset{(2a+3b)}{\cancel{(2a+3b)^2}}} \cdot \frac{\overset{3a}{\cancel{6a^2b}}}{\underset{2b}{\cancel{4ab^2}}\underset{1}{\cancel{(2a-3b)}}}$$

$$= \frac{3a}{2b(2a + 3b)}$$

DIVISION

It follows from the definition of division (that is, $A \div B = Q$ if and only if $A = BQ$ and Q is unique) that for all nonzero real numbers b, c, and d, and any real number a,

$$\frac{a}{b} \div \frac{c}{d} = \frac{a}{b} \cdot \frac{d}{c}$$

To verify this statement, multiply the quotient by the divisor to obtain the dividend. Thus, to divide one rational expression by another, we multiply by the reciprocal of the divisor.

EXAMPLE 2

$$\blacktriangleright \quad \frac{6a^2b^3}{5cd} \div \frac{3a^2c}{10bd} = \frac{6a^2b^3}{5cd} \cdot \frac{10bd}{3a^2c} = \frac{4b^4}{c^2}$$

$$\blacktriangleright \quad \frac{10x^3y}{3xy + 9y} \div \frac{4x^2 - 12x}{x^2 - 9} = \frac{10x^3y}{3y(x + 3)} \cdot \frac{(x + 3)(x - 3)}{4x(x - 3)} = \frac{5x^2}{6}$$

$$\blacktriangleright \quad \frac{4 - 2x}{4} \div (x - 2) = \frac{2(2 - x)}{4} \cdot \frac{1}{x - 2} = \frac{2 - x}{2(x - 2)} = \frac{(-1)(x - 2)}{2(x - 2)} = -\frac{1}{2}$$

EXERCISE 57

In problems 1 through 22 perform the indicated operations and simplify.

1. $\dfrac{6}{7} \cdot \dfrac{28}{9}$

2. $\dfrac{15}{16} \cdot \dfrac{24}{27}$

3. $\dfrac{4}{6} \div \dfrac{24}{8}$

4. $\dfrac{52}{81} \div \dfrac{39}{27}$

5. $\dfrac{6x^3y}{7u} \cdot \dfrac{14u^3}{12xy}$

6. $\dfrac{y^4}{3u^5} \cdot \dfrac{2u^3}{3y}$

7. $\dfrac{3c^2d}{a^3b^3} \div \dfrac{3a^3b^3}{cd}$

8. $\dfrac{uvw}{5xyz} \div \dfrac{5vy}{uwxz}$

9. $\left(\dfrac{-d^5}{3a} \div \dfrac{d^2}{6a^2}\right) \cdot \dfrac{a}{-4d^3}$

10. $\dfrac{-d^5}{3a} \div \left(\dfrac{d^2}{6a^2} \cdot \dfrac{a}{-4d^3}\right)$

11. $\dfrac{a^2 - a}{a - 1} \cdot \dfrac{a + 1}{a}$

12. $\dfrac{x + 3}{x^3 + 3x^2} \cdot \dfrac{x^3}{x - 3}$

13. $\dfrac{m + n}{m^2 - n^2} \div \dfrac{m^2 - mn}{m^2 - 2mn + n^2}$

14. $\dfrac{x^2 - 6x + 9}{x^2 - x - 6} \div \dfrac{x^2 + 2x - 15}{x^2 + 2x}$

15. $(t^2 - t - 12) \div \dfrac{t^2 - 9}{t^2 - 3t}$

16. $\dfrac{2y^2 + 7y + 3}{4y^2 - 1} \div (y + 3)$

17. $-(x^2 - 4) \cdot \dfrac{3}{x + 2}$

18. $-(x^2 - 3x) \cdot \dfrac{x - 2}{x - 3}$

19. $\dfrac{9 - x^2}{x^2 + 5x + 6} \cdot \dfrac{x + 2}{x - 3}$

20. $\dfrac{2 - m}{2m + m^2} \cdot \dfrac{m^2 + 4m + 4}{m^2 - 4}$

21. $\dfrac{x^2 - xy}{xy + y^2} \div \left(\dfrac{x^2 - y^2}{x^2 + 2xy + y^2} \div \dfrac{x^2 - 2xy + y^2}{x^2y + xy^2}\right)$

22. $\left(\dfrac{x^2 - xy}{xy + y^2} \div \dfrac{x^2 - y^2}{x^2 + 2xy + y^2}\right) \div \dfrac{x^2 - 2xy + y^2}{x^2y + xy^2}$

23. $(x^2 - 1)/(x - 1)$ and $x + 1$ name the same real number for (*all, all but one, no*) replacements of x by real numbers.

24. $(x^2 - x - 6)/(x - 3) = x + 2$, except for what values of x?

25. Can you evaluate the following arithmetic problem in less than 3 min?

$$\dfrac{(108{,}641)^2 - (108{,}643)^2}{(108{,}642)(108{,}646) - (108{,}644)^2}$$

51   ADDITION AND SUBTRACTION

Addition and subtraction of rational expressions are based on the following properties of real fractions:

$$\frac{a}{b} + \frac{c}{b} = \frac{a + c}{b} \tag{1}$$

$$\frac{a}{b} - \frac{c}{b} = \frac{a - c}{b} \tag{2}$$

$$\frac{a}{b} = \frac{ak}{bk} \qquad k \neq 0 \tag{3}$$

Thus, if the denominators of two rational expressions are the same, we may either add or subtract the expressions by adding or subtracting the numerators and placing the result over the common denominator; if the denominators are not the same, we use property (3) to change the form of each fraction so they have a common denominator and then use either (1) or (2).

Even though any common denominator will do, the problem will generally become less involved if the least common denominator (LCD) is used. If the LCD is not obvious (often it is), then we proceed as we did when we studied rational numbers in Chap. 3, that is, factor each denominator completely, including numerical coefficients. The LCD should then contain each different factor in the denominators to the highest power it occurs in any one denominator.

EXAMPLE 3

$$\frac{4(x+4)}{4x(x-3)} - \frac{2(x-3)}{4x(x-3)} = \frac{4(x+4) - 2(x-3)}{4x(x-3)} = \frac{4x+16-2x+6}{4x(x-3)}$$

$$= \frac{2x+22}{4x(x-3)} = \frac{2(x+11)}{4x(x-3)} = \frac{x+11}{2x(x-3)}$$

EXAMPLE 4

$$\frac{1}{2y} + \frac{1}{4y^2} - 1 = \frac{1(2y)}{(2y)(2y)} + \frac{1}{4y^2} - \frac{4y^2}{4y^2} = \frac{2y+1-4y^2}{4y^2} = \frac{1+2y-4y^2}{4y^2}$$

Note that the LCD is $4y^2$.

EXAMPLE 5

$$\frac{4}{x^2-4} - \frac{3}{x^2-x-2} = \frac{4}{(x-2)(x+2)} - \frac{3}{(x-2)(x+1)}$$

We see that the LCD is $(x-2)(x+2)(x+1)$. Then

$$\frac{4(x+1)}{(x-2)(x+2)(x+1)} - \frac{3(x+2)}{(x-2)(x+2)(x+1)} = \frac{4(x+1) - 3(x+2)}{(x-2)(x+2)(x+1)}$$

$$= \frac{4x+4-3x-6}{(x-2)(x+2)(x+1)} = \frac{(x-2)}{(x-2)(x+2)(x+1)} = \frac{1}{(x+2)(x+1)}$$

EXAMPLE 6

$$\frac{3}{x^2-6x+9} - \frac{2}{x^2-9} - \frac{5}{3-x} = \frac{3}{(x-3)^2} - \frac{2}{(x-3)(x+3)} + \frac{5}{x-3}$$

NOTE: $-\dfrac{5}{3-x} = \dfrac{5}{-(3-x)} = +\dfrac{5}{(x-3)}$

We see that the LCD is $(x-3)^2(x+3)$.   Then

$$\dfrac{3(x+3)}{(x-3)^2(x+3)} - \dfrac{2(x-3)}{(x-3)^2(x+3)} + \dfrac{5(x-3)(x+3)}{(x-3)^2(x+3)}$$

$$= \dfrac{3(x+3) - 2(x-3) + 5(x-3)(x+3)}{(x-3)^2(x+3)} = \dfrac{3x+9 - 2x+6 + 5x^2 - 45}{(x-3)^2(x+3)}$$

$$= \dfrac{5x^2 + x - 30}{(x-3)^2(x+3)}$$

EXERCISE 58

Combine into a single fraction and simplify.

1. $\dfrac{2x}{3y} + \dfrac{5}{3y}$

2. $\dfrac{3x}{2x^2y^2} + \dfrac{2y}{2x^2y^2}$

3. $\dfrac{3x-2}{2x} - \dfrac{x}{2x}$

4. $\dfrac{4t-1}{4mn} - \dfrac{3}{4mn}$

5. $\dfrac{1}{2a^2} - \dfrac{2b-1}{2a^2}$

6. $\dfrac{5}{3k} - \dfrac{6x-4}{3k}$

7. $\dfrac{3x}{y} + \dfrac{1}{4}$

8. $\dfrac{2}{x} - \dfrac{1}{3}$

9. $\dfrac{2}{x} + 1$

10. $x + \dfrac{1}{x}$

11. $\dfrac{1}{x} - \dfrac{y}{x^2} + \dfrac{y^2}{x^3}$

12. $\dfrac{u}{v^2} - \dfrac{1}{v} + \dfrac{u^2}{v^3}$

13. $\dfrac{3y+8}{4y^2} - \dfrac{2y-1}{y^3} - \dfrac{5}{8y}$

14. $\dfrac{4t-3}{18t^3} + \dfrac{3}{4t} - \dfrac{2t-1}{6t^2}$

15. $\dfrac{5a}{a-1} - \dfrac{5}{a-1}$

16. $\dfrac{2x}{4x^2-9} - \dfrac{3}{4x^2-9}$

17. $\dfrac{3}{x-1} + \dfrac{2}{1-x}$

18. $\dfrac{5}{y-3} - \dfrac{2}{3-y}$

19. $\dfrac{a}{a-1} - \dfrac{2}{a^2-1}$

20. $\dfrac{m+2}{m-2} - \dfrac{m^2+4}{m^2-4}$

21. $\dfrac{3x-1}{2x^2+x-3} - \dfrac{2}{x-1}$

22. $\dfrac{4}{2x-3} - \dfrac{2x+1}{(2x-3)(x+2)}$

23. $\dfrac{3}{x^2 - 1} - \dfrac{2}{x^2 - 2x + 1}$

24. $\dfrac{1}{m^2 - n^2} + \dfrac{1}{m^2 + 2mn + n^2}$

25. $2 + \dfrac{x + 1}{x - 3}$

26. $\dfrac{t + 1}{t - 1} - 1$

27. $x - 3 - \dfrac{x - 1}{x - 2}$

28. $\dfrac{x^2 - 2x}{x + 2} + x - 3$

29. $\dfrac{2x}{x^2 - y^2} + \dfrac{1}{x + y} - \dfrac{1}{x - y}$

30. $\dfrac{2}{x + 3} - \dfrac{1}{x - 3} + \dfrac{2x}{x^2 - 9}$

31. $5 + \dfrac{a}{a + 1} - \dfrac{a}{a - 1}$

32. $\dfrac{1}{y + 2} + 3 - \dfrac{2}{y - 2}$

33. $\dfrac{1}{5x - 5} - \dfrac{1}{3x - 3} + \dfrac{1}{1 - x}$

34. $\dfrac{x + 7}{ax - bx} + \dfrac{y + 9}{by - ay}$

35. $\dfrac{2t}{3t^2 - 48} + \dfrac{t}{4t + t^2}$

36. $\dfrac{3s}{3s^2 - 12s} + \dfrac{1}{2s + 4s}$

52   COMPLEX FRACTIONS

A fractional form with fractions in its numerator, denominator, or both is called a **complex fraction.**   It is often necessary to represent a complex fraction as a simple fraction, that is, in all cases that we will consider, as the quotient of two polynomials.   The process does not involve any new concepts.   It is a matter of applying old concepts in the right sequence.   We will discuss two general approaches, each with its own merits depending on the problem under consideration.   One of the methods makes very effective use of the property $a/b = ak/bk$, with $k \neq 0$.

EXAMPLE 7.   Express $\dfrac{1 + \dfrac{2}{x}}{3 - \dfrac{4}{x}}$ as a simple fraction.

SOLUTION

Method 1.   Multiply the numerator and denominator by the LCD of all fractions within the numerator and denominator.   Thus

$$\frac{1 + \dfrac{2}{x}}{3 - \dfrac{4}{x}} = \frac{\left(1 + \dfrac{2}{x}\right)x}{\left(3 - \dfrac{4}{x}\right)x} = \frac{x + 2}{3x - 4}$$

Method 2. Write the numerator and denominator as single fractions. Then treat as a quotient. Thus

$$\frac{1 + \dfrac{2}{x}}{3 - \dfrac{4}{x}} = \frac{\dfrac{x+2}{x}}{\dfrac{3x-4}{x}} = \frac{x+2}{x} \div \frac{3x-4}{x} = \frac{x+2}{x} \cdot \frac{x}{3x-4} = \frac{x+2}{3x-4}$$

EXAMPLE 8. Express $\dfrac{1 - \dfrac{1}{4c^2}}{1 + \dfrac{1}{2c}}$ as a simple fraction.

SOLUTION
Method 1

$$\frac{1 - \dfrac{1}{4c^2}}{1 + \dfrac{1}{2c}} = \frac{\left(1 - \dfrac{1}{4c^2}\right)4c^2}{\left(1 + \dfrac{1}{2c}\right)4c^2} = \frac{4c^2 - 1}{4c^2 + 2c} = \frac{(2c+1)(2c-1)}{2c(2c+1)} = \frac{2c-1}{2c}$$

Method 2

$$\frac{1 - \dfrac{1}{4c^2}}{1 + \dfrac{1}{2c}} = \frac{\dfrac{4c^2 - 1}{4c^2}}{\dfrac{2c+1}{2c}} = \frac{(2c+1)(2c-1)}{4c^2} \cdot \frac{2c}{2c+1} = \frac{2c-1}{2c}$$

EXERCISE 59

Write each of the problems 1 through 16 as simple fractions and reduce to lowest terms.

1. $\dfrac{\dfrac{2}{x}}{\dfrac{4}{x^2}}$

2. $\dfrac{\dfrac{6x^2}{y^2}}{\dfrac{3x}{y}}$

3. $\dfrac{\dfrac{x+3}{x^2}}{\dfrac{x+2}{x}}$

4. $\dfrac{\dfrac{c-3}{cd}}{\dfrac{c-3}{c^2}}$

5. $\dfrac{1 + \dfrac{3}{x}}{x - \dfrac{9}{x}}$

6. $\dfrac{1 - \dfrac{y^2}{x^2}}{1 - \dfrac{y}{x}}$

7. $\dfrac{\dfrac{a}{4}}{a - \dfrac{1}{8}}$

8. $\dfrac{m + \dfrac{1}{6}}{\dfrac{2m}{3}}$

9. $\dfrac{\dfrac{1}{x} + \dfrac{1}{y}}{\dfrac{y}{x} - \dfrac{x}{y}}$

10. $\dfrac{b - \dfrac{a^2}{b}}{\dfrac{1}{a} - \dfrac{1}{b}}$

11. $\dfrac{\dfrac{x}{y} - 2 + \dfrac{y}{x}}{\dfrac{x}{y} - \dfrac{y}{x}}$

12. $\dfrac{1 + \dfrac{2}{x} - \dfrac{15}{x^2}}{1 + \dfrac{4}{x} - \dfrac{5}{x^2}}$

13. $1 + \dfrac{1}{1 + \dfrac{1}{2}}$

14. $1 + \dfrac{1}{1 - \dfrac{1}{3}}$

15. $1 - \dfrac{1}{1 - \dfrac{1}{x}}$

16. $2 - \dfrac{1}{1 - \dfrac{2}{x + 2}}$

17. A boat traveling downstream at 30 mph relative to the water, which is in turn moving at 5 mph, would have a speed of 35 mph relative to the land, or would it? According to Einstein, velocities must be added according to the following formula:

$$v = \dfrac{v_1 + v_2}{1 + \dfrac{v_1 v_2}{c^2}}$$

where v is the resultant velocity, c is the speed of light, and v_1 and v_2 are the two velocities to be added. Convert the right side of the equation into a simple fraction.

18. Take the number 5 and its reciprocal $\frac{1}{5}$. Add 1 to each, and divide the first sum by the second. The quotient should be the number 5 you started with.

19. Show for any number x, with $x \neq 0$, that if we take it and its reciprocal and add 1 to each, the quotient of the two sums will be the number that we started with.

53   FRACTIONAL EQUATIONS AND APPLICATIONS

We have already considered equations with rational coefficients, such as $(x/2) - 3 = (2x + 5)/4$, and found that we could easily convert them to equivalent equations with integral coefficients by multiplying through by the least common multiple of all of the denominators.   If an equation involves variables in one or more denominators, such as

$$\frac{3}{x} - \frac{1}{2} = \frac{4}{x}$$

we may proceed in essentially the same way; however, the replacement set of the equation must exclude any value of the variable that will make a denominator zero.   Thus, in this example, the replacement set for x is the set of all real numbers except $x = 0$.   As long as we stay with the replacement set of the original equation, we may multiply through by a least common denominator containing a variable, and the new equation will be equivalent to the old.   When we solve the new equation, we must be particularly sure to check its solutions to see if they are elements of the replacement set of the original equation.   Remember, *the solution set of an equation is always a subset of its replacement set.*

EXAMPLE 9.   Solve and check: $\dfrac{3}{x} - \dfrac{1}{2} = \dfrac{4}{x}$.

SOLUTION

$$\frac{3}{x} - \frac{1}{2} = \frac{4}{x} \qquad \text{Replacement set: all real numbers except } x = 0$$

$$(2x)\frac{3}{x} - (2x)\frac{1}{2} = (2x)\frac{4}{x}$$

$$6 - x = 8$$

$$-x = 2$$

$$x = -2$$

CHECK:

$$\frac{3}{-2} - \frac{1}{2} \overset{?}{=} \frac{4}{-2}$$

$$-\frac{4}{2} \overset{\vee}{=} -\frac{4}{2}$$

EXAMPLE 10.   Solve and check: $\dfrac{3x}{x-2} - 4 = \dfrac{14 - 4x}{x - 2}$.

SOLUTION

$$\frac{3x}{x-2} - 4 = \frac{14 - 4x}{x-2} \qquad \text{Replacement set: all real numbers except } x = 2$$

$$(x-2)\frac{3x}{x-2} - 4(x-2) = (x-2)\frac{14 - 4x}{x-2}$$

$$3x - 4x + 8 = 14 - 4x$$

$$3x = 6$$

$$x = 2$$

Since 2 is not in the replacement set of the original equation, the original equation has no solution.

EXAMPLE 11.   A speedboat takes 1.5 times longer to go 120 miles up a river than to return. If the boat cruises at 25 mph in still water, what is the rate of the current.

SOLUTION

Let x = rate of current

$25 - x$ = rate of boat upstream

$25 + x$ = rate of boat downstream

$$\frac{\text{time going}}{\text{upstream}} = 1.5 \; \frac{\text{time going}}{\text{downstream}}$$

$$\frac{120}{25 - x} = (1.5)\frac{120}{25 + x} \qquad \text{Recall } t = d/r \text{ from } d = rt.$$

$$\frac{120}{25 - x} = \frac{180}{25 + x}$$

$$(25 + x)120 = (25 - x)180$$

$$3{,}000 + 120x = 4{,}500 - 180x$$

$$300x = 1{,}500$$

$$x = 5 \text{ mph (rate of current)}$$

CHECK

$$\text{Time upstream} = \frac{120}{20} = 6 \text{ hr}$$

$$\text{Time downstream} = \frac{120}{30} = 4 \text{ hr}$$

Therefore, time upstream is 1.5 times longer than time downstream.

EXERCISE 60

Solve each equation in problems 1 through 22.

1. $\dfrac{1}{x} + \dfrac{2}{3} = \dfrac{1}{2}$

2. $\dfrac{5}{6} - \dfrac{1}{y} = \dfrac{2}{3y}$

3. $\dfrac{1}{m} - \dfrac{1}{9} = \dfrac{4}{9} - \dfrac{2}{3m}$

4. $\dfrac{2}{3x} + \dfrac{1}{2} = \dfrac{4}{x} + \dfrac{4}{3}$

5. $\dfrac{4}{3k} - 2 = \dfrac{k + 4}{6k}$

6. $\dfrac{1}{2t} + \dfrac{1}{8} = \dfrac{2}{t} - \dfrac{1}{4}$

7. $\dfrac{7}{y - 2} - \dfrac{1}{2} = 3$

8. $\dfrac{9}{L + 1} - 1 = \dfrac{12}{L + 1}$

9. $\dfrac{5x}{x + 5} = 2 - \dfrac{25}{x + 5}$

10. $\dfrac{3}{2x - 1} + 4 = \dfrac{6x}{2x - 1}$

11. $\dfrac{2E}{E - 1} = 2 + \dfrac{5}{2E}$

12. $\dfrac{3N}{N - 2} - \dfrac{9}{4N} = 3$

13. $\dfrac{3x}{2 - x} + \dfrac{6}{x - 2} = 3$

14. $5 - \dfrac{2x}{3 - x} = \dfrac{6}{x - 3}$

15. $\dfrac{3x}{x - 4} - 2 = \dfrac{3}{4 - x}$

16. $\dfrac{2}{x - 2} = 3 - \dfrac{5}{2 - x}$

17. $\dfrac{1}{3} - \dfrac{s - 2}{2s + 4} = \dfrac{s + 2}{3s + 6}$

18. $\dfrac{n - 5}{6n - 6} = \dfrac{1}{9} - \dfrac{n - 3}{4n - 4}$

19. $\dfrac{D^2 + 2}{D^2 - 4} = \dfrac{D}{D - 2}$

20. $\dfrac{5}{x - 3} = \dfrac{33 - x}{x^2 - 6x + 9}$

21. $\dfrac{5t - 22}{t^2 - 6t + 9} - \dfrac{11}{t^2 - 3t} - \dfrac{5}{t} = 0$

22. $\dfrac{1}{c^2 - c - 2} - \dfrac{3}{c^2 - 2c - 3} = \dfrac{1}{c^2 - 5c + 6}$

23. One number is 3 larger than another.   Find the numbers if the sum of their reciprocals is equal to the reciprocal of their product.

24. What number added to the numerator and subtracted from the denominator of $\frac{7}{8}$ makes the resulting fraction equal $\frac{1}{2}$?

25. If one United States dollar can be exchanged for $1.08 in Canadian money, how many United States cents would a Canadian receive for each Canadian dollar?   HINT: Solve the proportion $108/100 = 100/x$.   Give the answer to the nearest tenth of a cent.

26. The ratio of the speed of an aircraft (v_a) to the speed of sound (v_s) in the surrounding air is called the Mach number (M).   Thus

$$M = \frac{v_a}{v_s}$$

If an aircraft traveling at 1,904 mph has a Mach number of 2.8, what is the speed of sound in the surrounding air?

27. A jet airliner goes 900 miles with the wind in the same time it takes it to go 700 miles against the wind.   If the wind velocity is 50 mph, what is the cruising speed of the airliner in still air?

28. A boat travels 40 miles upstream in the same time it takes it to travel 52 miles downstream.   If the boat can cruise at 23 mph on still water, what is the speed of the current?

54   ADDITIONAL APPLICATIONS

This section includes additional applications involving fractional equations associated with *optics, electricity, hydraulics, social science, distance-rate-time, work-rate-time, business,* and *puzzles.*   The problems are self contained and require no previous knowledge of the subjects concerned.

EXERCISE 61

OPTICS

In problems 1 through 4 refer to Fig. 1 for appropriate formulas and interpretation.

1. If the focal length f of a thin convex lens is 20 cm and an object is 30 cm from the lens, how far will the image be from the lens?   How much will the object be magnified?

2. If the focal length f of a thin convex lens is 20 cm and an object is 80 cm from the lens, how far will the image be from the lens?   How much will the object be magnified (or reduced)?

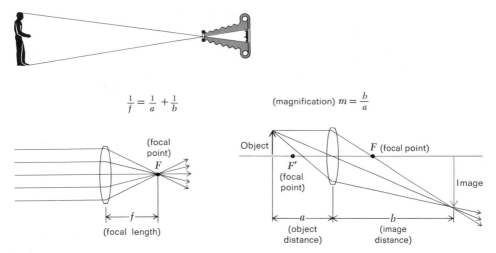

$$\frac{1}{f} = \frac{1}{a} + \frac{1}{b}$$

(magnification) $m = \dfrac{b}{a}$

Figure 1

3. In an experiment to determine the focal length f of a thin convex lens the object and image distances were measured and found to be 15 and 60 cm, respectively. What is the focal length of the lens?

4. Solve the preceding problem with the object and image distances reversed.

HYDRAULICS

In problems 5 and 6 refer to Fig. 2 for appropriate formulas and interpretation.

5. If the large cross-sectional area in a hydraulic lift is approximately 100 sq in. and a person wants to lift a weight of 5,000 lb with a 50-lb force, how large should the small cross-sectional area be?

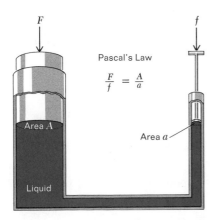

Pascal's Law

$$\frac{F}{f} = \frac{A}{a}$$

Figure 2

6. If the large cross-sectional area of a hydraulic lift is 200 sq in. and the cross-sectional area of the small pipe is 3 sq in., how much force f will be required to lift 5,000 lb?

SOCIAL SCIENCE

7. Anthropologists, in their study of race and human genetic groupings, use ratios called indices.   One widely used index is the cephalic index, the ratio of the breadth of the head to its length expressed as a percent (looking down from above).   Thus

$$C = \frac{100B}{L}$$

(long-headed, $C < 75$; intermediate, $75 \leq C \leq 80$; round-headed, $C > 80$.)   If an Indian tribe in Baja, California had a cephalic index of 66 and the average breadth of their heads was 6.6 in., what was the average length of their heads?

8. Psychologists define intelligence quotient as the ratio of a person's mental age to his chronological age expressed as a percent: $IQ = MA/CA \times 100$.   If a student has a mental age of 12 and an IQ of 150, what is his chronological age?

DISTANCE-RATE-TIME

9. An explosion is set off on the surface of the water 11,000 ft from a ship.   If the sound reaches the ship through the water 7.77 sec before it arrives through the air and if sound travels through water 4.5 times faster than through the air, how fast (to the nearest foot) does sound travel in air and in water?

10. A jet aircraft making a 600-mile trip travels at 200 mph for the first 300 miles and 600 mph for the last 300 miles.   What was its average velocity for the total trip?   The answer is not 400 mph!   REMEMBER: average velocity is defined to be the ratio of the total distance to the total time.

WORK-RATE-TIME

EXAMPLE 12.   It takes 8 hr for one pipe to fill a swimming pool.   Another pipe is installed to speed up the job, and together the pipes can now fill the pool in 3 hours.   How long would it take the second pipe to fill the pool by itself?

SOLUTION

Let x = the number of hours it takes the second pipe to fill the pool alone

$\dfrac{1}{8}$ = rate at which the first pipe fills the pool $\left(\dfrac{1}{8} \text{ of the pool per hour}\right)$

$\dfrac{1}{x}$ = rate at which the second pipe fills the pool $\left(\dfrac{1}{x} \text{ of the pool per hour}\right)$

$\dfrac{1}{8}(3)$ = part of pool filled by first pipe in 3 hr (rate $\cdot$ time)

$\frac{1}{x}(3)$ = part of pool filled by second pipe in 3 hr (rate · time)

1 = one full pool (one whole job)

$$\begin{array}{ccc} \text{part of pool filled by} & & \text{part of pool filled by} \\ \text{first pipe in 3 hr} & + & \text{second pipe in 3 hr} \end{array} = 1$$

$$\frac{3}{8} \quad + \quad \frac{3}{x} \quad = 1$$

$$(8x)\frac{3}{8} + (8x)\frac{3}{x} = (8x)1$$

$$3x + 24 = 8x$$

$$x = 4\tfrac{4}{5} \text{ hr}$$

11. At a family cabin water is pumped and stored in a large water tank. Two pumps are used for this purpose. One can fill the tank by itself in 6 hr and the other can do the job in 9 hr. How long will it take both pumps operating together to fill the tank?

12. If one girl can do a typing job in 5 hr and another in 8 hr, how long will it take both together to do the job?

13. In an electronic computer center a card-sorter operator is given the job of alphabetizing a given quantity of IBM cards. He knows that an older sorter can do the job by itself in 3 hr. With the help of a newer machine the job is completed in 1 hr. How long would it take the new machine to do the job alone?

14. A small-town newspaper owns two printing presses, an older one and a new modern one. The new press operates 2.5 times faster than the older one. Together, they can get out the evening paper in 2 hr. How long would it take each press alone to prepare the evening paper?

ELECTRICAL CIRCUITS

In problems 15 through 18 refer to Fig. 3 for appropriate formulas and interpretation.

15. If a household circuit of 110 volts is drawing a current of 25 amperes, what is the total resistance in the circuit?

16. Two lights with 11 ohms of resistance each are connected into a 110-volt household circuit.

(A) How much current will they draw if they are connected in series?

(B) How much current will they draw if they are connected in parallel?

17. If a 3-volt battery has two lights connected to it in series, find the resistance of the second light if the resistance of the first is 8 ohms and the current is $\frac{1}{4}$ ampere.

Ohm's Law

Simple circuit:

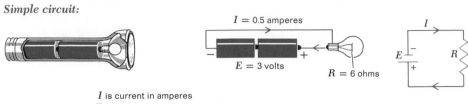

$I = 0.5$ amperes

$E = 3$ volts

$R = 6$ ohms

I is current in amperes
E is electromotive force in volts
R is resistance in ohms

$$I = \frac{E}{R}$$

Series circuit:

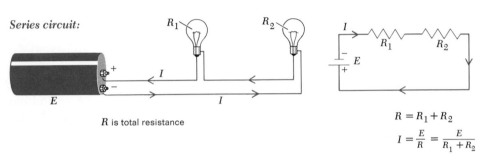

R is total resistance

$$R = R_1 + R_2$$
$$I = \frac{E}{R} = \frac{E}{R_1 + R_2}$$

Parallel circuit:

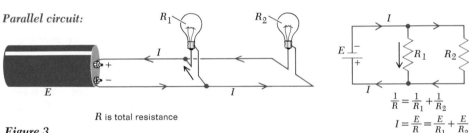

R is total resistance

$$\frac{1}{R} = \frac{1}{R_1} + \frac{1}{R_2}$$
$$I = \frac{E}{R} = \frac{E}{R_1} + \frac{E}{R_2}$$

Figure 3

18. If a 3-volt battery has two lights connected to it in parallel, find the resistance of the second light if the resistance of the first is 20 ohms and the current is $\frac{1}{4}$ ampere.

BUSINESS

19. The simple interest formula is occasionally found in the form $P = A/(1 + rt)$ where r is the annual rate, P the principal, and A the amount due after t years. Find r if $A = 114$, $P = 100$, and $t = 4$.

20. In the preceding problem find t if $P = 100$, $A = 127$, and $r = 4\frac{1}{2}$ percent.

PUZZLES

21. The following famous Hindu puzzle is found in various forms in many different books (the version included here is from Mr. Maurice Kraitchik's "Mathematical Recreations," Dover, 1953): While three watchmen were guarding an orchard, a thief slipped in and stole some apples. On his way out he met the three watchmen one after the other, and to each in turn he gave a half of the apples he then had, and two besides. Thus he managed to escape with one apple. How many had he stolen originally?

55   FORMULAS AND EQUATIONS WITH SEVERAL VARIABLES

One of the immediate applications you will have for algebra in other courses is the changing of formulas or equations to alternate equivalent forms. The following examples are more or less typical.

EXAMPLE 13.   Solve the formula $c = wrt/1{,}000$ for t (the formula gives the cost c of using an electrical appliance; w = power in watts, r = rate per kilowatt hour, t = time in hours).

SOLUTION

$$\frac{wrt}{1{,}000} = c$$

$$\frac{1{,}000}{wr} \cdot \frac{wrt}{1{,}000} = \frac{1{,}000}{wr} \cdot c$$

$$t = \frac{1{,}000c}{wr}$$

EXAMPLE 14.   Solve the formula $A = P + Prt$ for r (simple interest formula).

SOLUTION

$$P + Prt = A$$

$$Prt = A - P$$

$$r = \frac{A - P}{Pt}$$

EXAMPLE 15.   Solve the formula $A = P + Prt$ for P.

SOLUTION

$$P + Prt = A$$

$$P(1 + rt) = A$$

$$P = \frac{A}{1 + rt}$$

EXAMPLE 16. Solve the formula $I = (E/R_1) + (E/R_2)$ for R_1 (see Fig. 3, Sec. 54 for the physical interpretation).

SOLUTION

$$I = \frac{E}{R_1} + \frac{E}{R_2}$$

$$(R_1 R_2)I = (R_1 R_2)\frac{E}{R_1} + (R_1 R_2)\frac{E}{R_2}$$

$$R_1 R_2 I = R_2 E + R_1 E$$

$$R_1 R_2 I - R_1 E = R_2 E$$

$$R_1(R_2 I - E) = R_2 E$$

$$R_1 = \frac{R_2 E}{R_2 I - E}$$

EXERCISE 62

The following formulas and equations are widely used in science or mathematics.

1. Solve $A = P + I$ for I (SIMPLE INTEREST).
2. Solve $R = R_1 + R_2$ for R_2 (ELECTRICAL CIRCUITS—RESISTANCE IN SERIES).
3. Solve $d = rt$ for r (DISTANCE-RATE-TIME).
4. Solve $d = 1,100t$ for t (SOUND DISTANCE IN AIR).
5. Solve $I = Prt$ for t (SIMPLE INTEREST).
6. Solve $C = 2\pi r$ for r (CIRCUMFERENCE OF A CIRCLE).
7. Solve $C = \pi D$ for π (CIRCUMFERENCE OF A CIRCLE).
8. Solve $e = mc^2$ for m (MASS-ENERGY EQUATION).
9. Solve $ax + b = 0$ for x (FIRST-DEGREE POLYNOMIAL EQUATION IN ONE VARIABLE).
10. Solve $p = 2a + 2b$ for a (PERIMETER OF A RECTANGLE).
11. Solve $s = 2t - 5$ for t (SLOPE-INTERCEPT FORM FOR A LINE).
12. Solve $y = mx + b$ for m (SLOPE-INTERCEPT FORM FOR A LINE).
13. Solve $3x - 4y - 12 = 0$ for y (LINEAR EQUATION IN TWO VARIABLES).
14. Solve $Ax + By + C = 0$ for y (LINEAR EQUATION IN TWO VARIABLES).
15. Solve $I = \dfrac{E}{R}$ for E (ELECTRICAL CIRCUITS—OHM'S LAW).
16. Solve $m = \dfrac{b}{a}$ for a (OPTICS—MAGNIFICATION).

17. Solve $C = \dfrac{100B}{L}$ for L (ANTHROPOLOGY—CEPHALIC INDEX).

18. Solve IQ $= \dfrac{(100)(\text{MA})}{(\text{CA})}$ for (CA)   (PSYCHOLOGY—INTELLIGENCE QUOTIENT).

19. Solve $F = G\dfrac{m_1 m_2}{d^2}$ for m_1 (GRAVITATIONAL FORCE BETWEEN TWO MASSES).

20. Solve $F = G\dfrac{m_1 m_2}{d^2}$ for G (GRAVITATIONAL FORCE BETWEEN TWO MASSES).

21. Solve $A = \dfrac{h}{2}(b_1 + b_2)$ for h (AREA OF A TRAPEZOID).

22. Solve $A = \dfrac{h}{2}(b_1 + b_2)$ for b_2 (AREA OF A TRAPEZOID).

23. Solve C $= \frac{5}{9}$ (F $-$ 32) for F   (CENTIGRADE-FAHRENHEIT).
24. Solve F $= \frac{9}{5}$ C $+$ 32 for C   (FAHRENHEIT-CENTIGRADE).
25. Solve $\dfrac{1}{f} = \dfrac{1}{a} + \dfrac{1}{b}$ for f (OPTICS—FOCAL LENGTH).

26. Solve $\dfrac{1}{R} = \dfrac{1}{R_1} + \dfrac{1}{R_2}$ for R_1 (ELECTRICAL CIRCUITS—RESISTANCE IN PARALLEL).

56   CHAPTER SUMMARY

GENERAL

This chapter has been concerned with quotient of polynomial forms called rational expressions. We found that they have properties very similar to rational numbers, their addition, subtraction, multiplication, and division involve essentially the same rules.

Rational expressions are encountered with great frequency in science and mathematics. An early acquired skill in their use will be amply rewarded in many courses.

SPECIFIC

Describe, define, or give examples of each of the following:

1. **Rational expressions**
multiplication
division
addition
subtraction

2. Complex fractions
express as a simple fraction
3. Rational equations
solve and check
4. Changing formulas to alternate equivalent forms

EXERCISE 63   CHAPTER REVIEW

In problems 1 through 12 perform the indicated operations and simplify.

1. $\dfrac{-4x^2y^3}{3a^2b^2} \div \dfrac{-2xy^2}{3ab}$

2. $\dfrac{4x^2y}{3ab^2} \div \left(\dfrac{2a^2x^2}{b^2y} \cdot \dfrac{6a}{2y^2} \right)$

3. $\dfrac{x^3 - x}{x^2 - x} \div \dfrac{x^2 + 2x + 1}{x}$

4. $(d - 2)^2 \div \dfrac{d^2 - 4}{d - 2}$

5. $\dfrac{y^2 - y - 6}{(y + 2)^2} \cdot \dfrac{2 + y}{3 - y}$

6. $\dfrac{x^3 + x^2 - 6x}{(x + 3)(x - 2)} = x$

except for what values of x?

7. $\dfrac{1}{10p^2} - \dfrac{3}{4pq} + \dfrac{2}{5q^2}$

8. $\dfrac{x + 1}{x + 2} - \dfrac{x + 2}{x + 3}$

9. $1 - \dfrac{m - 1}{m + 1}$

10. $\dfrac{x}{4x + x^2} + \dfrac{2x}{3x^2 - 48}$

11. $\dfrac{2x + 4}{2x - y} + \dfrac{2x - y}{y - 2x}$

12. $\dfrac{\dfrac{x}{y} - \dfrac{y}{x}}{\dfrac{x}{y} + 1}$

Solve each equation (problems 13–15).

13. $\dfrac{2}{3m} - \dfrac{1}{4m} = \dfrac{1}{12}$

14. $\dfrac{5}{2x + 3} - 5 = \dfrac{-5x}{2x + 3}$

15. $\dfrac{3x}{x - 5} - 8 = \dfrac{15}{x - 5}$

16. One number is twice another. Find the two numbers if the reciprocal of the smaller minus the reciprocal of the larger is equal to the reciprocal of their product.

17. If an airplane can travel 300 miles against the wind in the same time it travels 400 miles with the wind and the speed of the wind is 25 mph, what is the cruising speed of the airplane in still air?

18. Solve $W = I^2R$ for R (ELECTRICAL CIRCUITS, POWER IN WATTS).

19. Solve $S = \dfrac{n(a + L)}{2}$ for L (ARITHMETIC PROGRESSION).

20. Solve $\dfrac{1}{f} = \dfrac{1}{f_1} + \dfrac{1}{f_2}$ for f_1 (OPTICS).

21. Solve $P = \dfrac{A}{1 + rt}$ for r (SIMPLE INTEREST).

22. Given $I = E/R$ and $W = IE$, write a formula for W in terms of E and R.

exponents and radicals

57 LAWS OF POSITIVE INTEGRAL EXPONENTS

Earlier we defined what we meant by a number raised to a positive integral power

$$a^n = a \cdot a \cdots a \qquad n \text{ factors of } a$$

and soon identified what we called the first law of exponents:

If m and n are positive integers and a is a real number, then

$$a^m a^n = a^{m+n}$$

By now you probably use this law almost subconsciously when multiplying polynomial forms.

When simplifying certain rational forms, such as $2x^2y^3/4xy^5$, we relied on the definition of a^n and the important property of fractions,

$$\frac{ak}{bk} = \frac{a}{b}$$

When we encountered exponent forms such as $(2y^2)^3$, we relied on the definition of a^n and the first law of exponents to write the alternate equivalent form $8y^6$. When you look back on it, we have developed quite a bit of algebra on the basis of these few elementary properties of exponents and fractions, and we will continue to use these properties where appropriate.

When more complicated expressions involving exponents are encountered, other exponent laws combined with the first law provide an efficient tool for simplifying and manipulating these expressions. In this section we will introduce and discuss four additional exponent properties. In the next section we will extend the meaning of exponent to include all integers (zero and negative integers as well as the positive integers), and we will do this in such a way that the five laws of exponents we discuss in this section continue to hold. These five laws should be learned well since they are used with considerable frequency almost any place that algebra is used. Each law will be introduced by an example, and at the conclusion of the discussion all five laws will be stated together for convenient reference.

In each of the following expressions, the replacement set for the variables m and n is the set of natural numbers; the replacement set for the variables a and b is the set of real numbers (excluding division by zero, of course).

EXAMPLE 1.
$$a^3 a^4 = \overset{\substack{3 \\ \text{factors}}}{(a \cdot a \cdot a)} \overset{\substack{4 \\ \text{factors}}}{(a \cdot a \cdot a \cdot a)} = \overset{\substack{3+4 \\ \text{factors}}}{(a \cdot a \cdot a \cdot a \cdot a \cdot a \cdot a)} = a^{3+4} = a^7$$

Law 1. $a^m a^n = a^{m+n}$

EXAMPLE 2.
$$(a^3)^4 = \overset{\substack{4 \text{ groups of} \\ 3 \text{ factors each}}}{a^3 \cdot a^3 \cdot a^3 \cdot a^3} = (a \cdot a \cdot a)(a \cdot a \cdot a)(a \cdot a \cdot a)(a \cdot a \cdot a)$$

$$= \overset{\substack{4 \cdot 3 \\ \text{factors}}}{(a \cdot a \cdot a \cdot a \cdot a \cdot a \cdot a \cdot a \cdot a \cdot a \cdot a \cdot a)} = a^{4 \cdot 3} = a^{12}$$

Law 2. $(a^n)^m = a^{mn}$

EXAMPLE 3.
$$(ab)^4 = \overset{\substack{4 \\ \text{factors of } (ab)}}{(ab)(ab)(ab)(ab)} = \overset{\substack{4 \\ \text{factors}}}{(a \cdot a \cdot a \cdot a)} \overset{\substack{4 \\ \text{factors}}}{(b \cdot b \cdot b \cdot b)} = a^4 b^4$$

Law 3. $(ab)^m = a^m b^m$

EXAMPLE 4.
$$\left(\frac{a}{b}\right)^5 = \overset{\substack{5 \\ \text{factors of } a/b}}{\left(\frac{a}{b} \cdot \frac{a}{b} \cdot \frac{a}{b} \cdot \frac{a}{b} \cdot \frac{a}{b}\right)} = \frac{a \cdot a \cdot a \cdot a \cdot a}{b \cdot b \cdot b \cdot b \cdot b} = \frac{a^5}{b^5}$$

Law 4. $\left(\dfrac{a}{b}\right)^m = \dfrac{a^m}{b^m}$

EXAMPLE 5. $\dfrac{a^7}{a^3} = \dfrac{a \cdot a \cdot a \cdot a \cdot a \cdot a \cdot a}{a \cdot a \cdot a} = \dfrac{(a \cdot a \cdot a)(a \cdot a \cdot a \cdot a)}{(a \cdot a \cdot a)} = a^{7-3} = a^4$

$\dfrac{a^3}{a^3} = \dfrac{a \cdot a \cdot a}{a \cdot a \cdot a} = 1$

$\dfrac{a^4}{a^7} = \dfrac{a \cdot a \cdot a \cdot a}{a \cdot a \cdot a \cdot a \cdot a \cdot a \cdot a} = \dfrac{(a \cdot a \cdot a \cdot a)}{(a \cdot a \cdot a \cdot a)(a \cdot a \cdot a)} = \dfrac{1}{a^{7-4}} = \dfrac{1}{a^3}$

Law 5. $\dfrac{a^m}{a^n} = \begin{cases} a^{m-n} & \textit{if } m > n \\[2mm] 1 & \textit{if } m = n \\[2mm] \dfrac{1}{a^{n-m}} & \textit{if } n > m \end{cases}$

The laws of exponents are theorems, and as such they require proofs. We have only given plausible arguments for each law; formal proofs of these laws require a property of the natural numbers, called the inductive property, which is beyond the scope of this course.

It is very important to observe and remember that the laws of exponents apply to products and quotients, and not to sums and differences. Many mistakes are made in algebra by people applying a law of exponents to the wrong algebraic form. The exponent laws are summarized below for convenient reference.

LAWS OF EXPONENTS

1. $a^m a^n = a^{m+n}$

2. $(a^n)^m = a^{mn}$

3. $(ab)^m = a^m b^m$

4. $\left(\dfrac{a}{b}\right)^m = \dfrac{a^m}{b^m}$

5. $\dfrac{a^m}{a^n} = \begin{cases} a^{m-n} & \textit{if } m > n \\[2mm] 1 & \textit{if } m = n \\[2mm] \dfrac{1}{a^{n-m}} & \textit{if } n > m \end{cases}$

EXAMPLE 6.

▶ $x^{12} x^{13} \boxed{= x^{12+13}} = x^{25}$

▶ $(t^7)^5 \boxed{= t^{5 \cdot 7}} = t^{35}$

▶ $(xy)^5 = x^5y^5$

▶ $\left(\dfrac{u}{v}\right)^3 = \dfrac{u^3}{v^3}$

▶ $\dfrac{x^{12}}{x^4} \boxed{= x^{12-4}} = x^8$

▶ $\dfrac{t^4}{t^9} \boxed{= \dfrac{1}{t^{9-4}}} = \dfrac{1}{t^5}$

▶ $(x^2y^3)^4 \boxed{= (x^2)^4(y^3)^4} = x^8y^{12}$

▶ $\left(\dfrac{u^3}{v^4}\right)^3 \boxed{= \dfrac{(u^3)^3}{(v^4)^3}} = \dfrac{u^9}{v^{12}}$

▶ $\dfrac{2x^9y^{11}}{4x^{12}y^7} \boxed{= \dfrac{2}{4}\cdot\dfrac{x^9}{x^{12}}\cdot\dfrac{y^{11}}{y^7} = \dfrac{1}{2}\cdot\dfrac{1}{x^3}\cdot\dfrac{y^4}{1}} = \dfrac{y^4}{2x^3}$

NOTE: As before, the "dotted boxes" are used to indicate steps that are usually carried out mentally.

Knowing the rules of the game of chess doesn't make one a good chess player; similarly, memorizing the laws of exponents doesn't necessarily make one good at using them. To acquire skill in their use, one must use these laws in a fairly large variety of problems. The following exercises should help you acquire this skill.

EXERCISE 64

Replace the question marks with appropriate numerals or expressions.

1. $x^5x^2 = x^?$

2. $10^5 \cdot 10^{13} = 10^?$

3. $y^8 = y^?y^3$

4. $10^9 = 10^6 \cdot 10^?$

5. $(u^4)^3 = u^?$

6. $(v^2)^3 = ?$

7. $x^{10} = (x^?)^5$

8. $y^{12} = (y^6)^?$

9. $(uv)^5 = u^5v^?$

10. $(xy)^8 = ?$

11. $x^3y^3 = (xy)^?$

12. $(p^4q^4) = (pq)^?$

13. $\left(\dfrac{x}{y}\right)^5 = \dfrac{x^5}{y^?}$

14. $\left(\dfrac{a}{b}\right)^8 = ?$

15. $\dfrac{u^7}{v^7} = \left(\dfrac{u}{v}\right)^?$

16. $\dfrac{x^3}{y^3} = \left(\dfrac{x}{y}\right)^?$ 17. $\dfrac{t^6}{t^4} = t^?$ 18. $\dfrac{m^{12}}{m^4} = ?$

19. $t^3 = \dfrac{t^?}{t^4}$ 20. $m^6 = \dfrac{m^8}{m^?}$ 21. $\dfrac{a^4}{a^{10}} = \dfrac{1}{a^?}$

22. $\dfrac{b^3}{b^8} = ?$ 23. $\dfrac{1}{u^2} = \dfrac{u^?}{u^9}$ 24. $\dfrac{1}{n^6} = \dfrac{n^8}{n^?}$

Simplify, using appropriate laws of exponents.

25. $(2 \times 10^3)(3 \times 10^{12})(4 \times 10^7)$ 26. $(2x^2)(3x^3)(x^4)$

27. $\dfrac{2x^3y^8}{6x^7y^2}$ 28. $\dfrac{9u^8v^6}{3u^4v^8}$ 29. $(x^3)^3$

30. $(10^4)^5$ 31. $(ab)^{10}$ 32. $(cd)^{12}$

33. $(x^2y^3)^4$ 34. $(p^2q^5)^3$ 35. $(3a^3b^2)^3$

36. $(2s^2t^4)^4$ 37. $2(c^2d)^4$ 38. $6(xy^3)^5$

39. $\left(\dfrac{m}{n}\right)^5$ 40. $\left(\dfrac{u}{v}\right)^6$ 41. $\left(\dfrac{a^3}{b^2}\right)^4$

42. $\left(\dfrac{c^2}{d^5}\right)^3$ 43. $\left(\dfrac{x^2y}{2w^2}\right)^3$ 44. $\left(\dfrac{ab^3}{c^2d}\right)^4$

45. $\dfrac{(2xy^3)^2}{(4x^2y)^3}$ 46. $\dfrac{(4u^3v)^3}{(2uv^2)^6}$ 47. $\dfrac{(-2x^2)^3}{(2^2x)^4}$

48. $\dfrac{(9x^3)^2}{(-3x)^2}$ 49. $\dfrac{-2^4}{(-2a^2)^4}$ 50. $\dfrac{(-x^2)^2}{(-x^3)^3}$

58   INTEGRAL EXPONENTS—POSITIVE, NEGATIVE, AND ZERO

In this section we will extend the meaning of exponent to include zero and negative integers; symbols such as 8^0 and 7^{-3} will then be defined. Thus, typical scientific expressions such as *"The focal length of a thin lens is given by $f^{-1} = a^{-1} + b^{-1}$,"* *"The diameter of a red blood corpuscle is approximately 8×10^{-5} cm,"* or *"The amount of water found in the air as vapor is about 9×10^{-6} times that found in the seas"* will then make sense.

In extending the concept of exponent beyond the natural numbers, we will require that any new exponent symbol be defined in such a way that all five laws of exponents for natural numbers continue to hold. This results in the necessity of having only one set of laws for all types of exponents rather than a different set of laws for each new kind of exponent introduced.

We will start by defining the zero exponent.   If all the exponent laws must hold even if some of the exponents are zero, then a^0 $(a \neq 0)$ should be defined so that when the first law of exponents is applied,

$$a^0 \cdot a^2 = a^{0+2} = a^2$$

This suggests that a^0 should be defined as 1 for all nonzero real numbers a, since 1 is the only real number that gives a^2 when multiplied by a^2 (that is, 1 is the only multiplicative identity in the real-number system).   If we let $a = 0$ and follow the same reasoning, we find that

$$0^0 \cdot 0^2 = 0^{0+2} = 0^2 = 0$$

and 0^0 could be any real number; hence it is not uniquely determined.   For this reason we choose not to define 0^0.

DEFINITION 1: $a^0 = 1$ *for all real numbers $a \neq 0$.*

EXAMPLE 7

▶ $5^0 = 1$

▶ $325^0 = 1$

▶ $(\frac{1}{3})^0 = 1$

▶ $t^0 = 1 \ (t \neq 0)$

▶ $(x^2 y^3)^0 = 1 \ (x \neq 0, \ y \neq 0)$

To get an idea of how a negative integral exponent should be defined, we can proceed as above.   If the first law of exponents is to hold, then a^{-2} $(a \neq 0)$ must be defined so that

$$a^{-2} \cdot a^2 = a^{-2+2} = a^0 = 1$$

Thus a^{-2} must be the reciprocal of a^2; that is,

$$a^{-2} = \frac{1}{a^2}$$

This kind of reasoning leads us to the following general definition.

DEFINITION 2: $a^{-n} = 1/a^n$ *where n is a positive integer and a is a nonzero real number.*

Of course, it follows from Definition 2 and properties of equality that

$$a^n = \frac{1}{a^{-n}}$$

EXAMPLE 8

▶ $10^{-3} = \dfrac{1}{10^3} = \dfrac{1}{1,000} = 0.001$

▶ $\dfrac{1}{x^{-8}} = x^8$

▶ $a^{-7} = \dfrac{1}{a^7}$

▶ $\dfrac{x^{-3}}{y^{-5}} = \dfrac{x^{-3}}{1} \cdot \dfrac{1}{y^{-5}} = \dfrac{1}{x^3} \cdot \dfrac{y^5}{1} = \dfrac{y^5}{x^3}$

It can be shown (though the demonstration is technically difficult) that *under the definitions of the zero exponent and the negative integral exponent given above that all of the exponent laws will continue to hold and that no contradictions will be introduced into our mathematical system.* We will accept the results of this theorem without proof.

With the definition of a negative exponent and a zero exponent behind us, we can now replace the fifth law of exponents with a simpler form that does not have any restrictions on the relative size of the exponents. Thus

$$\frac{a^m}{a^n} = a^{m-n} = \frac{1}{a^{n-m}}$$

Table 1 provides a summary of all of our work on exponents to this time.

TABLE 1   INTEGRAL EXPONENTS AND THEIR LAWS   (SUMMARY)

DEFINITION OF a^p *p an integer and a a real number*	LAWS OF EXPONENTS *n and m integers, a and b real numbers*
1. *If p is a positive integer, then* $a^p = a \cdot a \cdots a$ *p factors of a* EXAMPLE: $3^5 = 3 \cdot 3 \cdot 3 \cdot 3 \cdot 3$	1. $a^m a^n = a^{m+n}$
2. *If p = 0, then* $a^p = 1$ $a \neq 0$ EXAMPLE: $3^0 = 1$	2. $(a^n)^m = a^{mn}$ 3. $(ab)^m = a^m b^m$ 4. $\left(\dfrac{a}{b}\right)^m = \dfrac{a^m}{b^m}$
3. *If p is a negative integer, then* $a^p = \dfrac{1}{a^{-p}}$ $a \neq 0$ EXAMPLE: $3^{-4} = \dfrac{1}{3^{-(-4)}} = \dfrac{1}{3^4}$	5. $\dfrac{a^m}{a^n} = a^{m-n} = \dfrac{1}{a^{n-m}}$

EXAMPLE 9

▶ $\dfrac{2^5}{2^8} = 2^{5-8} = 2^{-3}$ or $\dfrac{2^5}{2^8} = \dfrac{1}{2^{8-5}} = \dfrac{1}{2^3}$

▶ $\dfrac{10^{-3}}{10^6} = 10^{-3-6} = 10^{-9}$ or $\dfrac{10^{-3}}{10^6} = \dfrac{1}{10^{6-(-3)}} = \dfrac{1}{10^{6+3}} = \dfrac{1}{10^9}$

EXAMPLE 10.   Simplify and express answers using positive exponents only.

▶ $a^5 a^{-2} \;\boxed{= a^{5-2}}\; = a^3$

▶ $(a^{-3}b^2)^{-2} \;\boxed{= (a^{-3})^{-2}(b^2)^{-2}}\; = a^6 b^{-4} = \dfrac{a^6}{b^4}$

▶ $\left(\dfrac{a^{-5}}{a^{-2}}\right)^{-1} \;\boxed{= \dfrac{(a^{-5})^{-1}}{(a^{-2})^{-1}}}\; = \dfrac{a^5}{a^2} = a^3$

▶ $\dfrac{4x^{-3}y^{-5}}{6x^{-4}y^3} \;\boxed{= \dfrac{2x^{-3-(-4)}}{3y^{3-(-5)}} = \dfrac{2x^{-3+4}}{3y^{3+5}}}\; = \dfrac{2x}{3y^8}$

or, changing to positive exponents first,

$\dfrac{4x^{-3}y^{-5}}{6x^{-4}y^3} = \dfrac{2x^4}{3x^3y^3y^5} = \dfrac{2x}{3y^8}$

▶ $\dfrac{10^{-4} \cdot 10^2}{10^{-3} \cdot 10^5} \;\boxed{= \dfrac{10^{-4+2}}{10^{-3+5}}}\; = \dfrac{10^{-2}}{10^2} = \dfrac{1}{10^4} = \dfrac{1}{10{,}000} = 0.0001$

▶ $\left(\dfrac{m^{-3}m^3}{n^{-2}}\right)^{-2} \;\boxed{= \left(\dfrac{m^{-3+3}}{n^{-2}}\right)^{-2} = \left(\dfrac{m^0}{n^{-2}}\right)^{-2}}\; = \left(\dfrac{1}{n^{-2}}\right)^{-2} = \dfrac{1^{-2}}{(n^{-2})^{-2}} = \dfrac{1}{n^4}$

▶ $\dfrac{3^{-2} + 2^{-1}}{11} = \dfrac{\dfrac{1}{3^2} + \dfrac{1}{2}}{11} = \dfrac{\dfrac{2}{18} + \dfrac{9}{18}}{11} \;\boxed{= \dfrac{11}{18} \div 11}\; = \dfrac{11}{18} \cdot \dfrac{1}{11} = \dfrac{1}{18}$

▶ $(a^{-1} - b^{-1})^2 = \left(\dfrac{1}{a} - \dfrac{1}{b}\right)^2 = \left(\dfrac{b - a}{ab}\right)^2 = \dfrac{b^2 - 2ab + a^2}{a^2b^2}$

EXERCISE 65

Simplify and write your answer using positive exponents only.

1. 10^0

2. $8,732^0$

3. 2^{-2}

4. 3^{-3}

5. $\dfrac{1}{3^{-2}}$

6. $\dfrac{1}{4^{-3}}$

7. $10^{-4} \cdot 10^4$

8. $2^{10} \cdot 2^{-10}$

9. $\dfrac{10^8}{10^{-3}}$

10. $\dfrac{10^3}{10^{-7}}$

11. $\dfrac{10^{-2}}{10^{-4}}$

12. $\dfrac{10^{-5}}{10^{-3}}$

13. $\dfrac{10^{23} \cdot 10^{-11}}{10^{-3} \cdot 10^{-2}}$

14. $\dfrac{10^{-13} \cdot 10^{-4}}{10^{-21} \cdot 10^3}$

15. $\dfrac{8 \times 10^{-3}}{2 \times 10^5}$

16. $\dfrac{18 \times 10^{12}}{6 \times 10^{-4}}$

17. $(2^{-3})^{-2}$

18. $(10^{-4})^{-3}$

19. $(10^{-4})^3$

20. $(3^{-2})^2$

21. $(2^{-3}3^2)^{-2}$

22. $(2^2 3^{-3})^{-1}$

23. $(10^2 3^0)^{-2}$

24. $(10^{12} 10^{-12})^{-1}$

25. $\dfrac{2^{-1} + 3^{-1}}{25}$

26. $\dfrac{12}{2^{-2} + 3^{-1}}$

27. $(10^{-1} + 10^{-1})^2$

28. $(2^{-2} + 2^{-2})^2$

29. $(2^{-2} + 3^{-2})^{-1}$

30. $(10^{-2} + 10^{-3})^{-1}$

31. $x^3 x^{-3}$

32. $y^{-5} y^5$

33. $\dfrac{a^8}{a^{-4}}$

34. $\dfrac{b^{-3}}{b^5}$

35. $(2cd^2)^{-3}$

36. $\dfrac{1}{(3mn)^{-2}}$

37. $(3x^3 y^{-2})^2$

38. $(2MN^{-3})^3$

39. $(x^{-3} y^2)^{-2}$

40. $(m^4 n^{-5})^{-3}$

41. $\dfrac{4x^{-2} y^{-3}}{2x^{-3} y^{-1}}$

42. $\dfrac{2a^6 b^{-2}}{16a^{-3} b^2}$

43. $\left(\dfrac{n^{-3}}{n^{-2}}\right)^{-2}$

44. $\left(\dfrac{x^{-1}}{x^{-8}}\right)^{-1}$

45. $\left(\dfrac{2x^{-3} y^2}{4xy^{-1}}\right)^{-2}$

46. $\left(\dfrac{6mn^{-2}}{3m^{-1} n^2}\right)^{-3}$

47. $(x + y)^{-2}$

48. $(a^2 - b^2)^{-1}$

49. $\dfrac{x^{-1} + y^{-1}}{x + y}$

50. $\dfrac{c - d}{c^{-1} - d^{-1}}$

51. $(x^{-1} + y^{-1})^{-1}$

52. $(x^{-1} - y^{-1})^2$

59   POWER–OF–TEN NOTATION AND APPLICATIONS

Work in science often involves the use of very, very large numbers. *The energy of a laser beam can go as high as 10,000,000,000,000 watts per sq cm.* Also involved is the use of very, very small numbers. *The mass of one water molecule is 0.00000000000000000000003 grams.* Writing and working with numbers of this type in standard decimal notation is generally awkward. Earlier in the course we used power-of-ten notation to represent very large numbers; now, with the introduction of negative exponents, we can also use power-of-ten notation to represent very small numbers (see Figs. 1 and 2). Together these power forms provide a valuable tool for the person working with large and small quantities.

For computational purposes, or simply for convenience, it is often desirable to convert a decimal fraction to a power-of-ten form. *Any decimal fraction, however large or small, can be represented as the product of a number between 1 and 10 and a power of 10.*

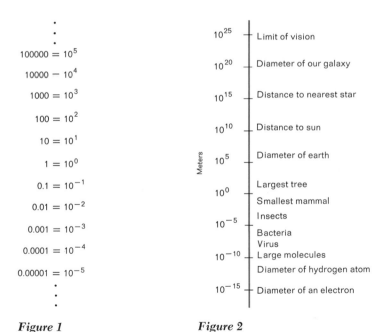

Figure 1   *Figure 2*

EXAMPLE 11:   DECIMAL FRACTIONS AND POWER-OF-TEN NOTATION.

$$5 = 5 \times 10^0$$
$$35 = 3.5 \times 10$$
$$430 = 4.3 \times 10^2$$
$$5{,}870 = 5.87 \times 10^3$$
$$8{,}910{,}000 = 8.91 \times 10^6$$

$$0.7 = 7 \times 10^{-1}$$
$$0.083 = 8.3 \times 10^{-2}$$
$$0.0043 = 4.3 \times 10^{-3}$$
$$0.000687 = 6.87 \times 10^{-4}$$
$$0.00000036 = 3.6 \times 10^{-7}$$

Can you discover a simple mechanical rule that relates the number of decimal places that the decimal is moved with the power of 10 that is used?

EXAMPLE 12:   EVALUATION OF A COMPLICATED ARITHMETIC PROBLEM.

$$\frac{(0.26)(720)}{(48{,}000{,}000)(0.0013)} = \frac{(2.6 \times 10^{-1})(7.2 \times 10^2)}{(4.8 \times 10^7)(1.3 \times 10^{-3})}$$

$$= \frac{(2.6)(7.2)}{(4.8)(1.3)} \cdot \frac{(10^{-1})(10^2)}{(10^7)(10^{-3})}$$

$$= 3 \times 10^{-3} \text{ or } 0.003$$

EXAMPLE 13:   SCIENTIFIC COMPUTATION.   Man is able to look back into time by looking out into space. Since light travels at a fast but finite rate, he is seeing heavenly bodies not as they exist now, but as they existed sometime in the past. If the distance between the sun and the earth is approximately 9.3×10^7 miles and if light travels at the rate of approximately 1.86×10^5 miles per sec, we see the sun as it was how many minutes ago?

SOLUTION

$$d = rt$$
$$t = d/r$$

$$t = \frac{9.3 \times 10^7}{1.86 \times 10^5} = 5 \times 10^2 = 500 \text{ sec or } 500/60 = 8.3 \text{ min}$$

Hence, we always see the sun as it was 8.3 min ago.

EXERCISE 66

Write each of the numbers in problems 1 through 18 as the product of a number between 1 and 10 and a power of 10.

1. 52   2. 47   3. 0.7
4. 0.2   5. 340   6. 283
7. 0.085   8. 0.017   9. 6,800

10. 4,930   **11.** 0.000723   **12.** 0.0000000729

13. 42,700,000,000,000   **14.** 5,460,000,000,000,000,000

15. The distance that light travels in one year is called a light-year. It is approximately 5,870,000,000,000 miles.

16. The energy of a laser beam can go as high as 10,000,000,000,000 watts.

17. The mass of one water molecule is 0.00000000000000000000003 grams.

18. The nucleus of an atom has a diameter of a little more than 1/100,000 that of the whole atom.

Write each of the numbers in problems 19 through 34 as a decimal fraction.

19. 3.7×10 **20.** 5.72×10 **21.** 7.1×10^3

22. 4×10^4 **23.** 8.37×10^{-1} **24.** 9.7×10^{-2}

25. 4×10^{-4} **26.** 5×10^{-3} **27.** 2.51×10^9

28. 6.5×10^{12} **29.** 5.9×10^{-7} **30.** 6.3×10^{-12}

31. The distance from the earth to the sun is approximately 9.3×10^7 miles.

32. The diameter of the sun is approximately 8.65×10^5 miles.

33. The probable mass of a hydrogen atom is 1.7×10^{-24} grams.

34. The diameter of a red corpuscle is approximately 7.5×10^{-5} cm.

35. Change each of the numerals in the following excerpt from Isaac Asimov's "The New Intelligent Man's Guide to Science" (p. 46 Basic Books, 1965) to power-of-ten notation: "The rate of radiation of energy by the sun requires the disappearance of solar mass at the rate of 4.2 million tons per second. At first blush this seems a frightening loss, but the total mass of the sun is 2,200,000,000,-000,000,000,000,000,000 tons, so the sun loses only 0.00000000000000000002 per cent of its mass each second. Assuming the sun to have been in existence for 6 billion years, as astronomers now believe, and if it has been radiating at its present rate all that time, it would have expended only 1/40,000 of its mass. It is easy to see, then, that the sun can continue to radiate energy at its present rate for billions of years to come."

36. Change each of the power-of-ten numerals in the following excerpt from "Principles of Animal Ecology" by W. C. Allee and others (p. 177, W. B. Saunders, 1949,) to decimal-fraction form: "The oceans are the great reservoirs of water. They occupy 70.8 percent of the 5.101×10^8 square kilometers of the earth's surface and have an average depth of 3795 meters. Their total volume is about 1.37×10^9 cubic kilometers. The amount of water frozen into the ice sheets equals some 9.3% of this amount. That found in the air as vapor is only about 9×10^{-6} of that in the sea. In more direct terms, if all moisture in the air were precipitated and collected in the ocean, the sea level would be raised only 3.5 centimeters."

Convert each of the numerals in problems 37 through 40 to power-of-ten notation, simplify, and express the final answer in power-of-ten form and as a decimal fraction.

37. $\dfrac{(90{,}000)(0.000002)}{0.006}$

38. $\dfrac{(0.0006)(4000)}{0.00012}$

39. $\dfrac{(60{,}000)(0.000003)}{(0.0004)(1{,}500{,}000)}$

40. $\dfrac{(0.000039)(140)}{(130{,}000)(0.00021)}$

41. If the mass of the earth is 6×10^{27} grams and each gram is 1.1×10^{-6} tons, find the mass of the earth in tons.

42. In 1929 Vernadsky, a biologist, estimated that all of the free oxygen of the earth is 1.5×10^{21} grams and that it is produced by life alone. If one gram is approximately 2.2×10^{-3} lb, what is the amount of free oxygen in pounds?

43. Some of the designers of high-speed computers are currently thinking of single-addition times of 10^{-7} sec (100 nanosec). How many additions would such a computer be able to perform in 1 sec? In 1 min?

44. If electricity travels in a computer circuit at the speed of light (1.86×10^5 miles per sec), how far will it travel in the time it takes the computer in the preceding problem to complete a single addition? (Size of circuits is becoming a critical problem in computer design.) Give the answer in miles and in feet.

60   SQUARE ROOTS AND RADICALS

Going from exponents to radicals in the same chapter may seem unnatural to many. However, exponents and radicals have a lot more in common than one might first expect. We will comment briefly on this relationship in this chapter; in more advanced courses the relationship is developed in detail.

In this section and the two following, we will take a careful look at the square-root symbol "$\sqrt{}$" and some of its properties. We discussed this symbol briefly in Chap. 3 where we found, among other things, that $\sqrt{2}$ does not name a rational number; that is, there is not rational number whose square is 2.

We define a **square root** of a number b to be a number a whose square is b.

EXAMPLE 14

▶ 2 is a square root of 4 since $2^2 = 4$.

▶ -2 is a square root of 4 since $(-2)^2 = 4$.

▶ 0 is *the* square root of 0 since 0 is the only number whose square is 0.

We state without proof the following important theorem.

THEOREM 6 *Every positive real number has two real square roots, each the negative of the other.*

Now, what is meant by the symbol "$\sqrt{4}$"? We often hear, "the square root of 4," as an answer. However, which square root of 4 does $\sqrt{4}$ represent? The following definition settles this matter once and for all. If a is a positive real number, then $\sqrt{a}$ names the **positive square root** of a. The symbol "$\sqrt{}$" is called the *square-root radical.* It of course follows from the definition of the negative of a number and a square root of a number that $-\sqrt{a}$ names the **negative square root** of a.

It can be shown (though we won't) that *if a is a positive integer and $\sqrt{a}$ is not an integer, then $\sqrt{a}$ is an irrational number.*

EXAMPLE 15. $-\sqrt{36} = -6$ and $\sqrt{81} = 9$.
$-\sqrt{7}$ and $\sqrt{7}$ name the negative and positive irrational numbers whose squares are 7.

SQUARE-ROOT PROPERTIES

Consider the following two special examples:

▶ $\sqrt{4}\,\sqrt{36} = 2 \cdot 6 = 12$ $\sqrt{4 \cdot 36} = \sqrt{144} = 12$

▶ $\dfrac{\sqrt{36}}{\sqrt{4}} = \dfrac{6}{2} = 3$ $\sqrt{\dfrac{36}{4}} = \sqrt{9} = 3$

These examples suggest two properties of radicals, $\sqrt{a}\,\sqrt{b} = \sqrt{ab}$ and $\sqrt{a}/\sqrt{b} = \sqrt{a/b}$, which might be very useful if true under general enough conditions. The following theorem shows that these product and quotient properties of radicals hold with only slight restrictions on a and b.

THEOREM 7 *If a and b are nonnegative real numbers, then*

$$\sqrt{a}\,\sqrt{b} = \sqrt{ab} \qquad and \qquad \frac{\sqrt{a}}{\sqrt{b}} = \sqrt{\frac{a}{b}} \qquad b \neq 0$$

PARTIAL PROOF
Let $N = \sqrt{a}$ and $M = \sqrt{b}$. Then $N^2 = a$ and $M^2 = b$.

$$\sqrt{a}\,\sqrt{b} = NM = \sqrt{(NM)^2} = \sqrt{N^2 M^2} = \sqrt{ab}$$

Note how the proof depends on a property of exponents.

EXAMPLE 16

▶ $\sqrt{5}\ \sqrt{10} = \sqrt{5\cdot 10} = \sqrt{50} = \sqrt{25\cdot 2} = \sqrt{25}\ \sqrt{2} = 5\sqrt{2}$

▶ $\dfrac{\sqrt{32}}{\sqrt{8}} = \sqrt{\dfrac{32}{8}} = \sqrt{4} = 2$

▶ $\sqrt{\dfrac{7}{4}} = \dfrac{\sqrt{7}}{\sqrt{4}} = \dfrac{\sqrt{7}}{2}$ or $\dfrac{1}{2}\sqrt{7}$

SIMPLEST RADICAL FORM

The foregoing definitions and theorems allow us to change algebraic expressions containing radicals to a variety of equivalent forms; one form that is often useful is called the "simplest radical form."

DEFINITION 3   *An algebraic expression that contains square-root radicals is said to be in the **simplest radical form** if all three of the following conditions are satisfied:*
(A) *No radicand (the expression within a radical sign) when expressed as a polynomial in a completely factored form contains a factor of power greater than 1.*
(B) *No radical appears in a denominator.*
(C) *No fraction appears within a radical.*

It should be understood that forms other than the simplest radical form may be more useful on occasion—one should remain flexible.

EXAMPLE 17:   RADICAL EXPRESSIONS CHANGED TO SIMPLEST RADICAL FORMS.   (All variables are assumed to represent positive real numbers.)

▶ $\sqrt{72} = \sqrt{6^2\cdot 2} = \sqrt{6^2}\ \sqrt{2} = 6\sqrt{2}$

▶ $\sqrt{12x^3y^5z^2} = \sqrt{(2^2x^2y^4z^2)(3xy)} = \sqrt{2^2x^2y^4z^2}\ \sqrt{3xy} = 2xy^2z\ \sqrt{3xy}$

▶ $\dfrac{3}{\sqrt{5}} = \dfrac{3\cdot\sqrt{5}}{\sqrt{5}\cdot\sqrt{5}} = \dfrac{3\sqrt{5}}{5}$ or $\dfrac{3}{5}\ \sqrt{5}$

▶ $\dfrac{6x^3}{\sqrt{3x}} = \dfrac{6x^3\sqrt{3x}}{\sqrt{3x}\sqrt{3x}} = \dfrac{6x^3\sqrt{3x}}{3x} = 2x^2\sqrt{3x}$

▶ $\sqrt{\dfrac{2a^2}{3b}} = \dfrac{\sqrt{2a^2}}{\sqrt{3b}} = \dfrac{a\sqrt{2}\sqrt{3b}}{\sqrt{3b}\sqrt{3b}} = \dfrac{a\sqrt{6b}}{3b}$ or $\dfrac{a}{3b}\sqrt{6b}$

▶ $\sqrt{x^2+y^2}$ is in the simplest radical form.

EXERCISE 67

In problems 1 through 40 simplify and express each answer in simplest radical form. All variables represent positive real numbers.

1. $\sqrt{81}$

2. $\sqrt{49}$

3. $-\sqrt{4}$

4. $-\sqrt{16}$

5. $\sqrt{5}$

6. $-\sqrt{2}$

7. $-\sqrt{\frac{4}{9}}$

8. $-\sqrt{\frac{16}{25}}$

9. $-\sqrt{16x^4y^6}$

10. $-\sqrt{4a^4b^8}$

11. $-\sqrt{\frac{9m^4}{4n^6}}$

12. $-\sqrt{\frac{a^2b^4}{4c^2}}$

13. $\sqrt{8}$

14. $\sqrt{18}$

15. $\frac{1}{\sqrt{3}}$

16. $\frac{1}{\sqrt{2}}$

17. $\frac{1}{\sqrt{3y}}$

18. $\frac{1}{\sqrt{2x}}$

19. $\sqrt{24m^5n^4}$

20. $\sqrt{27a^3b^4}$

21. $\frac{6x^2}{\sqrt{3x}}$

22. $\frac{4xy}{\sqrt{2y}}$

23. $\frac{7}{\sqrt{2}}$

24. $\frac{5}{\sqrt{3}}$

25. $\frac{2x^2y}{\sqrt{3xy}}$

26. $\frac{3a}{\sqrt{2ab}}$

27. $\sqrt{a^2 + b^2}$

28. $\sqrt{m^2 - n^2}$

29. $-\sqrt{\frac{2}{9}}$

30. $-\sqrt{\frac{3}{4}}$

31. $\sqrt{\frac{2}{3}}$

32. $\sqrt{\frac{3}{5}}$

33. $\sqrt{\frac{3m}{2n}}$

34. $\sqrt{\frac{6x}{7y}}$

35. $\frac{\sqrt{4a^3}}{\sqrt{3b}}$

36. $\frac{\sqrt{9m^5}}{\sqrt{2n}}$

37. $\frac{\sqrt{2x}\sqrt{5}}{\sqrt{20x}}$

38. $\frac{\sqrt{6}\sqrt{8x}}{\sqrt{3x}}$

39. $-\sqrt{x^4 - 2x^2}$

40. $\sqrt{m^3 + 4m^2}$

Approximate the radical expressions in problems 41 through 48 with decimal fractions. Use the square-root table (Appendix B) when necessary. (Writing expressions in simplest radical form first will be helpful in some cases.)

EXAMPLE 18

▶ $\sqrt{35}\sqrt{40} = \sqrt{35 \cdot 40} = \sqrt{(2^2 \cdot 5^2)(2 \cdot 7)} = 10\sqrt{14} = (10)(3.742) = 37.42$

▶ $\sqrt{\frac{7}{5}} = \frac{\sqrt{7}}{\sqrt{5}} = \frac{\sqrt{7}\sqrt{5}}{\sqrt{5}\sqrt{5}} = \frac{\sqrt{35}}{5} = \frac{5.916}{5} = 1.183$

41. $\sqrt{2}\sqrt{6}$

42. $\sqrt{6}\sqrt{3}$

43. $\sqrt{\frac{1}{3}}$

44. $\sqrt{\frac{1}{5}}$

45. $\sqrt{15}\,\sqrt{10}$ 46. $\sqrt{21}\,\sqrt{14}$ 47. $\dfrac{-\sqrt{33}}{\sqrt{2}}$ 48. $\dfrac{-\sqrt{23}}{\sqrt{5}}$

Find and graph (approximately) on the real-number line the elements in each of the sets in problems 49 through 52. The replacement set for each variable is the set of real numbers.

49. $\{x \mid x^2 = 4\}$ 50. $\{t \mid t^2 = 25\}$ 51. $\{m \mid m^2 = 7\}$ 52. $\{n \mid n^2 = 13\}$

53. In physics it is found that the distance y that an object falls in t sec, neglecting air resistance, is given by the formula $y = 16t^2$. How long would it take a steel marble to fall 40 ft? (Air resistance is negligible for small heavy objects falling a short distance.) Complete the answer to two decimal places.

54. It is claimed that an FBI agent, Delf Bryce, can drop a silver dollar from the level of his forehead, draw his gun and shoot it as it passes the gun. Find the time required (to two decimal places) for all of this action to take place if the silver dollar falls 3 ft before being hit. (Use the information in the preceding problem.)

55. When a bucket of water is twirled around in a vertical circle, the water will either stay in or spill out according to the balance between centripetal and gravitational forces. If the bucket is twirled fast enough, the centripetal forces will equal or exceed the gravitational forces and no water will spill. For a satellite to stay in orbit, the centripetal force must equal the gravitational force. Stated as an equation,

$$\frac{V^2}{R} = g$$

where V is the circular velocity of the satellite, R is the distance to the center of the earth, and g is the gravitational constant. (A) Find the required circular velocity (in miles per second) for a satellite to stay in orbit if $R = 4{,}130$ miles and $g = 6.06 \times 10^{-3}$ miles per sec per sec. (B) What is the circular velocity in miles per hour?

56. It is known that regardless of the shape of a container, the rate R in cubic feet per minute at which water flows out through circular orifice at the bottom is given by $R = 4.8a\sqrt{h}$, where a is the area of the orifice in square feet and h is the height of the water level in feet above the orifice. Find R for $a = 0.05$ sq ft and $h = 4.5$ ft. HINT: Use $\frac{9}{2}$ for 4.5.

57. Explain why the square root of a negative number cannot be a real number.

58. Are the real numbers closed under the operation of square root? Explain.

59. Prove the second part of Theorem 7.

60. Is $\sqrt{x^2} = x$ true for $x = 4$? For $x = -4$?

61. Is $\sqrt{x^2} = |x|$ true for $x = 4$? For $x = -4$?

62. Graph both $y = |x|$ and $y = \sqrt{x^2}$ on the same coordinate system for $-5 \le x \le 5$.

63. If we define the symbol $5^{1/2}$ in such a way that the laws of exponents continue to hold [in particular $(5^{1/2})^2 = 5^{2(1/2)} = 5$ or $5^{1/2} \cdot 5^{1/2} = 5^{1/2+1/2} = 5$], how should it be defined?

64. If $x^2 = y^2$, does it necessarily follow that $x = y$? HINT: Can you find a pair of numbers that make the first equation true, but the second equation false?

65. Find the fallacy in the following "proof" that all real numbers are equal: If m and n are any real numbers, then

$$(m - n)^2 = (n - m)^2$$

$$m - n = n - m$$

$$2m = 2n$$

$$m = n$$

61   SUMS AND DIFFERENCES OF RADICALS

Algebraic expressions can often be simplified by adding or subtracting terms that contain the same radicals.   We proceed in essentially the same way that we do when we combine like terms.   You will recall that the distributive law played a central role in this process.

EXAMPLE 19

▶ $3\sqrt{2} + 5\sqrt{2} = (3 + 5)\sqrt{2} = 8\sqrt{2}$

▶ $2\sqrt{m} - 7\sqrt{m} = (2 - 7)\sqrt{m} = -5\sqrt{m}$

▶ $3\sqrt{x} - 2\sqrt{5} + 4\sqrt{x} - 7\sqrt{5} = 3\sqrt{x} + 4\sqrt{x} - 2\sqrt{5} - 7\sqrt{5}$

$$= 7\sqrt{x} - 9\sqrt{5}$$

Occasionally terms containing radicals can be combined after they have been expressed in simplest radical form.

EXAMPLE 20

▶ $4\sqrt{8} - 2\sqrt{18} = 4 \cdot \sqrt{4} \cdot \sqrt{2} - 2 \cdot \sqrt{9} \cdot \sqrt{2}$

$$= 4 \cdot 2 \cdot \sqrt{2} - 2 \cdot 3 \cdot \sqrt{2}$$

$$= 8\sqrt{2} - 6\sqrt{2}$$

$$= 2\sqrt{2}$$

$$\blacktriangleright\ 2\sqrt{12} - \sqrt{\frac{1}{3}} = 2\cdot\sqrt{4}\cdot\sqrt{3} - \frac{1\cdot\sqrt{3}}{\sqrt{3}\cdot\sqrt{3}}$$

$$= 4\sqrt{3} - \frac{\sqrt{3}}{3}$$

$$= \left(4 - \frac{1}{3}\right)\sqrt{3}$$

$$= \frac{11}{3}\sqrt{3} \quad \text{or} \quad \frac{11\sqrt{3}}{3}$$

EXERCISE 68

Simplify by combining as many terms as possible.   All variables are assumed to represent positive real numbers.   Use exact radical forms only.

1. $5\sqrt{2} + 3\sqrt{2}$

2. $7\sqrt{3} + 2\sqrt{3}$

3. $6\sqrt{x} - 3\sqrt{x}$

4. $12\sqrt{m} - 3\sqrt{m}$

5. $4\sqrt{7} - 3\sqrt{5}$

6. $2\sqrt{3} + 5\sqrt{2}$

7. $\sqrt{y} - 4\sqrt{y}$

8. $2\sqrt{a} - 7\sqrt{a}$

9. $3\sqrt{5} - \sqrt{5} + 2\sqrt{5}$

10. $4\sqrt{7} - 6\sqrt{7} + \sqrt{7}$

11. $2\sqrt{x} - \sqrt{x} - 3\sqrt{x}$

12. $\sqrt{n} - 4\sqrt{n} - 2\sqrt{n}$

13. $3\sqrt{2} - 2\sqrt{3} - \sqrt{2}$

14. $\sqrt{5} - 2\sqrt{3} + 3\sqrt{5}$

15. $2\sqrt{x} - \sqrt{y} + 3\sqrt{y}$

16. $\sqrt{m} - \sqrt{n} - 2\sqrt{n}$

17. $\sqrt{8} - \sqrt{2}$

18. $\sqrt{18} + \sqrt{2}$

19. $\sqrt{27} - 3\sqrt{12}$

20. $\sqrt{8} - 2\sqrt{32}$

21. $\sqrt{8} + 2\sqrt{27}$

22. $2\sqrt{12} + 3\sqrt{18}$

23. $\sqrt{4x} - \sqrt{9x}$

24. $\sqrt{8mn} + 2\sqrt{18mn}$

25. $\sqrt{24} - \sqrt{12} + 3\sqrt{3}$

26. $\sqrt{8} - \sqrt{20} + 4\sqrt{2}$

27. $\sqrt{\frac{1}{2}} + \frac{\sqrt{2}}{2} + \sqrt{8}$

28. $\frac{\sqrt{3}}{3} + 2\sqrt{\frac{1}{3}} + \sqrt{12}$

29. $\sqrt{\frac{2}{3}} - \sqrt{\frac{3}{2}}$

30. $\sqrt{\frac{1}{8}} + \sqrt{8}$

31. $\sqrt{\frac{xy}{2}} + \sqrt{8xy}$

32. $\sqrt{\frac{3uv}{2}} - \sqrt{24uv}$

33. $\sqrt{12} - \sqrt{\frac{1}{2}}$

34. $\sqrt{\frac{3}{5}} + 2\sqrt{20}$

62   PRODUCTS AND QUOTIENTS INVOLVING RADICALS

We will conclude this chapter by considering several special types of products and quotients that involve radicals. The distributive law will play a central role in our approach to these problems. In the examples that follow all variables represent positive real numbers.

SPECIAL PRODUCTS

EXAMPLE 21.   Multiply and simplify:

▶ $2(3 - 2\sqrt{2}) = 6 - 4\sqrt{2}$

▶ $\sqrt{2}(\sqrt{10} - 3) \quad \boxed{= \sqrt{2}\sqrt{10} - 3\sqrt{2}} \quad = \sqrt{20} - 3\sqrt{2} = 2\sqrt{5} - 3\sqrt{2}$

▶ $(\sqrt{2} - 3)(\sqrt{2} + 5) = (\sqrt{2} - 3)\sqrt{2} + (\sqrt{2} - 3)5$
$$= \sqrt{2}\sqrt{2} - 3\sqrt{2} + 5\sqrt{2} - 15$$
$$= 2 + 2\sqrt{2} - 15$$
$$= 2\sqrt{2} - 13$$

▶ $\sqrt{x}(\sqrt{x} - 3) = \sqrt{x}\sqrt{x} - 3\sqrt{x} = x - 3\sqrt{x}$

▶ $(\sqrt{x} - 3)(\sqrt{x} + 5) = (\sqrt{x} - 3)\sqrt{x} + (\sqrt{x} - 3)5$
$$= \sqrt{x}\sqrt{x} - 3\sqrt{x} + 5\sqrt{x} - 15$$
$$= x + 2\sqrt{x} - 15$$

EXAMPLE 22.   Show that $(2 - \sqrt{3})$ is a solution of the equation $x^2 - 4x + 1 = 0$.

SOLUTION

$$x^2 - 4x + 1 = 0$$
$$(2 - \sqrt{3})^2 - 4(2 - \sqrt{3}) + 1 \overset{?}{=} 0$$
$$4 - 4\sqrt{3} + 3 - 8 + 4\sqrt{3} + 1 \overset{?}{=} 0$$
$$0 \overset{\vee}{=} 0$$

SPECIAL QUOTIENTS—RATIONALIZING DENOMINATORS

Recall that to express $\sqrt{2}/\sqrt{3}$ in simplest radical form, we multiplied the numerator and denominator by $\sqrt{3}$ to clear the denominator of the radical:

$$\frac{\sqrt{2}}{\sqrt{3}} = \frac{\sqrt{2} \cdot \sqrt{3}}{\sqrt{3} \cdot \sqrt{3}} = \frac{\sqrt{6}}{3}$$

The denominator is thus converted to a rational number. The process of converting irrational denominators to rational numbers is called **rationalizing the denominator.**

How can we rationalize the binomial denominator in $1/(\sqrt{3} - \sqrt{2})$? Multiplying the numerator and denominator by $\sqrt{3}$ or $\sqrt{2}$ doesn't help (Try it!). Recalling the special binomial product $(a - b)(a + b) = a^2 - b^2$ suggests that if we multiply the numerator and denominator by $\sqrt{3} + \sqrt{2}$, we will get $(\sqrt{3})^2 - (\sqrt{2})^2 = 1$, a rational number. Thus

$$\frac{1}{\sqrt{3} - \sqrt{2}} = \frac{1(\sqrt{3} + \sqrt{2})}{(\sqrt{3} - \sqrt{2})(\sqrt{3} + \sqrt{2})} = \frac{\sqrt{3} + \sqrt{2}}{3 - 2} = \sqrt{3} + \sqrt{2}$$

EXAMPLE 23.   Rationalize the denominators and simplify.

▶ $\dfrac{1}{\sqrt{2} + 3} = \dfrac{1(\sqrt{2} - 3)}{(\sqrt{2} + 3)(\sqrt{2} - 3)} = \dfrac{\sqrt{2} - 3}{2 - 9} = \dfrac{\sqrt{2} - 3}{-7}$ or $\dfrac{3 - \sqrt{2}}{7}$

▶ $\dfrac{\sqrt{2}}{\sqrt{6} - 2} = \dfrac{\sqrt{2}(\sqrt{6} + 2)}{(\sqrt{6} - 2)(\sqrt{6} + 2)} = \dfrac{\sqrt{12} + 2\sqrt{2}}{6 - 4}$

$$= \dfrac{2\sqrt{3} + 2\sqrt{2}}{2} = \dfrac{2(\sqrt{3} + \sqrt{2})}{2} = \sqrt{3} + \sqrt{2}$$

▶ $\dfrac{\sqrt{x} - \sqrt{y}}{\sqrt{x} + \sqrt{y}} = \dfrac{(\sqrt{x} - \sqrt{y})(\sqrt{x} - \sqrt{y})}{(\sqrt{x} + \sqrt{y})(\sqrt{x} - \sqrt{y})} = \dfrac{x - 2\sqrt{xy} + y}{x - y}$

EXERCISE 69

Multiply and simplify problems 1 through 24.

1. $3(\sqrt{3} - 4)$

2. $4(\sqrt{5} + 2)$

3. $\sqrt{2}(\sqrt{2} + 3)$

4. $\sqrt{7}(2 - \sqrt{7})$

5. $\sqrt{6}(\sqrt{2} - 1)$

6. $\sqrt{3}(5 + \sqrt{6})$

7. $\sqrt{5}(\sqrt{10} + \sqrt{5})$

8. $\sqrt{20}(\sqrt{5} - 1)$

9. $\sqrt{x}(\sqrt{x} - 3)$

10. $\sqrt{y}(5 - \sqrt{y})$

11. $(\sqrt{2} - 1)(\sqrt{2} + 3)$

12. $(2 - \sqrt{3})(3 + \sqrt{3})$

13. $(2 + \sqrt{x})(3 - \sqrt{x})$

14. $(\sqrt{m} - 3)(\sqrt{m} - 4)$

15. $(\sqrt{5} + 2)^2$

16. $(\sqrt{3} - 3)^2$

17. $(2\sqrt{2} - 5)(3\sqrt{2} + 2)$

18. $(4\sqrt{3} - 1)(3\sqrt{3} - 2)$

19. $(3 - 2\sqrt{5})(1 - 2\sqrt{5})$

20. $(2 + \sqrt{2})(3 + 2\sqrt{2})$

21. $(\sqrt{8} + 3)(\sqrt{18} + 2)$

22. $(\sqrt{20} - 4)(\sqrt{45} - 1)$

23. $(2\sqrt{x} - 3)^2$ 　　　　　　　　24. $(3\sqrt{y} + 1)^2$

25. Is $2 + \sqrt{3}$ a solution of the equation $x^2 - 4x + 1 = 0$?

26. Is $3 - \sqrt{2}$ a solution of the equation $x^2 - 6x + 3 = 0$?

Reduce to lowest terms by removing common factors from the numerator and denominator.

27. $\dfrac{6 - 2\sqrt{3}}{6}$ 　　　　　　　　28. $\dfrac{8 + 4\sqrt{2}}{12}$

29. $\dfrac{-4 + 2\sqrt{7}}{4}$ 　　　　　　　　30. $\dfrac{-3 - 6\sqrt{5}}{9}$

31. $\dfrac{6 - \sqrt{18}}{3}$ 　　　　　　　　32. $\dfrac{10 + \sqrt{8}}{2}$

Rationalize the denominators and simplify.

33. $\dfrac{1}{\sqrt{5} + 2}$ 　　　34. $\dfrac{1}{\sqrt{11} - 3}$ 　　　35. $\dfrac{4}{\sqrt{6} - 2}$

36. $\dfrac{2}{\sqrt{5} + 1}$ 　　　37. $\dfrac{\sqrt{2}}{\sqrt{6} + 2}$ 　　　38. $\dfrac{\sqrt{2}}{\sqrt{10} - 2}$

39. $\dfrac{\sqrt{x}}{\sqrt{x} - 2}$ 　　　40. $\dfrac{\sqrt{y}}{\sqrt{y} + 3}$ 　　　41. $\dfrac{\sqrt{2} - 1}{\sqrt{2} + 1}$

42. $\dfrac{\sqrt{3} + 2}{\sqrt{3} - 2}$ 　　　43. $\dfrac{\sqrt{2} + \sqrt{3}}{\sqrt{3} - \sqrt{2}}$ 　　　44. $\dfrac{\sqrt{5} - \sqrt{2}}{\sqrt{5} + \sqrt{2}}$

45. $\dfrac{2 + \sqrt{x}}{\sqrt{x} - 3}$ 　　　46. $\dfrac{3 - \sqrt{a}}{\sqrt{a} - 2}$

63 CHAPTER SUMMARY

GENERAL

In this chapter we extended the meaning of exponent to all integers. Thus the symbol a^r, where a is a real number, not only has meaning when r is a positive integer, but it also has meaning if r is a negative integer or zero. In a second course of algebra the meaning of exponent is again extended, this time to include all rational numbers; in particular, symbols such as $2^{1/2}$, $5^{3/5}$, $7^{-2/3}$, $6^{0.135}$, and $8^{-0.796}$ will be defined. In somewhat more advanced courses irrational exponents will be defined, and symbols such as $3^{\sqrt{2}}$ will take on meaning.   An important point to remember is that when these new exponent symbols are introduced, they will be defined in such a way that the five laws of exponents presented in this chapter will continue to hold.   It is very important that you learn these laws well and gain experience and confidence in their use.

We immediately found a useful application of integral exponents in the power-of-ten (sometimes called *scientific*) notation.   This notation is widely used, even in elementary scientific writings.

Many operations in mathematics have what are called *inverse operations*.   The inverse of addition is subtraction, and the inverse of multiplication is division. Now we have introduced the inverse operation of power, the operation of taking of roots, in particular square roots.   We note that each of the inverse operations are defined in terms of the original operation.   Subtraction is defined in terms of addition, division in terms of multiplication, and square root in terms of squaring.

In this course we have restricted our attention to square roots and associated notation and properties with the belief (and conviction) that if these are thoroughly understood, higher roots, when presented in a second course of algebra, will offer less difficulty.

SPECIFIC

Describe, define, or give examples of each of the following:

1. Integral Exponents
2^{12}, 3^{-5}, 4^0

a^r, a a real number and r an integer

five laws of exponents

power-of-ten notation

2. Square Roots and Radicals
a square root of a number

$\sqrt{a}$ $-\sqrt{a}$

simplest radical form

rationalizing a denominator

products and quotients of radicals—monomial and binomial forms

addition and subtraction of radicals

EXERCISE 70   CHAPTER REVIEW

1. Evaluate: (*a*) 2^5, (*b*) 3^{-3}, (*c*) $(\frac{1}{3})^0$.

2. Evaluate: (*a*) $(2^{-3})^2$, (*b*) $\dfrac{1}{2^{-3}}$, (*c*) $\dfrac{3^2}{3^{-2}}$.

In problems 3 through 14 simplify and write the answer using positive exponents only.

3. $(3x^3)(2x^4)(x^{-2})$

4. $\dfrac{(4x^7)(3x^{-2})}{6x^{10}}$

5. $(2m^2n^3)^4$

6. $\left(\dfrac{2x^2}{3y^3}\right)^3$

7. $\dfrac{-3^2}{(-3a^2)^2}$

8. $(x^2y^{-3})^{-1}$

9. $\dfrac{1}{(2x^2y)^{-2}}$

10. $\dfrac{8A^{-2}B^3}{2A^{-3}B^5}$

11. $\left(\dfrac{3a^{-2}b}{6a^2b^{-3}}\right)^{-2}$

12. (a) m^2m^{-2} (b) $m^2 + m^{-2}$

13. $\dfrac{7}{3^{-1} + 4^{-1}}$

14. $(x^{-1} + y^{-1})^2$

15. Express $(3.6 \times 10^4)(2 \times 10^{-6})$ as a single-decimal fraction.

16. Change $(480{,}000)(0.005)/(1{,}200{,}000)$ to power-of-ten notation and evaluate. Express the answer in power-of-ten form and as a decimal fraction.

17. The volume of mercury increases linearly with temperature over a fairly wide temperature range (this is why mercury is often used in thermometers). If 1 cc of mercury at $0°C$ is heated to a temperature of $1°C$, its volume will be 1.00018 cc, an increase of 1.8×10^{-4} cc. For each degree rise the increase is the same and equal to 1.8×10^{-4} cc; thus $V = 1 + (1.8 \times 10^{-4})T$, where V is volume and T is temperature. What would be the volume of this sample of mercury if the temperature were increased to $(2 \times 10^2)°C$? Write the answer as a decimal fraction.

18. If a is a square root of b, then is $a^2 = b$ or is $b^2 = a$?

In problems 19 through 30 simplify and express each answer in simplest radical form. All variables represent positive real numbers.

19. $\sqrt{8m^2n^3}$

20. $-\sqrt{\frac{5}{4}}$

21. $\sqrt{\frac{1}{3}}$

22. (a) $\sqrt{x^2y^2}$ (b) $\sqrt{x^2 + y^2}$

23. $\dfrac{\sqrt{2x^3}}{\sqrt{10x}}$

24. $\sqrt{12} + 2\sqrt{3}$

25. $\sqrt{45xy} - \sqrt{20xy} - 2\sqrt{x+y}$

26. $\sqrt{\frac{2}{3}} + \sqrt{\frac{3}{2}}$

27. $(\sqrt{2} + 5)(\sqrt{2} - 3)$

28. $(\sqrt{2x} + \sqrt{3y})^2$

29. $\dfrac{\sqrt{2}}{\sqrt{6} + 2}$

30. $\dfrac{\sqrt{x} - 2}{\sqrt{x} + 2}$

31. Use properties of radicals and the square-root table to approximate $\sqrt{\tfrac{7}{5}}$ to three decimal places.

32. Describe the set $\{x \mid \sqrt{x^2} = x,\ x \text{ a real number}\}$.

second-degree polynomial equations in one variable

64 INTRODUCTORY REMARKS

In the preceding chapters we concentrated our attention on first-degree polynomial equations (often called linear equations) in one and two variables.   We found that linear equations occur in many different forms and are generated by a large variety of significant problems from many different fields.

You will recall that we defined a first-degree polynomial equation in one variable as any equation that can be written in the form

$$ax + b = 0 \qquad a \neq 0$$

where x is a variable and a and b are constants, and we found that for each pair of constants this equation always has the unique solution $x = -b/a$. From a mathematical point of view this pretty well takes care of linear equations in one variable.

In this chapter we will consider the next class of polynomial equations in one variable, called second-degree polynomial equations or quadratic equations. A **quadratic equation** in one variable is any equation that can be written in the form

$$ax^2 + bx + c = 0 \qquad a \neq 0$$

where x is a variable and a, b, and c are constants.° We will refer to this form as the **standard form** for the quadratic equation.

EXAMPLE 1.   The equation $\frac{2}{3}x - \frac{1}{2}(x + 3) = 2 - x$ is a linear equation in one variable since it can be transformed into the equivalent equation $7x - 21 = 0$, which is of the form $ax + b = 0$.

EXAMPLE 2.   The equations $2x^2 - 3x + 5 = 0$, $m^2 = 27$, $15 = 180t - 16t^2$, and $(x - 3)^2 = (3 - x)(3 + x)$ are all quadratic equations in one variable since they either are in the form $ax^2 + bx + c = 0$ or can be transformed into this form.

EXAMPLE 3.   The equations $2x^3 - 3x^2 + 5x - 2 = 0$, $\sqrt{x - 2} = 5$, and $x^2 - (1/x^3) = 3$ are neither linear nor quadratic.

Problems that give rise to quadratic equations are many and varied. For example, to find the dimensions of a rectangle with an area of 78 sq in. and a length twice its width, we are led to the equation

$$(2x)(x) = 78$$
or $$2x^2 - 78 = 0$$

If an arrow is shot vertically in the air (from the ground) with an initial velocity of 176 fps, its distance y above the ground t sec after it is released (neglecting air resistance) is given by $y = 176t - 16t^2$. To find the times when y is zero, we are led to the equation

$$176t - 16t^2 = 0$$
or $$16t^2 - 176t = 0$$

To find the times when the arrow is 16 ft off the ground, we are led to the equation

$$176t - 16t^2 = 16$$
or $$16t^2 - 176t + 16 = 0$$

° Strictly speaking, a and b in $ax + b = 0$ and a, b, and c in $ax^2 + bx + c = 0$ are a special type of variable called *parameters*. What we are really interested in is the behavior of $ax + b$ or $ax^2 + bx + c$ for any given a, b, or a, b, c as x varies.

You might try solving these quadratic equations using the material presented in the course to date.   We actually have at hand, particularly since the last chapter on exponents and radicals, all of the tools we need to solve these three equations—it is a matter of putting this material together in the right way. Putting this material together in the right way will be the subject matter for next five sections.

65   SOLUTION BY FACTORING

If the coefficients a, b, and c in the quadratic equation

$$ax^2 + bx + c = 0$$

are such that $ax^2 + bx + c$ can be written as the product of two first-degree factors with integral coefficients, then the quadratic equation can be quickly and easily solved.   The method of solution by factoring rests on the following property of the real numbers: *If a and b are real numbers, then*

$$ab = 0 \text{ if and only if } a = 0 \text{ or } b = 0 \text{ (or both)}$$

EXAMPLE 4.   Solve $x^2 + 2x - 15 = 0$ by factoring.

SOLUTION

$$x^2 + 2x - 15 = 0$$
$$(x - 3)(x + 5) = 0$$
$$x - 3 = 0 \quad \text{or} \quad x + 5 = 0$$
$$x = 3 \quad \text{or} \quad x = -5$$

$(x - 3)(x + 5) = 0$ if and only if $(x - 3) = 0$ or $(x + 5) = 0$

CHECK

$$x = 3: \qquad 3^2 + 2(3) - 15 = 9 + 6 - 15 = 0$$
$$x = -5: \qquad (-5)^2 + 2(-5) - 15 = 25 - 10 - 15 = 0$$

Thus, $\{x \mid x^2 + 2x - 15 = 0\} = \{3, -5\}$.

EXAMPLE 5.   Solve $2x^2 = 3x$.

SOLUTION

$$2x^2 = 3x \qquad \text{Why shouldn't both sides be divided by } x?$$
$$2x^2 - 3x = 0$$
$$x(2x - 3) = 0$$
$$x = 0 \quad \text{or} \quad 2x - 3 = 0$$
$$x = 0 \quad \text{or} \quad x = \tfrac{3}{2}$$

$x(2x - 3) = 0$ if and only if $x = 0$ or $2x - 3 = 0$

CHECK

$$x = 0: \quad 2(0)^2 \overset{?}{=} 3(0) \qquad x = \tfrac{3}{2}: \quad 2(\tfrac{3}{2})^2 \overset{?}{=} 3(\tfrac{3}{2})$$
$$0 \overset{\vee}{=} 0 \qquad\qquad\qquad \tfrac{9}{2} \overset{\vee}{=} \tfrac{9}{2}$$

Thus, $\{x \mid 2x^2 = 3x\} = \{0, \tfrac{3}{2}\}$.

The method of factoring is very fast and easy to use when it applies. However, as you recall, not all second-degree polynomials with integral coefficients can be factored into linear factors with integral coefficients. In this regard, recall the very useful and important theorem in Chap. 6: *A second-degree polynomial $ax^2 + bx + c$ with integral coefficients has linear factors with integral coefficients if and only if ac has integral factors whose sum is b.*

EXAMPLE 6. Solve $6x^2 - 19x - 7 = 0$ by factoring, if possible.

SOLUTION
Does ac have factors whose sum is b?

$$ac = 6(-7) = -42$$

$-42 = (-21)(2)$ and $(-21) + (2) = -19 = b$; thus $6x^2 - 19x - 7$ can be factored.

$$6x^2 - 19x - 7 = 0$$
$$(2x - 7)(3x + 1) = 0$$
$$2x - 7 = 0 \quad \text{or} \quad 3x + 1 = 0$$
$$x = \tfrac{7}{2} \quad \text{or} \quad x = -\tfrac{1}{3}$$

The checking of the solutions is left to the reader.

EXAMPLE 7. Solve $2x^2 - 8x + 3 = 0$ by factoring, if possible.

SOLUTION
Does ac have factors whose sum is b? $ac = (2)(3) = 6$, but 6 has no integral factors whose sum is $b = -8$; hence $2x^2 - 8x + 3$ cannot be factored as specified. Another method must be used to solve $2x^2 - 8x + 3 = 0$.

EXERCISE 71

Solve each of the following quadratic equations.

1. $(x - 3)(x - 5) = 0$
2. $(x - 9)(x + 3) = 0$
3. $(2x - 1)(x + 2) = 0$
4. $(x + 4)(3x - 2) = 0$

5. $(2m + 3)(3m - 2) = 0$ 6. $(5t - 2)(4t + 3) = 0$

7. $z(3z + 5) = 0$ 8. $u(4u - 1) = 0$

Find the solution set for each quadratic equation by factoring.

9. $x^2 - 5x + 6 = 0$ 10. $x^2 - 6x + 5 = 0$

11. $x^2 - 3x = 0$ 12. $x^2 + 5x = 0$

13. $N^2 - 4N - 12 = 0$ 14. $Q^2 + 4Q - 5 = 0$

15. $4t^2 - 8t = 0$ 16. $3m^2 + 12m = 0$

17. $2y^2 + 15y - 8 = 0$ 18. $3z^2 - 10z - 8 = 0$

19. $A^2 - 25 = 0$ 20. $3D^2 - 12 = 0$

Solve each of the following equations by factoring. If an equation cannot be solved by factoring, state this as your answer.

NOTE: (A) *Clear the equation of fractions (if they are present) by multiplying through by the least common multiple of all of the denominators.* (B) *Write the equation in standard quadratic form.* (C) *If all numerical coefficients contain a common factor, divide it out.* (D) *Test for factorability.* (E) *If factorable, solve.*

21. $2x(x - 1) = 3(x + 1)$ 22. $3x(x - 2) = 2(x - 2)$

23. $y^2 = 5y - 2$ 24. $3 = t^2 + 7t$

25. $\dfrac{m^2}{2} = m + 4$ 26. $\dfrac{L}{4}(L + 1) = 3$

27. $3M^2 + 12M = 36$ 28. $4N^2 = 16N + 128$

29. $2x - 3 = \dfrac{2}{x}$ 30. $y = \dfrac{15}{y - 2}$

31. $4x^2 = 12x + 8$ 32. $4y^2 + 6 = 16y$

33. $1 - \dfrac{3}{x} = \dfrac{10}{x^2}$ 34. $2 + \dfrac{2}{x^2} = \dfrac{5}{x}$

35. $y = \dfrac{9}{y}$ 36. $\dfrac{t}{2} = \dfrac{2}{t}$

In problems 37 through 42 find quadratic equations having solution sets as indicated. Write each equation in standard form with integral coefficients.

37. $\{3, 5\}$ 38. $\{2, 9\}$

39. $\{-2, 1\}$ 40. $\{3, -7\}$

41. $\{\frac{1}{2}, -2\}$ 42. $\{2, -\frac{3}{4}\}$

43. The width of a rectangle is 8 in. less than its length. If its area is 33 sq in., find its dimensions.

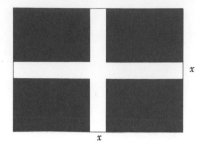

Figure 1

44. Find the base and height of a triangle with area of 2 sq ft if its base is 3 ft longer than its height $(A = \frac{1}{2}bh)$.

45. The sum of a number and its reciprocal is $\frac{13}{6}$. Find the number.

46. The difference between a number and its reciprocal is $\frac{7}{12}$. Find the number.

47. A flag has a cross of uniform width centered on a red background (Fig. 1). Find the width of the cross so that it takes up exactly half of the total area of a 4-by-3-ft flag.

66   EQUATIONS OF THE FORM $ax^2 + c = 0$

We have already solved many equations of the type $ax^2 + c = 0$. A few examples will serve to refresh your memory and extend some of the ideas that we have considered.

EXAMPLE 8

$$x^2 - 9 = 0$$

$$x^2 = 9 \qquad \text{What number squared is 9?}$$

$$\boxed{x = \pm\sqrt{9}}$$

$$x = \pm 3$$

In Example 8 is important to note that in going from the second to the third step we used the definition of square root and not the ill-conceived notion of "taking the square root of both sides." (Example 8 could also have been done by factoring, but the method shown is often faster for this type of problem.)

EXAMPLE 9

$$x^2 - 7 = 0$$

$$x^2 = 7$$

$$x = \pm\sqrt{7}$$

EXAMPLE 10
$$2x^2 - 3 = 0$$
$$2x^2 = 3$$
$$x^2 = \tfrac{3}{2}$$
$$x = \pm\sqrt{\tfrac{3}{2}} \text{ or } \pm\frac{\sqrt{6}}{2}$$

EXAMPLE 11
$$(x - 2)^2 = 16$$
$$x - 2 = \pm 4$$
$$x = 2 \pm 4$$
$$x = 6, -2$$

EXAMPLE 12
$$(x + \tfrac{1}{2})^2 = \tfrac{5}{4}$$
$$x + \tfrac{1}{2} = \pm\sqrt{\tfrac{5}{4}}$$
$$x = -\frac{1}{2} \pm \frac{\sqrt{5}}{2}$$
$$x = \frac{-1 \pm \sqrt{5}}{2}$$

EXAMPLE 13
$$(x - 5)^2 = -4$$

No solution in the real numbers, since no real number squared can be negative.

It is recommended that the reader check some of the solutions in the above examples.

EXERCISE 72

Solve problems 1 through 32 by the method discussed in this section, and write answers in simplest radical form. The replacement set for each variable is the set of real numbers.

1. $x^2 = 4$ 2. $x^2 = 64$
3. $m^2 - 25 = 0$ 4. $n^2 - 49 = 0$
5. $t^2 - 5 = 0$ 6. $y^2 - 13 = 0$
7. $u^2 + 9 = 0$ 8. $x^2 + 4 = 0$
9. $a^2 - 27 = 0$ 10. $b^2 - 8 = 0$
11. $x^2 = 12$ 12. $y^2 = 45$
13. $A^2 = \tfrac{9}{4}$ 14. $B^2 = \tfrac{16}{9}$
15. $9x^2 - 16 = 0$ 16. $4y^2 - 9 = 0$

Figure 2

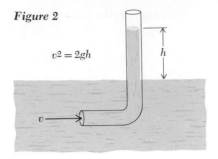

$v^2 = 2gh$

17. $2t^2 - 5 = 0$ 18. $3u^2 - 7 = 0$

19. $3D^2 - 1 = 0$ 20. $5E^2 - 1 = 0$

21. $A^2 = 4$ 22. $B^2 = 25$

23. $(x - 3)^2 = 4$ 24. $(x + 2)^2 = 25$

25. $(y + 2)^2 = 3$ 26. $(y - 3)^2 = 5$

27. $(x - 3)^2 = -4$ 28. $(t + 1)^2 = -9$

29. $(m - \frac{1}{2})^2 = \frac{5}{4}$ 30. $(n + \frac{1}{2})^2 = \frac{3}{4}$

31. $(x - \frac{3}{2})^2 = \frac{3}{2}$ 32. $(y + \frac{5}{2})^2 = \frac{5}{2}$

33. Solve for b: $a^2 + b^2 = c^2$ 34. Solve for v: $k = \frac{1}{2}mv^2$

35. The pressure p in pounds per square foot from a wind blowing at v mph is $p = 0.003v^2$. If a pressure gauge on a bridge registers a wind pressure of 14.7 lb per sq ft, what is the velocity of the wind?

36. One method of measuring the velocity of water in a stream or river is to use an L-shaped tube as indicated in Fig. 2. Torricelli's law in physics tells us that the height (in feet) that the water is pushed up into the tube above the surface is related to the water's velocity (in feet per second) by the formula $v^2 = 2gh$, where g is approximately 32 ft per sec per sec. (NOTE: The device can also be used as a simple speedometer for a boat.) How fast is a stream flowing if $h = 0.5$ ft? Find the answer to two decimal places.

37. A barrel 2 ft in diameter and 4 ft in height has a 1-in.-diameter drainpipe in the bottom. It can be shown that the height h of the surface of the water above the bottom of the barrel at time t min after the drain has been opened is given by the formula $h = [\sqrt{h_0} - (t/240)]^2$, where h_0 is the water level above the drain at time $t = 0$. If the barrel is full and the drain opened, how long will it take to empty half of the contents? HINT: The problem is very easily solved if the right side of the equation is not squared.

67   SOLUTION BY COMPLETING THE SQUARE

The methods discussed in the last two sections are both fast and easy to use, but unfortunately many quadratic equations will not yield to either of the methods.

For example, the very simple-looking quadratic equation

$$x^2 + 6x - 2 = 0$$

cannot be factored (as defined earlier). It requires a new method if it can be solved at all.

In this section we will discuss a method, called "solution by completing the square," that will work for all quadratic equations. In the next section we will use this method to develop a general formula that will be used in the future whenever the methods of the two preceding sections fail.

The method of completing the square is based on the process of transforming the standard quadratic equation,

$$ax^2 + bx + c = 0$$

into the form

$$(x + A)^2 = B$$

where A and B are constants. This last equation can easily be solved (assuming $B \geq 0$) by the method discussed in the last section. Thus

$$(x + A)^2 = B$$
$$x + A = \pm \sqrt{B}$$
$$x = -A \pm \sqrt{B}$$

Before considering how the first part is accomplished, let's pause for a moment and consider a related problem: What number must be added to $x^2 + 6x$ so that the result is the square of a linear expression? There is an easy mechanical rule for finding this number based on the squares of the following binomials:

$$(x + m)^2 = x^2 + 2mx + m^2$$
$$(x - m)^2 = x^2 - 2mx + m^2$$

In either case, we see that the third term on the right is the square of one-half of the coefficient of x in the second term on the right. This observation leads directly to the rule. To **complete the square** of a quadratic of the form $x^2 + bx$, add the square of one-half of the coefficient of x [that is, $(b/2)^2$].

EXAMPLE 14

To complete the square of $x^2 + 6x$, add $(\frac{6}{2})^2$, that is, 9; thus $x^2 + 6x + 9 = (x + 3)^2$.

To complete the square of $x^2 - 3x$, add $(-\frac{3}{2})^2$, that is $\frac{9}{4}$; thus $x^2 - 3x + \frac{9}{4} = (x - \frac{3}{2})^2$.

To complete the square of $x^2 + bx$, add $(b/2)^2$, that is $b^2/4$; thus $x^2 + bx + (b^2/4) = [x + (b/2)]^2$.

It is important to note that the rule stated above applies only to quadratic forms where the coefficient of the second-degree term is 1.

SOLUTION OF QUADRATIC EQUATIONS BY COMPLETING THE SQUARE

Solving quadratic equations by the method of completing the square is best illustrated by examples. In the following examples the replacement set for all variables is the set of real numbers.

EXAMPLE 15. Solve $x^2 + 6x - 2 = 0$ by the method of completing the square.

SOLUTION

$$x^2 + 6x - 2 = 0 \qquad \text{Add 2 to both sides of the equation to remove } -2 \text{ from the left side.}$$

$$x^2 + 6x \quad = 2 \qquad \text{To complete the square of the left side, add the square of one-half of the coefficient of } x \text{ to each side of the equation.}$$

$$x^2 + 6x + 9 = 2 + 9$$

$$(x + 3)^2 = 11 \qquad \text{Factor the left side.}$$

$$x + 3 = \pm\sqrt{11} \qquad \text{Proceed as in the last section.}$$

$$x = -3 \pm \sqrt{11}$$

Thus, $\{x \mid x^2 + 6x - 2 = 0, x \text{ a real number}\} = \{-3 + \sqrt{11}, -3 - \sqrt{11}\}$.

CHECK

$$(-3 + \sqrt{11})^2 + 6(-3 + \sqrt{11}) - 2 \overset{?}{=} 0$$

$$9 - 6\sqrt{11} + 11 - 18 + 6\sqrt{11} - 2 \overset{?}{=} 0$$

$$0 \overset{\checkmark}{=} 0$$

$$(-3 - \sqrt{11})^2 + 6(-3 - \sqrt{11}) - 2 \overset{?}{=} 0$$

$$9 + 6\sqrt{11} + 11 - 18 - 6\sqrt{11} - 2 \overset{?}{=} 0$$

$$0 \overset{\checkmark}{=} 0$$

NOTE: If desired, decimal approximations of the roots may be obtained from a square-root table; that is, $-3 + \sqrt{11} \doteq -3 + 3.32 = 0.32$ and $-3 - \sqrt{11} \doteq -3 - 3.32 = -6.32$. It should be remembered, however, that these decimal quantities are approximate and not exact solutions of the equation.

EXAMPLE 16.   Solve $2x^2 - 4x - 3 = 0$ by the method of completing the square.

SOLUTION

$$2x^2 - 4x - 3 = 0$$
$$x^2 - 2x - \tfrac{3}{2} = 0$$

Note that the coefficient of x^2 is not 1. Divide through by the leading coefficient and proceed as in the last example.

$$x^2 - 2x \quad\quad = \tfrac{3}{2}$$
$$x^2 - 2x + 1 = \tfrac{3}{2} + 1$$
$$(x - 1)^2 = \tfrac{5}{2}$$
$$x - 1 = \pm \sqrt{\tfrac{5}{2}}$$
$$x = 1 \pm \frac{\sqrt{10}}{2}$$
$$x = \frac{2 \pm \sqrt{10}}{2}$$

$\{(2 + \sqrt{10})/2, (2 - \sqrt{10})/2\}$ is the solution set of the given equation.

The checking of the solution is left to the reader.

EXAMPLE 17.   Solve $m^2 - 3m + 4 = 0$ by the method of completing the square.

SOLUTION

$$m^2 - 3m + 4 = 0$$
$$m^2 - 3m \quad\quad = -4$$
$$m^2 - 3m + \tfrac{9}{4} = \tfrac{9}{4} - 4$$
$$(m - \tfrac{3}{2})^2 = -\tfrac{7}{4}$$

No real solutions; hence $\{m \mid m^2 - 3m + 4 = 0,\ m \text{ a real number}\} = \phi$.

EXERCISE 73

Complete the square of each quadratic form and factor.

1. $x^2 + 4x$
2. $x^2 + 8x$
3. $x^2 - 6x$
4. $y^2 - 10y$
5. $t^2 + 3t$
6. $u^2 + u$
7. $x^2 - 5x$
8. $Z^2 - 7Z$

In problems 9 through 20 solve each of the equations by the method of completing the square. Remember that whatever you add to the left of the equation, you must also add to the right. The replacement set for each variable is the set of real numbers.

9. $x^2 + 4x + 2 = 0$ 　　　　　　　　　10. $x^2 + 8x + 3 = 0$

11. $y^2 - 6y - 3 = 0$ 　　　　　　　　12. $y^2 - 10y - 3 = 0$

13. $t^2 + 3t - 1 = 0$ 　　　　　　　　14. $u^2 + u - 1 = 0$

15. $x^2 - 2x + 3 = 0$ 　　　　　　　　16. $Z^2 - 4Z + 8 = 0$

17. $2x^2 - 6x + 3 = 0$ 　　　　　　　18. $2y^2 - 4y + 1 = 0$

19. $3Z^2 + Z - 1 = 0$ 　　　　　　　20. $2u^2 + 3u - 1 = 0$

21. Solve for x:　$x^2 + mx + n = 0$

22. Solve for x:　$ax^2 + bx + c = 0$, with $a \neq 0$.

68　THE QUADRATIC FORMULA

The method of completing the square discussed in the last section can be used to solve any quadratic equation, but the process is often tedious. If you had a very large number of quadratic equations to solve by completing the square, before you finished you would probably ask yourself if the process could not be made more efficient. "Why not take the general quadratic equation $ax^2 + bx + c = 0$, with $a \neq 0$, and solve it once and for all for x in terms of the coefficients a, b, and c by the method of completing the square, and thus obtain a formula that could be memorized and used whenever a, b, and c are known?" If you worked the last problem in the last exercise, this is exactly what you did—you derived the well-known and widely used quadratic formula! The formula will be developed here in case you had difficulty with the problem or omitted it.

We are dealing with the equation

$$ax^2 + bx + c = 0 \qquad a \neq 0$$

and we solve it by completing the square exactly as we did when the coefficients were specified. The replacement set for the variable x is assumed to be the set of real numbers. To make the leading coefficient 1, multiply both sides of the equation by $1/a$. Thus

$$x^2 + \frac{b}{a}x + \frac{c}{a} = 0$$

Adding $-c/a$ to each side, we get

$$x^2 + \frac{b}{a}x = -\frac{c}{a}$$

Add the square of one-half of the coefficient of x, which is $(b/2a)^2$, to each side to complete the square of the left side.   Thus

$$x^2 + \frac{b}{a}x + \frac{b^2}{4a^2} = \frac{b^2}{4a^2} - \frac{c}{a}$$

Factor the left side and combine the right side into a single term, leaving

$$\left(x + \frac{b}{2a}\right)^2 = \frac{b^2 - 4ac}{4a^2}$$

If $b^2 - 4ac \geq 0$, then by the definition of square root of positive real numbers,

$$x + \frac{b}{2a} = \pm \sqrt{\frac{b^2 - 4ac}{4a^2}}$$

$$x = -\frac{b}{2a} \pm \frac{\sqrt{b^2 - 4ac}}{2a}$$

$$x = \frac{-b \pm \sqrt{b^2 - 4ac}}{2a} \qquad a \neq 0$$

The last equation is called the **quadratic formula.**   It should be memorized and used to solve quadratic equations when simpler methods fail.   The following examples illustrate the use of the formula.

EXAMPLE 18.   Solve $2x + \frac{3}{2} = x^2$ by use of the quadratic formula.

SOLUTION

$2x + \frac{3}{2} = x^2$ Clear the equation of fractions.

$4x + 3 = 2x^2$ Write in standard form.

$2x^2 - 4x - 3 = 0$

$x = \dfrac{-b \pm \sqrt{b^2 - 4ac}}{2a}$ $\begin{aligned} a &= 2 \\ b &= -4 \\ c &= -3 \end{aligned}$ Write down the quadratic formula, and identify a, b, and c.

$x = \dfrac{-(-4) \pm \sqrt{(-4)^2 - 4(2)(-3)}}{2(2)}$ Substitute into formula and simplify.

$x = \dfrac{4 \pm \sqrt{40}}{4} = \dfrac{4 \pm 2\sqrt{10}}{4}$

$x = \dfrac{2 \pm \sqrt{10}}{2}$

$\{(2 + \sqrt{10})/2, (2 - \sqrt{10})/2\}$ is the solution set for the given equation.

EXAMPLE 19.   An artist with a painting measuring 6 by 8 in. wishes to frame it with a frame of uniform width that has a total area equal to the area of the painting.   How wide should he make the frame?   Give the answer in simplest radical form and as a decimal fraction to two decimal places.

SOLUTION

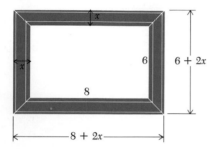

$$\frac{\text{Total area of picture}}{\text{and frame}} = \frac{\text{Twice the area of}}{\text{the picture}}$$

$$(6 + 2x)(8 + 2x) = 2(6 \cdot 8)$$
$$48 + 28x + 4x^2 = 96$$
$$x^2 + 7x - 12 = 0$$

$$x = \frac{-b \pm \sqrt{b^2 - 4ac}}{2a} \qquad \begin{aligned} a &= 1 \\ b &= 7 \\ c &= 12 \end{aligned}$$

$$x = \frac{-7 \pm \sqrt{7^2 - 4(1)(-12)}}{2(1)}$$

$$x = \frac{-7 \pm \sqrt{97}}{2}$$

The negative answer must be rejected since it has no meaning relative to the original problem; hence

$$x = \frac{-7 + \sqrt{97}}{2} \doteq 1.43 \text{ in.}$$

The check is left to the reader.   (Is it possible for 1.43, or any rational number, to check exactly?)

EXERCISE 74

Specify the constants a, b, and c for each quadratic equation when written in the standard form $ax^2 + bx + c = 0$.

1. $x^2 + 8x + 3 = 0$

2. $x^2 + 4x + 2 = 0$

3. $z^2 = 4z - 8$

4. $x^2 = 2x - 3$

5. $2u^2 + 3u = 1$

6. $z = 1 - 3z^2$

7. $x^2 + \frac{3}{2} = 3x$

8. $\frac{1}{2} + y^2 = 2y$

9. $3y^2 = 5$

10. $2x^2 = 5x$

Solve each of the following quadratic equations by using the quadratic formula. The replacement set for each variable is the set of real numbers.

11. $x^2 + 8x + 3 = 0$

12. $x^2 + 4x + 2 = 0$

13. $y^2 - 10y - 3 = 0$

14. $y^2 - 6y - 3 = 0$

15. $u^2 = 1 - u$

16. $3t + t^2 = 1$

17. $z^2 + 8 = 4z$

18. $x^2 = 2x - 3$

19. $2y^2 - 4y + 1 = 0$

20. $2x^2 + 3 = 6x$

21. $3u + 2u^2 = 1$

22. $3z^2 = 1 - z$

23. $x + \dfrac{2}{x} = 6$

24. $2x = 3 + \dfrac{3}{x}$

25. $x^2 = 3x + \frac{1}{2}$

26. $m^2 = \dfrac{8m - 1}{5}$

27. $t^2 - \sqrt{5}t - 11 = 0$

28. $3u^2 = \sqrt{3}u + 2$

In problems 29 through 32 indicate which statements are true.

29. If $b^2 - 4ac < 0$, the quadratic equation has no real solutions.

30. If $b^2 - 4ac > 0$, the quadratic equation has two real solutions.

31. If $b^2 - 4ac = 0$, the quadratic equation has one real solution.

32. If $b^2 - 4ac = 0$, the quadratic equation has two real solutions.

33. The width of a rectangle is 2 in. less than its length. Find its dimensions to two decimal places if its area is 12 sq in.

34. If the length and width of a 4-by-2-in. rectangle are each increased by the same amount, the area of the new rectangle will be twice the old. What are the dimensions to two decimal places of the new rectangle?

69   WHICH METHOD?

In everyday encounters with quadratic equations the quadratic formula is used whenever the equation is not of the form $ax^2 + c = 0$ or the factoring method is not applicable. If the factoring method is applicable, it will generally produce results faster and easier than the formula and should be used.

EXAMPLE 20.   Solve $2x^2 + 7x - 15 = 0$.

SOLUTION

Test for factorability: Does $ac = (2)(-15) = -30$ have factors whose sum is $b = 7$? Yes, $(10)(-3) = -30$ and $(10) + (-3) = 7$. Therefore, $2x^2 + 7x - 15$ can be factored and the equation can be solved by factoring. Thus

$$2x^2 + 7x - 15 = 0$$
$$(2x - 3)(x + 5) = 0$$
$$2x - 3 = 0 \quad \text{or} \quad x + 5 = 0$$
$$x = \tfrac{3}{2} \qquad\qquad x = -5$$

Suppose you had used the quadratic formula instead?

$$x = \frac{-b \pm \sqrt{b^2 - 4ac}}{2a} \qquad \begin{array}{l} a = 2 \\ b = 7 \\ c = -15 \end{array}$$

$$x = \frac{-(7) \pm \sqrt{7^2 - 4(2)(-15)}}{2(2)}$$

$$x = \frac{-7 \pm \sqrt{169}}{4} = \frac{-7 \pm 13}{4}$$

$$x = \tfrac{3}{2}, -5$$

The formula produces the same result (as it should), but with a little more work.

In the exercises for this section the problems will be mixed up, and it will be up to you to use the most efficient method—formula, factoring, or square root— for each particular problem.

EXERCISE 75

Solve each of the following quadratic equations by the most efficient method. The replacement set for all variables is the set of real numbers.

1. $x^2 + 2x - 15 = 0$

2. $x^2 = 2x + 3$

3. $m^2 - 3m = 1$

4. $2n + n^2 = 2$

5. $A^2 + 4 = 0$

6. $(x - 2)^2 = -9$

7. $2x^2 = 4x$

8. $2y^2 + 3y = 0$

9. $t^2 = \frac{3}{2}(t + 1)$

10. $E^2 = 3E - \frac{3}{2}$

11. $2x + 1 = \dfrac{6}{x}$

12. $6y = \dfrac{1 - y}{y}$

13. $M = M^2$

14. $t(t - 3) = 0$

15. $t(t - 3) = 1$

16. $(x - 3)(x + 2) = 1$

17. $I^2 - 50 = 0$

18. $(B - 2)^2 = 3$

19. $3x = \dfrac{84 - 9x}{x}$

20. $\dfrac{24}{d} = 12d - 28$

21. $\dfrac{24}{10 + x} + 1 = \dfrac{24}{10 - x}$

22. $\dfrac{1.2}{x - 1} + \dfrac{1.2}{x} = 1$

In problems 23 through 26 solve for the indicated letter in terms of the other letters.   Use positive square roots only.

23. $d = \frac{1}{2}gt^2$ (solve for t).

24. $a^2 + b^2 = c^2$ (solve for a).

25. $A = P(1 + r)^2$ (solve for r).

26. $P = EI - RI^2$ (solve for I).

27. Find the elements of the set $\left\{ x \mid \dfrac{1}{x - 2} + 1 = \dfrac{6 - x}{x^2 - 4} + \dfrac{1}{x + 2} \right\}$.

70   ADDITIONAL APPLICATIONS

We conclude this chapter with a number of applications from several different areas: *communications, economics-business, geometry, number problems, police science, physics-engineering, and rate-time.*

Since quadratic equations often have two solutions, it is important to check both of the solutions in the original problem to see if one or the other must be rejected.

EXERCISE 76

COMMUNICATIONS

1. The number of telephone connections possible through a switchboard to which n telephones are connected is given by the formula $c = n(n - 1)/2$. How many telephones could be handled by a switchboard that had the capacity of 190 connections?

ECONOMICS AND BUSINESS

2. If P dollars is invested at r percent compounded annually, at the end of two years it will grow to $A = P(1 + r)^2$. At what interest rate will $100 grow to $144 in two years?   NOTE: $A = 144$ and $P = 100$.

3. Cost equations for manufacturing companies are often quadratic in nature. (At very high or very low outputs the costs are more per unit because of inefficiency of plant operation at these extremes.)   If the cost equation for manufacturing transistor radios is $C = x^2 - 10x + 31$, where C is the cost of manufacturing x units per week (both in thousands), find (A) the output for a $15,000 weekly cost and (B) the output for a $6,000 weekly cost.

4. The manufacturing company in the preceding problem sells its transistor radios for $3 each.   Thus its revenue equation is $R = 3x$, where R is revenue and x is the number of units sold per week (both in thousands).   Find the break-even points for the company, that is, the output at which revenue equals cost. (In the next chapter we will solve this problem using graphing techniques, and the reason for two break-even points will then be clear.)

5. In a certain city the demand equation for popular records is $q_d = 3{,}000/p$, where q_d would be the quantity of records demanded on a given day if the selling price were p dollars per record. (Notice as the price goes up, the number of records the people are willing to buy goes down, and vice versa.)   On the other hand, the supply equation is $q_s = 1{,}000p - 500$, where q_s is the quantity of records a supplier is willing to supply at p dollars per record. (Notice as the price goes up, the number of records a supplier is willing to sell goes up, and vice versa.) At what price will supply equal demand; that is, at what price will $q_d = q_s$?   In economic theory the price at which supply equals demand is called the *equilibrium point*, the point at which the price ceases to change.

GEOMETRY

The following theorem may be used where needed:

PYTHAGOREAN THEOREM   *A triangle is a right triangle if and only if the square of the longest side is equal to the sum of the squares of the two shorter sides.*

$$c^2 = a^2 + b^2$$

6. Approximately how far would a person be able to see from the top of a mountain 2 miles high (Fig. 3)?   Use the square-root table to estimate the answer to the nearest mile.

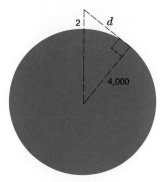

Figure 3

7. Find the length of each side of a right triangle if the second longest side is 1 in. longer than the shortest side and the longest side is 2 in. longer than the shortest side.

This right triangle has been well known for over 2,000 years.   It has many interesting properties and has been put to many interesting uses.   For example, it can be shown that any triangle whose sides are in the same ratio must be a right triangle.   The ancients used this fact to lay out right angles when surveying land and constructing buildings.   An appropriately knotted piece of rope is all of the equipment that is needed.

Also, by stretching a guitar string around three pulleys nailed to a board and spaced so that distances between them are in the ratio of the sides of the triangle under consideration, the three sides of the triangle thus formed will sound the same chord as the top three strings of a guitar if the longest side is tuned to G.

8. Find r in Fig. 4.   Express the answer in simplest radical form.

9. A golden rectangle is defined to be one that has the property that when a

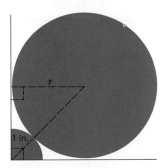

Figure 4

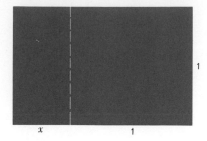

Figure 5

square of side equal to the shorter side of the rectangle is removed, the ratio of the sides of the remaining rectangle is the same as the ratio of the sides of the original rectangle. If the shorter side of the original rectangle is 1, find the shorter side of the remaining rectangle (see Fig. 5). This number is called the golden ratio, and it turns up frequently in the history of mathematics.

NUMBER PROBLEMS

10. Separate 21 into two parts whose product is 104.

11. Find two consecutive positive even integers whose product is 168.

12. Find all numbers with the property that when the number is added to itself, the sum is the same as when the number is multiplied by itself.

13. Find a number whose square exceeds itself by 56.

14. The sum of a number and its reciprocal is $\frac{10}{3}$. Find the number.

POLICE SCIENCE

15. Skid marks are often used to estimate the speed of a car in an accident. It is common practice for an officer to drive the car in question (if it is still running) at a speed of 20 to 30 mph and skid it to a stop near the original skid marks. It is known (from physics) that the speed of the car and the length of the skid marks are related by the formula

$$\frac{d_a}{v_a^2} = \frac{d_t}{v_t^2}$$

where $d_a =$ length of accident car's skid marks

$\quad d_t =$ length of test car's skid marks

$\quad v_a =$ speed of accident car (to be found)

$\quad v_t =$ speed of test car

Estimate the speed of an accident vehicle if its skid marks are 120 ft and the test car driven at 30 mph produces skid marks of 36 ft.

16. At 20 mph a car collides with a stationary object with the same force it would have if it had been dropped $13\frac{1}{2}$ ft, that is, if it had been pushed off the roof of an average one-story house. In general, a car moving at r mph hits a stationary object with a force of impact that is equivalent to that force with which it would hit the ground when falling from a certain height h given by the formula $h = 0.0336r^2$. Approximately how fast would a car have to be moving if it crashed as hard as if it had been pushed off the top of a 12-story building 121 ft high?

PHYSICS–ENGINEERING

17. In physics it is found that the illumination I in foot-candles on a surface d ft from a light source of c candlepower is given by the formula $I = c/d^2$. How far should a light of 20 candlepower be placed from a surface to produce the same illumination as a light of 10 candlepower at 10 ft? Write the answer in simplest radical form, and approximate it to two decimal places.

18. If an arrow is shot vertically in the air (from the ground) with an initial velocity of 176 fps, its distance y above the ground t sec after it is released (neglecting air resistance) is given by $y = 176t - 16t^2$.

(A) Find the times when y is zero, and interpret physically.

(B) Find the times when the arrow is 16 ft off the ground. Compute answers to two decimal places.

19. A *Pitot tube* is a device (based on Bernoulli's principles) that is used to measure the flow speed of a gas (Fig. 6). If mounted on an airplane, it indicates the plane's velocity relative to the surrounding air and is known as an airspeed indicator. A simple equation relates the height differential of the fluid in the tube with the velocity of the gas. Thus

$$v^2 = 2gkh$$

where v = velocity of gas (feet per second)

g = gravitational constant (approximately 32 ft per sec per sec)

k = ratio of the density of the fluid in the tube to the density of the gas

h = height differential (in feet)

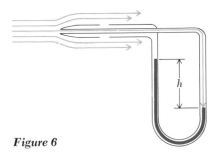

Figure 6

Approximate an aircraft's speed in feet per second and miles per hour if $k = 625$ and $h = 0.81$.

RATE–TIME PROBLEMS

20. Two boats travel at right angles to each other after leaving the same dock at the same time. One hour later they are 13 miles apart. If one travels 7 mph faster than the other, what is the rate of each?

21. A new printing press can do a job in 1 hr less than an older press. Together they can do the same job in 1.2 hr. How long would it take each alone to do the job?

22. One pipe can fill a tank in 5 hr less than another; together they fill the tank in 5 hr. How long would it take each alone to fill the tank? Compute answer to two decimal places.

23. A speedboat takes 1 hr longer to go 24 miles up a river than to return. If the boat cruises at 10 mph in still water, what is the rate of the current?

71   CHAPTER SUMMARY

GENERAL

The quadratic equation occurs in many different places in mathematics and science as well as in trade-technical areas and business. The quadratic formula should be memorized so that it will be available for use when needed, that is, when a quadratic equation cannot be solved by factoring or is not of the form $ax^2 + c = 0$.

In all of the problems we considered in this chapter we restricted the replacement set of the variables to the set of real numbers; in other words, we asked only for real-number solutions to the quadratic equations. We found that there are quadratic equations that do not have real-number solutions, for example, $x^2 + 4 = 0$ or $x^2 - x + 1 = 0$. In order for $x^2 + 4 = 0$ to have a solution, we would have to have a number whose square is -4. No such real number exists since the square of any real number is positive. A new number must be invented if this equation is to have a solution.

It is precisely this type of thinking that motivates the extension of the real-number system to an enlarged set of numbers called the *complex numbers*. We will not undertake this extension in this course; it will be undertaken in the next course, and at that time a number will be defined so that when it is squared, it will equal -4! In addition, with this new number system every quadratic equation will have a solution, without exception.

SPECIFIC

Describe, define, or give examples of each of the following:

1. **Second-degree polynomial in one variable**
2. **Second-degree polynomial equation in one variable**
3. **Quadratic expression in one variable**
4. **Quadratic equation in one variable**
5. **Solution by factoring:**

$$(ax + b)(cx + d) = 0 \text{ if and only if } (ax + b) = 0 \text{ or } (cx + d) = 0$$

6. **Solution by square root:**

$$ax^2 + c = 0 \qquad -\frac{c}{a} \geq 0$$

$$x = \pm \sqrt{-\frac{c}{a}}$$

7. **Solution by quadratic formula:**

$$ax^2 + bx + c = 0$$

$$x = \frac{-b \pm \sqrt{b^2 - 4ac}}{2a}$$

No real solutions: $b^2 - 4ac < 0$
One real solution: $b^2 - 4ac = 0$
Two real solutions: $b^2 - 4ac > 0$

EXERCISE 77   CHAPTER REVIEW

Solve each of the quadratic equations in problems 1 through 11.   The replacement set for each variable is the set of real numbers.

1. $u^2 - 81 = 0$

2. $10I^2 = 20I$

3. $2t^2 + 3 = 0$

4. $2y^2 - 16 = 0$

5. $(m + \frac{1}{2})^2 = \frac{5}{4}$

6. $2r^2 + 3r - 2 = 0$

7. $13x = 6 + 6x^2$

8. $4u^2 - 1 = 2u$

9. $A^2 - A + 1 = 0$

10. $N = \dfrac{15}{N - 2}$

11. $3x - 1 = \dfrac{2(x + 1)}{x + 2}$

12. Solve $2x^2 + x - 6 = 0$ three ways: (*a*) by factoring, (*b*) by completing the square, and (*c*) by using quadratic formula.

13. Find a quadratic equation with integral coefficients that has the solution set $\{-\frac{1}{2}, 3\}$.

14. If $b^2 - 4c > 0$, then the quadratic equation has two real solutions. (True or false?)

15. Separate 17 into two parts whose product is 42.

16. The perimeter of a rectangle is 22 in. If its area is 30 sq in. find the length of each side.

17. The hypotenuse (the side opposite the right angle) of a right triangle is 13 in. Find the length of the two legs of the triangle if one is 7 in. longer than the other.

Additional applications may be found in Sec. 70.

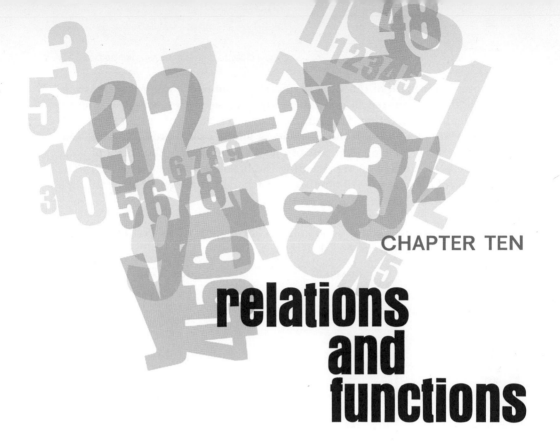

CHAPTER TEN

relations
and
functions

72 INTRODUCTION

Seeking relationships between various types of phenomena is undoubtedly one of
the most important aspects of science.   In physics one attempts to find a relationship between the pressure of an enclosed gas and its temperature; in chemistry,
a relationship between the speed of a chemical reaction and the concentration of
a given substance; in geometry, a relationship between the radius of a sphere and
its volume; in psychology, a relationship between IQ and school performance; in
space science, a relationship between the velocity of a rocket and the size of its
orbit; in cooking, a relationship between the amount of rise in bread and the
quantity of yeast used; in police science, a relationship between driving speed
and breaking distance; . . . .   The list could be continued indefinitely.

We note that in spite of the varied types of phenomena considered, the scientist is essentially interested in one thing—the pairing of elements from one set with the elements of another (for example, pairing elements of one set representing the pressure of a gas with the elements of another set representing the temperature of a gas or pairing elements of one set representing the speed of a car with elements of another set representing the breaking distance of a car).   The resulting sets of ordered pairs of numbers are generally represented by a table or a graph or (if possible) in terms of an equation.

EXAMPLE 1:   THE DISTANCE d IN FEET THAT AN OBJECT FALLS (NEGLECTING AIR RESISTANCE) IN t SEC, WHERE $t = 0, 1, 2, 3, 4, 5$.

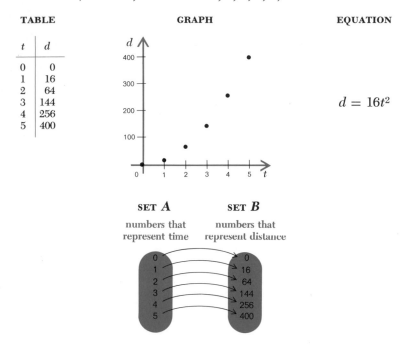

TABLE		GRAPH	EQUATION

t	d
0	0
1	16
2	64
3	144
4	256
5	400

$$d = 16t^2$$

SET A — numbers that represent time

SET B — numbers that represent distance

We note that the table, the graph, and the equation each correctly matches elements of set A with elements of set B.

Establishing and working with sets of ordered pairs of matched numbers—whether it is through tables, graphs, or equations—permeates almost all of pure and applied science.   This pairing activity is so broad and so fundamental in the activities of man in his attempt to understand and control his environment that he has found it necessary to describe it in the precise language of mathematics.   The result has been the extensive development of a subject—the theory and applications of relations and functions—that stands high on the list of the most important mathematical concepts.

We will only scratch the surface of this important subject in this course; the concept of function will be discussed and extended in almost any mathematics course you take after this one, and eventually some of you will take whole courses devoted entirely to this one topic.

73   RELATIONS AND FUNCTIONS

To be able to talk about relationships of the type discussed in the preceding section with more precision, it is necessary to introduce two new technical terms, "relation" and "function." A **relation** is any set of ordered pairs of elements (generally numbers in this course). The choice of the word "relation" for this definition is quite natural since any set of ordered pairs of numbers establishes a relationship between two sets of numbers, the set of first components of the set of ordered pairs and the set of second components. The set of first components of the set of ordered pairs is called the **domain** of the relation, and the set of second components is called the **range** of the relation.

Relations are specified in many different ways; the most usual ways are through set notation, tables, graphs, or equations—use dictates the choice. If in this course an equation is used to specify a relation and the domain and range are not indicated, then it is assumed that the domain and range include those real numbers for which the equation is meaningful.

EXAMPLE 2:   A RELATION SPECIFIED BY A SET.

$$A = \{(-2, 0), (-1, 1), (-1, -1), (0, 1), (0, -1), (1, 1), (1, -1), (2, 0)\}$$

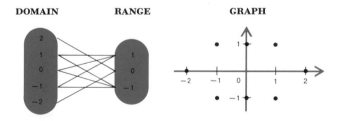

EXAMPLE 3:   A RELATION SPECIFIED BY A GRAPH.

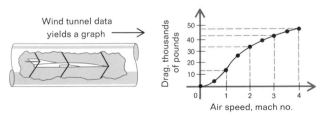

DOMAIN

The set of all real numbers from 0 to 4

RANGE

The set of all real numbers from 0 to 50,000

The domain of a relation is generally associated with the horizontal axis and the range with the vertical axis. The graph in example 3 enables us to pair elements from the domain (air speed) with elements from the range (drag), yielding a set of ordered pairs of matched numbers (a relation).

EXAMPLE 4:   A RELATION SPECIFIED BY AN EQUATION.

$y = 16x^2$, $x \geq 0$ (or more formally, $\{(x, y) \mid y = 16x^2, x \geq 0\}$)

GRAPH

DOMAIN

Set of all nonnegative real numbers

RANGE

Set of all nonnegative real numbers

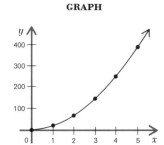

We emphasize the fact that *any* set of ordered pairs of elements is a relation; whether it has physical meaning or not is entirely beside the point. The concept is purely mathematical in nature, and as such it is completely free to be applied to a variety of practical or theoretical problems. Many different practical problems give rise to exactly the same relation. For example, the area of 16 squares each with side x and the distance that an object falls in a vacuum at the end of x sec is each described by the same relation: $y = 16x^2$, with $x \geq 0$.

In many problems in science and mathematics it is necessary to restrict a relation so that each element in the domain is paired with one and only one element in the range. A relation so restricted is called a **function**. All functions are relations, but some relations are not functions. In this course we will be primarily interested in relations that are functions. Which of the relations in the three examples above are functions? The relation in example 2 is not a function since certain domain elements are paired with more than one range element; for example, 0 is paired with 1 and also -1. The relations in examples 3 and 4 are both functions; each element in the domain is paired with exactly one element in the range.

An element in the range of a function may be paired with more than one element in the domain (see example 5).

EXAMPLE 5. If an arrow is shot straight up from the ground with an initial velocity of 160 fps, its distance d in feet above the ground at the end of t sec (neglecting air resistance) is given by

$$d = 160t - 16t^2 \qquad 0 \leq t \leq 10$$

PARTIAL TABLE

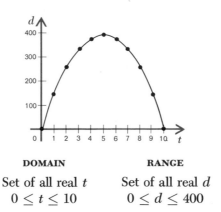

t	d
0	0
1	144
2	256
3	336
4	384
5	400
6	384
7	336
8	256
9	144
10	0

DOMAIN	**RANGE**
Set of all real t	Set of all real d
$0 \le t \le 10$	$0 \le d \le 400$

The relation in example 5 is a function since each number in the domain (time) is associated with exactly one number in the range (distance). Note that there are values in the range that are associated with more than one value in the domain; for example, 144 is associated with both 1 and 9. (What is the physical meaning of this?)

It is very easy to tell if a relation is a function if one has its graph. *A relation is a function if each vertical line in the coordinate system contains at most one point of the graph.* Example 2 obviously does not meet this test; examples 3, 4, and 5 all do.

EXAMPLE 6

RELATIONS SPECIFIED BY GRAPHS	FUNCTION?	DOMAIN	RANGE
	No	All real x $-3 \le x \le 3$	All real y $-3 \le y \le 3$
	Yes	All real n $-4 \le n \le 3$	All real m $-1 \le m \le 4$

RELATIONS SPECIFIED BY GRAPHS	FUNCTION?	DOMAIN	RANGE
	Yes	All real u $-5 \leq u \leq 5$	All real v $0 \leq v \leq 3$
	No	$\{0, 1, 2, 3, 4\}$	$\{0, 1, 2, 3, 4\}$

Any variable that is used as a place holder for elements from the domain of a function is called an **independent variable**; any variable that is used as a place holder for elements from the range of a function is called a **dependent variable**. In example 6, x, n, and u are independent variables, and y, m, and v are dependent variables.

EXERCISE 78

State the domain and range for each of the following relations and indicate whether the relation is a function.

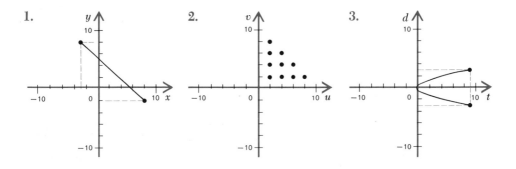

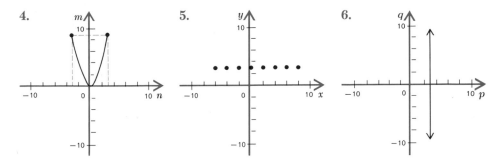

Graph each of the relations in problems 7 through 12. State the domain and range of each and indicate whether the relation is a function.

7. $f = \{(-2, 0), (0, 2), (2, 0)\}$
8. $g = \{(-1, -2), (0, -1), (1, 0), (2, 1), (3, 2), (4, 1)\}$
9. $F = \{(1, 1), (2, 1), (3, 2), (3, 3)\}$
10. $G = \{(2, 4), (4, 2), (2, 0), (4, -2)\}$

11. $\{(x, y) \mid y = \dfrac{x}{2} - 4,\ 0 \le x \le 6\}$

12. $\{(x, y) \mid y = 6 - 2x,\ 0 \le x \le 6\}$

13. Graph each relation for the domain $\{0, 1, 4\}$. What is the range of each and which is a function?
(A) $\{(x, y) \mid y = x^2\}$ (B) $\{(x, y) \mid y^2 = x\}$

14. Graph each relation for the domain $\{0, 2, 4\}$. What is the range of each and which is a function?
(A) $\{(x, y) \mid y = |x|\}$ (B) $\{(x, y) \mid |y| = x\}$

Each of the statements in problems 15 through 23 can be described by a function. Write an equation that specifies the function, and graph it for an appropriate set of values.

15. The cost C of x records at \$2 per record. (The cost depends on the number of records purchased.)

16. The distance d that a car travels in t hr at 30 mph. (The distance depends on time.)

17. The cost C of manufacturing x pairs of skis if fixed costs are \$300 per day and the variable costs are \$50 per pair of skis. (The cost per day depends on the number of pairs of skis manufactured per day.)

18. The cost per day C for renting a car at \$5 per day plus 5 cents a mile for x miles. (The rental cost per day depends on the mileage per day.)

19. The amount A to be repaid on a loan of \$100 at the end of t years at

4 percent simple interest is $100 more than four times the number of years. (The amount to be repaid on the loan depends on the number of years that a loan is outstanding.)

20. The temperature F in Fahrenheit degrees is 32° more than nine-fifths the temperature C in Centigrade degrees. (Temperature in Fahrenheit degrees depends on temperature in Centigrade degrees.)

21. The area A of a square is the square of its side x. (The area of a square depends on the size of its side.)

22. The area A of a circle is the product of π (use 3.14) and the square of its radius r. (The area of a circle depends on the size of its radius.)

23. The distance d in feet that an object falls in a vacuum is 16 times the square of the time t in sec. (The distance that an object falls depends on time.)

24. If an object is projected straight up from the ground with an initial velocity of v_0 fps, its distance d in feet above the ground at the end of t sec (neglecting air resistance) is given by $d = v_0 t - (g/2)t^2$, where g is the gravitational constant (assume $g = 32$). For an initial launching velocity of $v_0 = 128$ fps, graph the function for $0 \leq t \leq 8$.

74 FUNCTION NOTATION

In the last section we saw that a function involves two sets of elements, a domain and range, and a rule that enables one to assign each element in the domain to exactly one element in the range. We have used different letters as names for numbers; in essentially the same way we will use different letters as names for functions. The letter f is most often used, but letters such as g, F, and G (or any other handy letter), will do. If more than one function is involved in a given discussion, then each function should be named by a different letter. For example, f and g may be used to name the two functions

$$f = \{(x, y) \mid y = 2x + 1\}$$
$$g = \{(x, y) \mid y = x^2\}$$

If x represents an element in the domain of a function f, then we will often use the symbol "$f(x)$" in place of y to designate the number in the range of f to which x is paired. It is important not to confuse this new symbol and think of it as the product of f and x. The symbol "$f(x)$" is read "f of x," or "the value of f at x."

This new function symbol is extremely useful, and its correct use should be mastered early. For example, in place of the more formal representation of the functions f and g above we can now write

$$f(x) = 2x + 1 \qquad \text{and} \qquad g(x) = x^2$$

Thus, "$f(x)$" and "$2x + 1$" name the same number in the range of f for each replacement of the variable x from the domain of f; "$g(x)$" and "x^2" name the same number in the range of g for each replacement of the variable x from the domain of g. In particular,

$$f(3) = 2(3) + 1 = 7 \quad \text{and} \quad g(5) = 5^2 = 25$$

That is, the function f assigns 7 to the number 3, and g assigns 25 to 5. The ordered pair $(3, 7)$ belongs to the function f and $(5, 25)$ belongs to the function g.

EXAMPLE 7. Let F and G be functions defined by $F(x) = 3x - 1$ and $G(x) = 1 - x^2$, respectively. Then

▶ $F(2) = 3(2) - 1 = 5$

▶ $F(-3) = 3(-3) - 1 = -10$

▶ $G(-5) = 1 - (-5)^2 = 1 - 25 = -24$

▶ $G(-1) = 1 - (-1)^2 = 1 - 1 = 0$

▶ $F(0) + G(3) = [3(0) - 1] + [1 - (3)^2] = (-1) + (-8) = -9$

▶ $F(c) = 3(c) - 1 = 3c - 1$

▶ $G(a + b) = 1 - (a + b)^2$

Some people seem to improve their feeling for the symbol "$f(x)$" by thinking of a function as a calculating machine which takes in an element from the domain at one end and turns out the matched element from the range at the other (see Fig. 1).

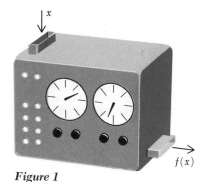

Figure 1

EXERCISE 79

1. If $f(x) = 10x - 7$, find $f(1)$, $f(2)$, $f(-3)$, and $f(0)$.
2. If $g(t) = 6 - 2t$, find $g(2)$, $g(3)$, $g(-3)$, and $g(0)$.
3. If $G(u) = 3u^2$, find $G(2)$, $G(0)$, $G(-2)$, and $G(-1)$.

4. If $Q(x) = 2x^3$, find $Q(-1)$, $Q(1)$, $Q(0)$, and $Q(-2)$.
5. If $f(x) = 2x + 5$, find $f(a)$, $f(c)$, and $f(a + 1)$.
6. If $F(m) = 8 - 2m$, find $F(T)$, $F(d)$, and $F(k - 1)$.
7. If $P(x) = x^2 - 2x + 3$, find $P(2)$, $P(-2)$, $P(0)$, and $P(2 + h)$.
8. If $Q(t) = 2t^2 - t - 1$, find $Q(3)$, $Q(-1)$, $Q(0)$, and $Q(2 + h)$.
9. If $h(s) = \dfrac{s}{s - 2}$, find $h(3)$, $h(0)$, and $h(2)$.
10. If $A(w) = \dfrac{w - 3}{w + 5}$, find $A(5)$, $A(0)$, and $A(-5)$.
11. For $f(x) = 3 - 2x$ and $g(x) = 2x^2$, find (A) $f(2) + g(-2)$, (B) $[f(0)][g(3)]$, and (C) $\dfrac{g(4)}{f(1)}$.
12. For $F(t) = t^2 - 1$ and $G(t) = 5 - t$, find (A) $F(1) + G(1)$, (B) $[F(-2)][G(3)]$, and (C) $\dfrac{G(8)}{F(2)}$.
13. For $g(t) = 3 - 2t$, find (A) $g(1 + h)$, (B) $g(1 + h) - g(1)$, and (C) $\dfrac{g(1 + h) - g(1)}{h}$.
14. For $f(x) = 3x + 5$, find (A) $f(2 + h)$, (B) $f(2 + h) - f(2)$, and (C) $\dfrac{f(2 + h) - f(2)}{h}$.
15. For $P(x) = 2x^2 + 3$, find $\dfrac{P(2 + h) - P(2)}{h}$.
16. For $Q(x) = x^2 - 2x + 1$, find $\dfrac{Q(1 + h) - Q(1)}{h}$.
17. Let f be a function that describes the relationship between the distance that a car travels at 30 mph and time t.   (A) Write a formula for $f(t)$.   (B) Find $f(1)$, $f(10)$, and $[f(2 + h) - f(2)]/h$.
18. Let g be a function that describes the relationship between the distance in feet that an object falls in a vacuum and the time t in seconds that it falls ($d = 16t^2$). (A) Write a formula for $g(t)$.   (B) Find $g(0)$, $g(1)$, $g(2)$, and $g(3)$.   (C) Find $\dfrac{g(2 + h) - g(2)}{h}$ and interpret physically.
19. $f = \{[x, f(x)] \mid f(x) = 3x - 1, x \varepsilon \{-1, 0, 2\}\} = \{$(list the elements in the set)$\}$.
20. $g = \{[t, g(t)] \mid g(t) = 16t^2, t \varepsilon \{0, 1, 2, 3\}\} = \{$(list the elements in the set)$\}$.
21. For $f(x) = 5x$, (A) Does $f(at) = af(t)$?   (B) Does $f(a + b) = f(a) + f(b)$? (C) Does $f(ab) = f(a) \cdot f(b)$?
22. For $g(x) = x^2$, (A) Does $g(at) = ag(t)$?   (B) Does $g(a + b) = g(a) + g(b)$? (C) Does $g(ab) = g(a) \cdot g(b)$?

75   LINEAR AND QUADRATIC FUNCTIONS

Functions are often classified and studied according to the nature of the rule of correspondence between the elements in the domain and the elements of the range of the function. This is a very efficient and productive way to approach the subject. In fact, the study of different classes of functions is the main unifying idea in the organization of a very large number of courses in mathematics from the very elementary to the very advanced. Two important and widely used functions are the linear and quadratic functions. We have studied linear and quadratic equations in two variables in some detail in this course. These equations (with certain restrictions) define linear and quadratic functions. In this section we will review some of the important properties of these equations within the framework of the function concept and notation introduced in the last two sections.

Any function defined by an equation of the form

$$f(x) = ax + b$$

where a and b are constants and x is a variable, is called a **linear function.** The graph, of course (see Chap. 4), is a straight line with slope a and y intercept b.

EXAMPLE 8.   Given $f(x) = x/2 - 3$.   (A) Find $f(0)$, $f(6)$, and $f(10)$.   (B) Graph f and indicate its slope and y intercept.   (C) State the domain and range of f.

SOLUTION

(A) $f(0) = \frac{0}{2} - 3 = -3$ $f(6) = \frac{6}{2} - 3 = 0$ $f(10) = \frac{10}{2} - 3 = 2$

(B)

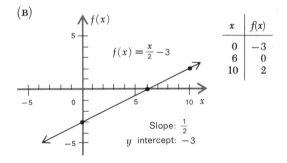

x	$f(x)$
0	-3
6	0
10	2

Slope: $\frac{1}{2}$

y intercept: -3

(C) Domain: all real numbers.   Range: all real numbers.

Any function defined by an equation of the form

$$f(x) = ax^2 + bx + c \qquad a \neq 0$$

where a, b, and c are constants and x is a variable, is called a **quadratic function.** You have had more experience with quadratic functions now than you probably realize. For example, in the preceding sections we considered the equations

$f(x) = x^2$, $g(t) = 16t^2$, $F(t) = 160t - 16t^2$, and $G(x) = 2x^2 - 2x + 1$; these are all examples of quadratic functions. In addition, you have even graphed some of these and found that the graphs are not linear. In more advanced courses one shows that the graph of any equation of the form

$$f(x) = ax^2 + bx + c \qquad a \neq 0$$

is a parabola opening either upward or downward respectively depending on whether $a > 0$ or $a < 0$. The curve looks either like this ⌣ or like this ⌢.

To graph a quadratic function, plot enough points so that when they are joined by a smooth curve, the resulting figure will look like one or the other of the two figures just indicated (or part of the figure if the domain of the function is restricted).

EXAMPLE 9:   GRAPHS OF QUADRATIC FUNCTIONS.

▶ $f(x) = x^2$

▶ $g(t) = 16t^2$
  $0 \le t \le 4$

▶ $G(t) = 12t - 2t^2$
  $= 2t(6 - t)$
  $0 \le t \le 6$

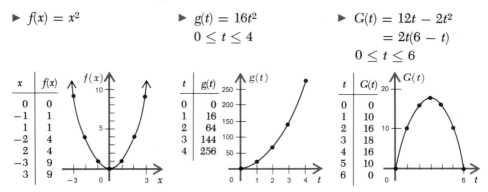

x	$f(x)$
0	0
−1	1
1	1
−2	4
2	4
−3	9
3	9

t	$g(t)$
0	0
1	16
2	64
3	144
4	256

t	$G(t)$
0	0
1	10
2	16
3	18
4	16
5	10
6	0

Parabolas are encountered with considerable frequency in the physical world. Suspension bridges, arch bridges, reflecting telescopes, radar telescopes, solar furnaces, and searchlights are a few examples of many that utilize parabolic forms in their design (Fig. 2). More will be said about these special applications in future courses.

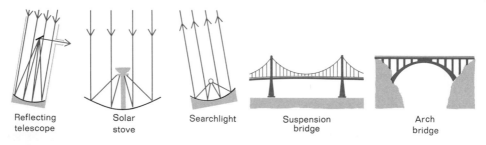

Reflecting telescope   Solar stove   Searchlight   Suspension bridge   Arch bridge

Figure 2

EXERCISE 80

Graph each of the functions in problems 1 through 24. Indicate if the function is linear, quadratic, or neither. If the function is linear, give its slope.

1. $f(t) = t$

2. $f(x) = -x$

3. $g(t) = t^2$

4. $g(x) = -x^2$

5. $f(u) = 2u - 4$

6. $g(u) = 4 - 2u$

7. $F = \{(t, F(t)) \mid F(t) = 4t^2, t \geq 0\}$

8. $h = \{(t, h(t)) \mid h(t) = \dfrac{t^2}{4}, t \geq 0\}$

9. $P(x) = x^3, -3 \leq x \leq 3$

10. $Q(x) = -x^3, -3 \leq x \leq 3$

11. $f(x) = 4, -6 \leq x \leq 6$

12. $g(x) = -3, -1 \leq x \leq 5$

13. $g(x) = \sqrt{x}, 0 \leq x \leq 9$

14. $F(x) = \sqrt{x - 1}, 1 \leq x \leq 10$

15. $f = \{(x, y) \mid y = 4 - x^2, -4 \leq x \leq 4\}$

16. $g = \{(x, y) \mid y = x^2 - 4, -4 \leq x \leq 4\}$

17. $g(w) = |w|, -5 \leq w \leq 5$

18. $G(t) = |t - 1|, -4 \leq t \leq 5$

19. $G(x) = 16x - 2x^2, 0 \leq x \leq 8$

20. $g(t) = 96t - 16t^2, 0 \leq t \leq 6$

21. $h(t) = t^2 - 2t - 3, -1 \leq t \leq 5$

22. $f(x) = 3 + 2x - x^2, -1 \leq x \leq 5$

23. $f(x) = \dfrac{|x|}{x}, -3 \leq x \leq 3$

24. $g(x) = 2 - \dfrac{|x|}{x}, -3 \leq x \leq 3$

25. Solve the following system of equations by graphing:

$$y = x^2$$
$$y = 2x$$

26. Solve the following system of equations by graphing:

$$y = x^2$$
$$y = 2x + 3$$

27. In spring and early summer periodic phenomena, such as blossoming for certain trees, appearance of certain insects, and ripening of fruit, usually come about four days later for each 500 additional feet of altitude. The difference in days is then a function of altitude and we can write $d(h) = 4 \cdot (h/500)$. Graph the function d for $0 \leq h \leq 4{,}000$.

28. Professor Brown found that motivation was a function of the distance that the rat was placed from the goal (food). Stated in terms of an equation $M(d) = -\frac{1}{5}d + 70$, where $M(d)$ is the motivation (pull in grams) and d is the distance to food in centimeters. Graph the function M for $30 \leq d \leq 175$.

29. A rectangular dog pen is to be made with 100 ft of fence wire. (A) If x represents the length of the pen, express its area $A(x)$ in terms of x. (B) What is the domain of the resulting function? (C) Graph the function for this domain. (D) From the graph estimate the dimension of the rectangle that will make the area maximum.

30. Work the preceding problem with the added assumption that an existing yard fence will be used for one side of the pen.

31. The number of telephone connections possible through a switchboard is a function of the number of telephones n connected to the switchboard. Stated as an equation

$$c(n) = \frac{n(n-1)}{2}$$

Graph the function c for integral values of n, with $1 \leq n \leq 10$.

32. The minimum distance required to stop a car (including reaction time) is a function of the rate r of the car. Stated in terms of an emperical equation

$$d(r) = 0.045r^2 + 1.1r$$

Graph the function d for $0 \leq r \leq 100$.

33. In the six preceding problems indicate which functions are linear and which are quadratic.

34. In Exercise 78, problems 15 through 24, indicate which functions are linear and which are quadratic.

76   QUADRATIC FUNCTIONS AND QUADRATIC EQUATIONS

In Chap. 9 we discussed the quadratic equation

$$ax^2 + bx + c = 0 \qquad a \neq 0$$

in detail and found, among other things, that this equation has two real, one real, or no real roots depending on $b^2 - 4ac$ being positive, zero, or negative. Now that we have studied quadratic functions and their graphs, we have another way of looking at solutions of quadratic equations.

For a given function f, if r is a number such that $f(r) = 0$, then r is called a **zero of f.** Thus if r is a zero of a quadratic function $f(x) = ax^2 + bx + c$, then r is a solution of the corresponding quadratic equation $ax^2 + bx + c = 0$ (and vice versa). Consider the quadratic equations and their related quadratic functions in the next three examples.

EXAMPLE 10

$$x^2 - 2x - 3 = 0$$
$$(x + 1)(x - 3) = 0$$

$x + 1 = 0$ or $x - 3 = 0$

$x = -1$ or $x = 3$

NOTE: $b^2 - 4ac = 16 > 0$

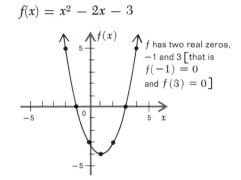

$f(x) = x^2 - 2x - 3$

f has two real zeros, -1 and 3 $\left[\text{that is } f(-1) = 0 \text{ and } f(3) = 0\right]$

EXAMPLE 11

$$x^2 - 6x + 9 = 0$$
$$(x - 3)^2 = 0$$
$$x = 3$$

NOTE: $b^2 - 4ac = 0$

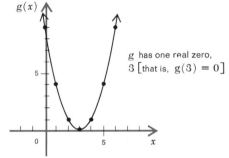

$g(x) = x^2 - 6x + 9$

g has one real zero, 3 $\left[\text{that is, } g(3) = 0\right]$

EXAMPLE 12

$$x^2 + 2x + 2 = 0$$

$$x = \frac{-b \pm \sqrt{b^2 - 4ac}}{2a}$$

$$x = \frac{-2 \pm \sqrt{-4}}{2}$$

No real solutions since $\sqrt{-4}$ is not a real number.

NOTE: $b^2 - 4ac = -4 < 0$

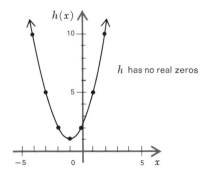

$h(x) = x^2 + 2x + 2$

h has no real zeros

The above three examples illustrate the following general property:

SOLUTIONS OF THE QUADRATIC EQUATION—THREE CASES

Case	$b^2 - 4ac$	Graph of $f(x) = ax^2 + bx + c$	$ax^2 + bx + c = 0$ has
1	positive	crosses x axis twice	two real roots
2	zero	crosses x axis once	one real root
3	negative	does not cross x axis	no real root

To solve a quadratic equation by graphing, one forms the related quadratic function, graphs the function, and estimates the x intercepts if they exist.

EXAMPLE 13.   Solve $x^2 - 4x + 3 = 0$ by graphing.

SOLUTION: Form the related function $f(x) = x^2 - 4x + 3$, and graph f.

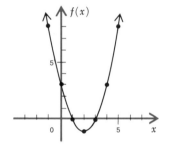

We see that $f(1) = 0$ and $f(3) = 0$. Thus 1 and 3 are solutions of $x^2 - 4x + 3 = 0$.

EXAMPLE 14.   Solve $x^2 - 4x + 5 = 0$ by graphing.

SOLUTION: Form the related function $f(x) = x^2 - 4x + 5$, and graph f.

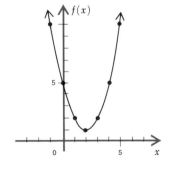

Since the graph of f does not cross the x axis, $x^2 - 4x + 5 = 0$ has no real solutions.

EXERCISE 81

Solve each of the quadratic equations in problems 1 through 12 by graphing.

1. $x^2 - 4 = 0$ 2. $x^2 + 9 = 0$
3. $x^2 + 1 = 0$ 4. $x^2 - 16 = 0$
5. $x^2 - 2x - 3 = 0$ 6. $x^2 + x + 1 = 0$
7. $x^2 - 2x + 4 = 0$ 8. $x^2 + 8x + 16 = 0$
9. $x^2 - 10x + 25 = 0$ 10. $x^2 + x - 6 = 0$
11. $6x - x^2 = 0$ 12. $4 + 3x - x^2 = 0$

13. If an object is projected vertically from the ground at 96 fps, then (neglecting air resistance) its velocity $v(t)$ at time t is given by the equation $v(t) = 96 - 32t$. (A) Graph the function v for $0 \leq t \leq 6$. (B) Find the zero(s) of the function from the graph, and interpret physically.

14. If an object is projected vertically from the ground at 96 fps, then (neglecting air resistance) its distance $d(t)$ above the ground at time t is given by the equation $d(t) = 96t - 16t^2$. (A) Graph the function d for a suitable set of values of t. (B) Determine from the graph the zero(s) of the function (interpret physically), the domain of the function, and the maximum height of the object.

Solve each of the following equations graphically, and give your answer to the nearest tenth of a unit.

15. $x^2 - 2 = 0$ 16. $x^2 - 5 = 0$
17. $x^3 - 2 = 0$ 18. $x^3 - 7 = 0$

77 CHAPTER SUMMARY

GENERAL

In reviewing the history of function we are once again made aware of an interesting example of the tendency of mathematicians to extend and generalize a concept. The word "function" appears to have been first used by Leibnitz in 1694 to stand for any quantity associated with a curve. By 1718 Johann Bernoulli was thinking of a function as any expression made up of constants and a variable. Euler later in this same century had come to regard a function as any equation made up of constants and variables. Euler made extensive use of the extremely useful notation $f(x)$ although its origin is generally attributed to Clairaut (1734).

The form of the definition of function that has been used until well into this century (many texts still contain this definition) was formulated by Dirichlet

(1805–1859). He stated that if two variables x and y are so related that for each value of x there corresponds exactly one value of y, then y is said to be a (single-valued) *function* of x. He called x, the variable to which values were assigned at will, the *independent variable,* and y, the variable whose values depended on the values assigned to x, the *dependent variable.* He called the values assumed by x the *domain of the function,* and the corresponding values assumed by y the *range of the function.*

Now, with set concepts permeating almost all of mathematics, we have the more general definition of function: A *function* is a set of ordered pairs of elements with the added property that no two distinct ordered pairs have the same first element. The set of first elements of the set of ordered pairs is called the *domain of the function;* the set of second elements of the set of ordered pairs is called the *range of the function.* Any symbol used as a place holder for elements from the domain is called an *independent variable,* and any symbol used as a place holder for elements from the range is called a *dependent variable.* The important symbol $f(x)$ is thus a dependent variable. It represents the element in the range of the function f corresponding to the x in the domain.

The set definition of function is very general. It stresses the fundamental idea of a relationship between two sets of numbers. The relationship between the two sets of numbers (the domain and range) may be established in many different ways; equations, graphs, tables, and set notation are the methods most frequently used.

The function concept is one of the most important concepts in mathematics, and as such it plays a central and natural role as a guide for the selection and development of material for elementary mathematics courses. Functions are often classified according to the nature of the rule of correspondence used between the domain and range. In this course we have restricted our attention to linear and quadratic functions; in future courses you will study polynomial functions, algebraic functions, exponential functions, logarithmic functions, and trigonometric functions, to name the most important types you are likely to encounter soon.

SPECIFIC

Describe, define, or give examples of each of the following:

1. **Relation**
domain
range
methods of representation

2. **Function**
domain
range
independent variable

dependent variable

methods of representation

3. Function notation

$f(x)$

4. Linear Functions: $f(x) = ax + b$

nature of graph

slope

y intercept

5. Quadratic functions: $f(x) = ax^2 + bx + c$, with $a \neq 0$

nature of graph

zeros of the function

relationship to quadratic equations

EXERCISE 82   CHAPTER REVIEW

1. What is a relation?

2. Which of the following relations are functions?

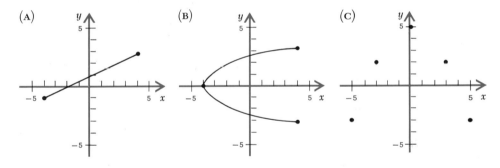

(A)   (B)   (C)

3. Indicate the domain and range of each function in the preceding problem.

4. Graph each of the following relations.   State the domain and range of each and indicate whether it is a function.

(A) $f = \{(-2, -2), (0, 0), (2, 2), (2, 5)\}$

(B) $g = \{(x, y) \mid y = 2 - x\}$

(C) $h = \{(x, y) \mid y = x^2 - 4, -3 \leq x \leq 3\}$

5. Identify linear and quadratic functions (if any) in the preceding problem.

6. If $g(t) = 7 - 2t$, find $g(0)$, $g(2)$, $g(-2)$, and $g(a)$.

7. If $F(u) = 2u^2 - u$, find $F(0)$, $F(3)$, $F(-2)$, and $F(e)$.

8. If $f(x) = 2x - 4$ and $g(x) = x^2 - 2$, find (A) $f(2) + g(-2)$, (B) $[f(-1)][g(0)]$, and (C) $g(t) - f(t)$.

9. If $f(x) = x^2 - 3$, find $f(2 + h)$ and $\dfrac{f(2 + h) - f(2)}{h}$.

10. The cost $C(x)$ for riding in a taxi is 50 cents plus 20 cents a mile for x miles. Express this functional relationship in terms of an equation, and graph it for an appropriate set of values.

Graph each of the functions in problems 11 through 15. Indicate if the function is linear, quadratic, or neither. If the function is linear, give its slope.

11. $F(t) = 4t^2, t \geq 0$.
12. $f = \{(u, v) \mid u = -v, -5 \leq v \leq 1\}$.
13. $G(t) = 6t - t^2, 0 \leq t \leq 8$.
14. $h(x) = x + |x|, x \, \varepsilon \, \{-4, -2, 0, 2, 4\}$.
15. Find the real zeros of the quadratic function $f(x) = x^2 - 2x - 8$ graphically.
16. Solve the quadratic equation $x^2 - 2x - 8 = 0$ graphically.

CHAPTER ELEVEN the postulational method

78 IS MATHEMATICS MORE THAN A SERIES OF TECHNIQUES?

Many think of mathematics as just a series of techniques.

These are indeed the least important aspect, and fall as far short of representing mathematics as color mixing does of painting. The techniques are mathematics stripped of motivation, reasoning, beauty, and significance. . . . Primarily, mathematics is a method of inquiry known as postulational thinking. The method consists in carefully formulating definitions of the concepts to be discussed and in explicitly stating the assumptions that shall be the basis for reasoning. From these definitions and assumptions conclusions are deduced by the application of the most rigorous logic man is capable of using. °

The postulational method, less than 100 years old in its modern form, permeates almost all of mathematics and a significant part of the social and physical sciences.

° Morris Kline, "Mathematics in Western Culture," p. 4, Oxford University Press, Fair Lawn, N.J., 1953.

There is no doubt that this method of inquiry ranks among man's greatest intellectual achievements.

You will recall that in the process of proving theorems, such as "$a - b = a + (-b)$ *for all integers a and b*," we made use of certain definitions and theorems that had been defined and proved earlier. These definitions and theorems in turn depended on still earlier definitions and theorems, and so on. But what do we mean by "and so on"? Do we continue back in an endless chain? (This is physically impossible.) Do we go in a circle? (Circular reasoning is comparable to picking oneself up by one's own boot straps.) If we don't go back in an endless chain and if we don't go in a circle, then we must eventually arrive at a starting place! In this course the starting place was the set of natural numbers with the operations of addition and multiplication (none of which we defined) and certain postulated properties of the natural numbers relative to these operations (remember the closure, associative, commutative, and distributive axioms). From this beginning we defined other concepts and proved many theorems. In short, we made use of a postulational approach in the development of algebra.

Once we realize that mathematics is concerned with the construction of mathematical systems, we can better appreciate the fact that it is as much concerned with method as it is with conclusions. In this chapter we will take a more careful look at the very important postulational method.

79   WHAT IS A POSTULATIONAL OR AXIOMATIC SYSTEM?

In addition to the algebra we have been studying, the postulational method is used to develop a large variety of other important mathematical systems. It is also widely used to develop significant theoretical systems in the physical and social sciences. Every axiomatic or postulational system has essentially the same features, and these are listed below.

1. **Undefined Elements.** The system contains a set of terms, relations, or operations that are not defined.

2. **Defined Elements.** All other terms, relations, or operations in the system are defined (ultimately) in terms of the initial set of undefined elements.

3. **Postulates.** The system contains a set of statements about the undefined terms, relations, or operations which are purposely stated without proof. These are called the postulates or axioms of the system.

4. **Theorems.** All other statements about the defined and undefined elements of the system are logically deduced from the postulates, and these are called the theorems of the system.

In the early stages of one's mathematical studies "common sense" rules of logic are usually used to "prove" theorems; gradually, as experience is gained, these rules are extended and are made more precise. Eventually many of you will take a course in formal logic, and at that time the rules of logic will be made explicit, and you will study them in detail.

80   AN ABSTRACT POSTULATIONAL SYSTEM

Does the following structure look familiar?

> Let S be a set of elements with two binary operations $\oplus$ and $\odot$ satisfying the following postulates:
>   If x, y, and z are elements of S, then
>
> 1. **Closure properties**   (A) $x \oplus y$ is a unique element in S
>   (B) $x \odot y$ is a unique element in S
> 2. **Associative properties** (A) $x \oplus (y \oplus z) = (x \oplus y) \oplus z$
>   (B) $x \odot (y \odot z) = (x \odot y) \odot z$
> 3. **Commutative properties** (A) $x \oplus y = y \oplus x$
>   (B) $x \odot y = y \odot x$
> 4. **Distributive property** $x \odot (y \oplus z) = (x \odot y) \oplus (x \odot z)$
> 5. **Identity elements**   (A) There exists a unique element Q in S so that for any element x in S, $x \oplus Q = x$.   (Q is called the **zero** of the system.)
> (B) There exists a unique element I in S so that for any element x in S, $x \odot I = x$.   (I is called the **one** of the system.)
> 6. **Inverse elements**   (A) For each element x in S there exists a unique element $\bar{x}$ in S so that $x \oplus \bar{x} = Q$.   ($\bar{x}$ is called the inverse of x relative to $\oplus$.)   (B) For each element x in S $(x \neq Q)$ there exists a unique element x' in S so that $x \odot x' = I$.   (x' is called the inverse of x relative to $\odot$.)

We started this course by identifying S with the set of natural numbers and the binary operations $\oplus$ and $\odot$ as "ordinary" addition and multiplication on the natural numbers. The first four postulates were stated, and we were under way. By the time we finished Chap. 3, we had extended the natural numbers to the real numbers, and in this extended system all six statements (where $Q = 0$, $I = 1$, $\bar{x} = -x$, and $x' = 1/x$) were accepted as properties of the real numbers. Many definitions were formulated, and many theorems were stated and proved.

We are now going to look at this structure as an abstract structure; that is, we will take the elements of S to be variables (undefined) and the binary operations $\oplus$ and $\odot$ as distinct, but unspecified. The theorems in the next box (a few of the many theorems possible) follow logically from the material in the first box irrespective of any meaning we assign to the elements of S or the two binary operations $\oplus$ and $\odot$! (If you really understand this statement by the time we finish this chapter, you will have made a giant step forward in your understanding of a very important aspect of mathematics.)

THEOREM 1 $Q \odot x = Q$ for each element x of S

    PROOF

$$Q \oplus Q = Q$$ Postulate 5a

$$x \odot (Q \oplus Q) = x \odot Q$$ property of equality

$$(x \odot Q) \oplus (x \odot Q) = x \odot Q$$ Postulate 4

$$x \odot Q = Q$$ Postulate 5a—uniqueness part

$$Q \odot x = Q$$ Postulate 3b

THEOREM 2 $x \odot \bar{y} = \overline{(x \odot y)}$

    PROOF

$$y \oplus \bar{y} = Q$$ Postulate 6a

$$x \odot (y \oplus \bar{y}) = x \odot Q$$ property of equality

$$(x \odot y) \oplus (x \odot \bar{y}) = Q$$ Postulate 4 and Theorem 1

$$x \odot \bar{y} = \overline{(x \odot y)}$$ Postulate 6a—uniqueness part

THEOREM 3 $\bar{x} \odot \bar{y} = x \odot y$

Proof similar to that of Theorem 2.

DEFINITION 1 $x \ominus y = z$ if and only if $x = y \oplus z$.

THEOREM 4 $x \ominus y = x \oplus \bar{y}$

    PROOF

$$x = Q \oplus x$$ Postulates 5a and 3a

$$x = (y \oplus \bar{y}) \oplus x$$ Postulate 6a and substitution principle

$$x = y \oplus (\bar{y} \oplus x)$$ Postulate 2a

$$x = y \oplus (x \oplus \bar{y})$$ Postulate 3a

$$x \ominus y = x \oplus \bar{y}$$ Definition 1

DEFINITION 2 $x \oslash y = z$ if and only if z is a unique element of S so that $x = y \odot z$

81   SEVERAL INTERPRETATIONS OF THE SAME POSTULATIONAL SYSTEM

If in an abstract postulational system the undefined terms, relations, and operations are defined in such a way that the postulates become true statements, the result is called **an interpretation** of the abstract system. We will present three interpretations of the abstract postulational system presented in the preceding section.   You are already familiar with one of these, but the other two may surprise you.

FIRST INTERPRETATION: RATIONAL NUMBER SYSTEM

Let S be the set of rational numbers with $\oplus$ and $\odot$ defined to be the ordinary addition and multiplication operations of the rational numbers.   For x a rational number, the identity and inverse elements in S are then $Q = 0$, $I = 1$, $\bar{x} = -x$, and $x' = 1/x$ $(x \neq 0)$.   The definitions and theorems in the second box in the last section (where x, y, and z are rational numbers) should now look more familiar.

THEOREM 1

$$0 \cdot x = 0 \text{ for each rational number } x$$

THEOREM 2

$$x(-y) = -(xy)$$

THEOREM 3

$$(-x)(-y) = xy$$

DEFINITION 1

$$x - y = z \text{ if and only if } x = y + z$$

THEOREM 4

$$x - y = x + (-y)$$

DEFINITION 2

$$x/y = z \text{ if and only if } z \text{ is a unique rational number so that } x = yz$$

It is important to recognize that Theorems 1 through 4 above do not need to be proved again. We saw that these theorems followed logically from the postulates and undefined elements of the system irrespective of any particular interpretation of the undefined elements. This illustrates the power, efficiency, and beauty of the postulational method—a single abstract system may represent many different concrete systems.

We will now consider an interpretation of our abstract system that you probably have not encountered. This interpretation will involve a set S with only two elements!

SECOND INTERPRETATION: EVEN-ODD SYSTEM

The special system we will now construct will be based on the following relationships of odd and even numbers:

$$\text{odd} + \text{odd} = \text{even} \qquad \text{odd} \cdot \text{odd} = \text{odd}$$
$$\text{odd} + \text{even} = \text{odd} \qquad \text{odd} \cdot \text{even} = \text{even}$$
$$\text{even} + \text{even} = \text{even} \qquad \text{even} \cdot \text{even} = \text{even}$$

Let S and the binary operations of $\oplus$ and $\odot$ be defined as follows:

$$S = \{\text{even, odd}\}$$

$x \oplus y$

$x \backslash y$	even	odd
even	even	odd
odd	odd	even

$x \odot y$

$x \backslash y$	even	odd
even	even	even
odd	even	odd

We will call $\oplus$ addition and $\odot$ multiplication.

Does this system have identity elements? That is, does the system have a zero and a 1? Looking at the addition table we see that the element "even" is the zero of the system since it is the only element with the property $x \oplus \text{even} = x$, where x is an arbitrary element of the system (that is, either even or odd). Hence,

$$Q = \text{even}$$

Looking at the multiplication table we see that the element odd is the 1 of the system since it is the only element that has the property $x \odot \text{odd} = x$, where x is an arbitrary element of the system (that is, either even or odd). Hence,

$$I = \text{odd}$$

Something interesting happens when we replace even and odd with the simpler symbols Q and I.   Thus

$$S = \{Q, I\}$$

$x \oplus y$				$x \odot y$		
x \ y	Q	I		x \ y	Q	I
Q	Q	I		Q	Q	Q
I	I	Q		I	Q	I

It is apparent that Q and I behave in much the same way that 0 and 1 do in ordinary arithmetic.   The main exception is found in the lower right-hand corner of the addition table where we have defined 1 plus 1 to be zero.   This exception should not seem strange, however, when you recall that in our new system 1 means odd and zero means even.

All of the postulates in the abstract system can be shown to be true statements relative to the definition of the undefined elements given above; hence the theorems in the second box of Sec. 80 are true statements about the odd-even system.

First, it is clear from the addition and multiplication tables that the system is closed relative to these operations, and, in addition, these operations are commutative.   We have already shown that the system has unique identity elements Q and I.   What about inverse elements?   Does each element in S have a unique inverse relative to addition?   That is, are there unique elements $\overline{Q}$ and $\overline{I}$ in S so that

$$Q \oplus \overline{Q} = Q \quad \text{and} \quad I \oplus \overline{I} = I$$

From the addition table we see that $\overline{Q} = Q$ and $\overline{I} = I$; that is, each element is its own inverse relative to addition.

Does the nonzero element in S have a unique inverse relative to multiplication? That is, is there a unique element I' in S so that

$$I \odot I' = I$$

From the multiplication table we see that $I' = I$; thus, I is its own inverse relative to multiplication.

To show that the associative and distributive postulates are true, we simply substitute the elements of S into the equations in all possible ways and check that the resulting statements are true.   Since S has only two elements, the number of cases to consider is small.   The checking will be left as an exercise.

We now have an odd-even arithmetic that has the same structure as the rational numbers.   Calculations in this arithmetic are illustrated in the following examples.

EXAMPLE 1:   **ODD-EVEN ARITHMETIC.**

▶ $I \oplus (I \oplus Q) = I \oplus I = Q$

▶ $(I \odot I) \oplus [I \odot (I \oplus I)] = I \oplus (I \odot Q) = I \oplus Q = I$

▶ $(I \oplus I) \odot [I \oplus (I \odot I)] = Q \odot [I \oplus (I \odot I)] = Q$

Zero times any number in the system is zero

EXAMPLE 2.   Suppose you are interested in whether the final answer to the arithmetic problem

$$379 \cdot 4305 + 5078(27 + 36 \cdot 49)$$

is even or odd.   The odd-even arithmetic can produce an answer very quickly. Simply replace each number with I or Q, depending on whether the number is odd or even, and use odd-even arithmetic to determine the nature of the final answer.

$$(I \odot I) \oplus Q \odot [I \oplus (Q \odot I)] \qquad Q \text{ times any "number" is } Q$$
$$= I \oplus Q$$
$$= I$$

Thus, the answer to the problem is an odd number.

EXERCISE 83

Evaluate each of the problems 1 through 10.

1. $I \oplus (I \oplus Q)$ and $(I \oplus I) \oplus Q$
2. $I \oplus (Q \oplus Q)$ and $(I \oplus Q) \oplus Q$
3. $I \odot (I \odot Q)$ and $(I \odot Q) \odot Q$
4. $I \odot (Q \odot Q)$ and $(I \odot Q) \odot Q$
5. $I \oplus I \oplus I$
6. $I \oplus I \oplus Q$
7. $Q \oplus I \oplus Q \oplus I$
8. $(I \odot I) \oplus (I \odot I)$
9. $(I \oplus I) \odot (I \oplus I)$
10. $[I \odot (I \oplus Q)] \oplus [I \odot (I \oplus I)]$

11. Fill in the subtraction table using the definition of subtraction in the second box in Sec. 80.

$$x \ominus y$$

x \ y	Q	I
Q		
I		

12. Fill in the division table using the definition of division in the second box in Sec. 80.

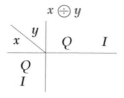

13. Evaluate $I \odot I$ and $(I \odot I)$

14. Evaluate $I \odot I$ and $I \odot I$

THIRD INTERPRETATION: CALENDAR SYSTEM

Let the days of the week be arranged clockwise around a circle and assigned numbers from 0 to 6, starting with 0 for Sunday (Fig. 1).

Consider the following problem: A sales office needs a quick way of determining the day of return for the traveling salesmen it sends out. If, for example, a man leaves on Thursday and is to be gone 5 days, what day is he due back? We can find the day easily by starting at 4 on the circle and moving five units clockwise to 2 (which corresponds to Tuesday). Thus we might think of $4 + 5 = 2$.

Keeping this illustration in mind, we will construct a mathematical system called a "calendar system" where the set S will contain only six elements called calendar numbers. Thus

$$S = \{0, 1, 2, 3, 4, 5, 6\}$$

To find $x \oplus y$ in this system, where $x \, \varepsilon \, S$ and $y \, \varepsilon \, S$, we start at x on the circle and move y units clockwise to the point which we call the sum of x and y. Thus $2 \oplus 3 = 5$, and $6 \oplus 3 = 2$.

We multiply in this system by repeated addition. For example, $3 \odot 4 = 4 \oplus 4 \oplus 4 = 5$; that is, start at 4, move four units clockwise, and then another four units clockwise to end at 5.

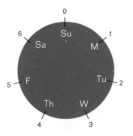

Figure 1

Subtraction can be accomplished by simply moving counterclockwise from the initial point: $5 \ominus 3 = 2$, $3 \ominus 5 = 5$, and $2 \ominus 3 = 6$ are examples.

Addition and multiplication tables can easily be constructed from these definitions.

$x \oplus y$

x \ y	0	1	2	3	4	5	6
0	0	1	2	3	4	5	6
1	1	2	3	4	5	6	0
2	2	3	4	5	6	0	1
3	3	4	5	6	0	1	2
4	4	5	6	0	1	2	3
5	5	6	0	1	2	3	4
6	6	0	1	2	3	4	5

$x \odot y$

x \ y	0	1	2	3	4	5	6
0	0	0	0	0	0	0	0
1	0	1	2	3	4	5	6
2	0	2	4	6	1	3	5
3	0	3	6	2	5	1	4
4	0	4	1	5	2	6	3
5	0	5	3	1	6	4	2
6	0	6	5	4	3	2	1

With the above interpretation of the undefined elements in our abstract postulation system, it can be shown (though we won't show it in detail) that all the postulates of the abstract system become true statements, and thus the theorems that follow from the postulates become true statements. We will assume that this has been done. You can use these results in the exercises unless directed to the contrary.

EXERCISE 84

Using the calendar system, evaluate each of the problems 1 through 20.

1. $3 \oplus 6$
2. $5 \oplus 1$
3. $3 \oplus 3$
4. $2 \oplus 1$
5. $4 \oplus 5$ and $5 \oplus 4$
6. $6 \oplus 5$ and $5 \oplus 6$
7. $5 \ominus 4$ and $4 \ominus 5$
8. $6 \ominus 2$ and $2 \ominus 6$
9. $3 \odot 5$ and $5 \odot 3$
10. $5 \odot 4$ and $4 \odot 5$
11. $3 \oplus (5 \oplus 4)$ and $(3 \oplus 5) \oplus 4$
12. $5 \oplus (4 \oplus 3)$ and $(5 \oplus 4) \oplus 3$
13. $3 \odot (5 \odot 4)$ and $(3 \odot 5) \odot 4$
14. $5 \odot (4 \odot 3)$ and $(5 \odot 4) \odot 3$
15. $4 \odot (2 \oplus 6)$ and $(4 \odot 2) \oplus (4 \odot 6)$
16. $5 \odot (3 \oplus 5)$ and $(5 \odot 3) \oplus (5 \odot 5)$

EXAMPLE 3. To divide, say, $6 \oslash 4$, recall the definition of division, write $6 = 4 \odot x$, and find x from the multiplication table. Thus $6 \oslash 4 = 5$ since $6 = 4 \odot 5$.

17. $3 \oplus 2$ and $2 \oplus 3$

18. $6 \oplus 3$ and $3 \oplus 6$

19. $4 \oplus 1$ and $1 \oplus 4$

20. $4 \oplus 2$ and $2 \oplus 4$

Solve and check each of the equations in problems 21 through 24 in the calendar system. (You will find Fig. 1 and the addition and multiplication tables useful in this regard.)

EXAMPLE 4. $4x \ominus 3 = 5$ CHECK: $(4 \odot 2) \ominus 3 \stackrel{?}{=} 5$

$$4x = 5 \oplus 3$$
$$1 \ominus 3 \stackrel{?}{=} 5$$
$$4x = 1$$
$$5 \stackrel{\vee}{=} 5$$
$$x = 2$$

21. $2x \ominus 3 = 5$

22. $5x \ominus 4 = 4$

23. $3x \oplus 3 = 1$

24. $6x \oplus 5 = 3$

25. What are the identity elements of the calendar system?   That is, what are the zero and one of the system?

26. (A) Is the sum of two calendar numbers always a calendar number?   (B) Is the product of two calendar numbers always a calendar number?

27. Is the calendar system closed with respect to subtraction?

28. Is the calendar system closed with respect to division, excluding division by zero?

29. Find the inverse of each calendar number relative to addition.

30. Find the inverse of each calendar number, except zero, relative to multiplication.

In the abstract system Theorem 4 states that $x \ominus y = x \oplus \bar{y}$. *As an illustration of this theorem, evaluate each of the following:*

31. $3 \ominus 5$ and $3 \oplus \bar{5}$

32. $1 \ominus 6$ and $1 \oplus \bar{6}$

In the abstract system Theorem 2 states that $x \odot \bar{y} = \overline{(x \odot y)}$. *As an illustration of this theorem, evaluate each of the following:*

33. $3 \odot \bar{4}$ and $\overline{(3 \odot 4)}$

34. $5 \odot \bar{2}$ and $\overline{(5 \odot 2)}$

In the abstract system Theorem 3 states that $x \odot y = x \odot y$. *As an illustration of this theorem, evaluate each of the following:*

35. $\bar{2} \odot \bar{3}$ and $2 \odot 3$

36. $\bar{4} \odot \bar{6}$ and $4 \odot 6$

Another theorem that might have been added to the abstract system is $x \oplus y = x \odot y'$, *for* $y \neq 0$. *Evaluate each of the following as an illustration of this theorem:*

37. $3 \oplus 2$ and $3 \odot 2'$ **38.** $2 \oplus 5$ and $2 \odot 5'$

82   CHAPTER SUMMARY

GENERAL

The postulational method is the process of reasoning that starts with undefined elements (terms, relations, and operations) and certain assumed statements about the undefined elements called postulates or axioms; uses the undefined elements to define new terms, relations, and operations; and applies the rules of deductive logic to arrive at new statements called theorems.

The true value and power of the postulational method and resulting postulational systems lie in the fact that those who grant the postulates of a system as true statements about a special interpretation of the undefined elements of the system must also grant as true statements any of the theorems of the system. Unsuspected and surprising results may be the outcome.

This method, applied with such spectacular results in mathematics, can be applied to any field. Its successful use in mathematics has led to its being adopted as a basic tool in the physical sciences, and, to a lesser but increasing extent, in the social sciences.

A scientist does not often remain satisfied with relations established by experiment alone; frequently, he attempts to derive these relations from a set of formulated postulates. In general, he attempts to formulate a postulational system that will not only let him deduce the already known relations (obtained by experiment) but will, in addition, enable him to predict new relations which have not yet been observed.

SPECIFIC

Describe, define, or give examples of each of the following:

1. **The postulational method.**
2. **An abstract postulational system.**
undefined elements (terms, relations, operations)
defined elements (terms, relations, operations)
postulates or axioms
theorems
3. **An interpretation of an abstract postulational system.**

EXERCISE 85   CHAPTER REVIEW

Let S in the abstract postulational system (Sec. 80) be defined as $S = \{0, 1, 2\}$ and $\oplus$ and $\odot$ be defined as in the calendar system except for the replacement of the calendar circle by

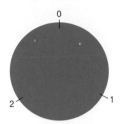

We will refer to this new system as a clock system *(with three elements).*

1. Write down an addition and multiplication table for the clock system.

Using the clock system, evaluate problems 2 through 9.

2. $1 \oplus 2$ and $2 \oplus 1$

3. $2 \oplus 2$

4. $1 \odot 2$ and $2 \odot 1$

5. $2 \odot 2$

6. $2 \oplus (1 \oplus 2)$ and $(2 \oplus 1) \oplus 2$

7. $2 \odot (1 \odot 2)$ and $(2 \odot 1) \odot 2$

8. $2 \ominus 1$ and $1 \ominus 2$

9. $2 \oslash 1$ and $1 \oslash 2$

10. Solve and check in the clock system:

(A) $2x \oplus 2 = 0$

(B) $2x \ominus 1 = 2$

11. What are the identity elements of the clock system; that is, what are the zero and 1 of the system?

12. Is the clock system closed with respect to the four basic arithmetic operations (addition, multiplication, subtraction, and division, except for division by zero)?

13. Are addition and multiplication commutative and associative?

14. Is the distributive postulate true for the clock system?

15. Find the inverse of each clock number relative to addition.

16. Find the inverse of each clock number relative to multiplication.

17. Theorem 4 in the abstract system states that $x \ominus y = x \oplus \overline{y}$. Evaluate $1 \ominus 2$ and $1 \oplus \overline{2}$.

18. Theorem 3 in the abstract system states that $\overline{x} \odot \overline{y} = x \odot y$. Evaluate $\overline{1} \odot \overline{2}$ and $1 \odot 2$.

appendixes

APPENDIX A SYMBOLIC FORMS

$\{a, b, c\}$	A set whose elements are a, b, and c.
$a \, \varepsilon \, A$	a is an element of set A.
$a \notin A$	a is not an element of set A.
$\{x \mid (\text{conditions on } x)\}$	The set of all x such that x meets the indicated conditions.
$a = b$	a is equal to b.
$a \neq b$	a is not equal to b.
$a \doteq b$	a is approximately equal to b.
$a < b$	a is less than b.
$a \leq b$	a is less than or equal to b.
$a > b$	a is greater than b.
$a \geq b$	a is greater than or equal to b.
$(\ ), [\ ], \{\ \}$	symbols of grouping.
$\sqrt{n}$	The positive square root of n.
$\pm a$	Plus or minus a.
$a \cdot b, \ ab, \ a(b)$	The product of a and b.
$a/b, \ \dfrac{a}{b}, \ a \div b, \ b\overline{)a}$	a divided by b.
$f(x)$	The value of a function f at x.
(a, b)	An ordered pair of numbers; a is called the first component and b the second component.
$\lvert a \rvert$	The absolute value of a.
$-a$	The negative of a.

n	n^2	$\sqrt{n}$	n	n^2	$\sqrt{n}$	n	n^2	$\sqrt{n}$	n	n^2	$\sqrt{n}$
0	0	0.000	50	2,500	7.071	100	10,000	10.000	150	22,500	12.247
1	1	1.000	51	2,601	7.141	101	10,201	10.050	151	22,801	12.288
2	4	1.414	52	2,704	7.211	102	10,404	10.100	152	23,104	12.329
3	9	1.732	53	2,809	7.280	103	10,609	10.149	153	23,409	12.369
4	16	2.000	54	2,916	7.348	104	10,816	10.198	154	23,716	12.410
5	25	2.236	55	3,025	7.416	105	11,025	10.247	155	24,025	12.450
6	36	2.449	56	3,136	7.483	106	11,236	10.296	156	24,336	12.490
7	49	2.646	57	3,249	7.550	107	11,449	10.344	157	24,649	12.530
8	64	2.828	58	3,364	7.616	108	11,664	10.392	158	24,964	12.570
9	81	3.000	59	3,481	7.681	109	11,881	10.440	159	25,281	12.610
10	100	3.162	60	3,600	7.746	110	12,100	10.488	160	25,600	12.649
11	121	3.317	61	3,721	7.810	111	12,321	10.536	161	25,921	12.689
12	144	3.464	62	3,844	7.874	112	12,544	10.583	162	26,244	12.728
13	169	3.606	63	3,969	7.937	113	12,769	10.630	163	26,569	12.767
14	196	3.742	64	4,096	8.000	114	12,996	10.677	164	26,896	12.806
15	225	3.873	65	4,225	8.062	115	13,225	10.724	165	27,225	12.845
16	256	4.000	66	4,356	8.124	116	13,456	10.770	166	27,556	12.884
17	289	4.123	67	4,489	8.185	117	13,689	10.817	167	27,889	12.923
18	324	4.243	68	4,624	8.246	118	13,924	10.863	168	28,224	12.961
19	361	4.359	69	4,761	8.307	119	14,161	10.909	169	28,561	13.000
20	400	4.472	70	4,900	8.367	120	14,400	10.954	170	28,900	13.038
21	441	4.583	71	5,041	8.426	121	14,641	11.000	171	29,241	13.077
22	484	4.690	72	5,184	8.485	122	14,884	11.045	172	29,584	13.115
23	529	4.796	73	5,329	8.544	123	15,129	11.091	173	29,929	13.153
24	576	4.899	74	5,476	8.602	124	15,376	11.136	174	30,276	13.191
25	625	5.000	75	5,625	8.660	125	15,625	11.180	175	30,625	13.229
26	676	5.099	76	5,776	8.718	126	15,876	11.225	176	30,976	13.266
27	729	5.196	77	5,929	8.775	127	16,129	11.269	177	31,329	13.304
28	784	5.292	78	6,084	8.832	128	16,384	11.314	178	31,684	13.342
29	841	5.385	79	6,241	8.888	129	16,641	11.358	179	32,041	13.379
30	900	5.477	80	6,400	8.944	130	16,900	11.402	180	32,400	13.416
31	961	5.568	81	6,561	9.000	131	17,161	11.446	181	32,761	13.454
32	1,024	5.657	82	6,724	9.055	132	17,424	11.489	182	33,124	13.491
33	1,089	5.745	83	6,889	9.110	133	17,689	11.533	183	33,489	13.528
34	1,156	5.831	84	7,056	9.165	134	17,956	11.576	184	33,856	13.565
35	1,225	5.916	85	7,225	9.220	135	18,225	11.619	185	34,225	13.601
36	1,296	6.000	86	7,396	9.274	136	18,496	11.662	186	34,596	13.638
37	1,369	6.083	87	7,569	9.327	137	18,769	11.705	187	34,969	13.675
38	1,444	6.164	88	7,744	9.381	138	19,044	11.747	188	35,344	13.711
39	1,521	6.245	89	7,921	9.434	139	19,321	11.790	189	35,721	13.748
40	1,600	6.325	90	8,100	9.487	140	19,600	11.832	190	36,100	13.784
41	1,681	6.403	91	8,281	9.539	141	19,881	11.874	191	36,481	13.820
42	1,764	6.481	92	8,464	9.592	142	20,164	11:916	192	36,864	13.856
43	1,849	6.557	93	8,649	9.644	143	20,449	11.958	193	37,249	13.892
44	1,936	6.633	94	8,836	9.659	144	20,736	12.000	194	37,636	13.928
45	2,025	6.708	95	9,025	9.747	145	21,025	12.042	195	38,025	13.964
46	2,116	6.782	96	9,216	9.798	146	21,316	12.083	196	38,416	14.000
47	2,209	6.856	97	9,409	9.849	147	21,609	12.124	197	38,809	14.036
48	2,304	6.928	98	9,604	9.899	148	21,904	12.166	198	39,204	14.071
49	2,401	7.000	99	9,801	9.950	149	22,201	12.207	199	39,601	14.107
n	n^2	$\sqrt{n}$	n	n^2	$\sqrt{n}$	n	n^2	$\sqrt{n}$	n	n^2	$\sqrt{n}$

APPENDIX C   THEOREM ON FACTORING QUADRATIC FORMS

THEOREM 1   *Given integers a, b, and c, (a ≠ 0), there exist integers d, e, f, and g such that*

$$ax^2 + bx + c = (dx + e)(fx + g)$$

if and only if ac can be written as the product of two integers whose sum is b.

PROOF (SKETCH)

Part 1. (Necessity)   Assume that $ax^2 + bx + c$ can be factored as indicated; show that ac can be written as the product of two integers whose sum is b.

$$ax^2 + bx + c = (dx + e)(fx + g)$$
$$= (df)x^2 + (dg + ef)x + (eg)$$

Hence, $a = df$, $b = (dg + ef)$, $c = eg$

$$ac = (df)(eg) = (dg)(ef) \qquad \text{and} \qquad dg + ef = b$$

That is, ac can be written as the product of two integers whose sum is b.

Part 2. (Sufficiency)   Assume that ac can be written as the product of two integers, say s and t, whose sum is b; show that $ax^2 + bx + c$ has first-degree factors with integral coefficients.

$$ac = st \qquad \text{and} \qquad s + t = b \qquad\qquad \text{given}$$

If $ac = st$, then, by the prime factorization theorem and partitioning theory, we know that there must exist integers m, n, p, and q (not necessarily prime) so that $a = mn$, $c = pq$, $s = mp$, and $t = nq$.   Hence,

$$ax^2 + bx + c = (mn)x^2 + (mp + nq)x + pq$$
$$= (mn)x^2 + (mp)x + (nq)x + (pq)$$
$$= (mx)(nx + p) + q(nx + p)$$
$$= (nx + p)(mx + q)$$

APPENDIX D   THERE IS NO RATIONAL NUMBER
WHOSE SQUARE IS 2

PROOF: Let us assume the contrary; that is, let us assume that there is a rational number a/b such that $(a/b)^2 = 2$. In addition we will assume, without loss of generality, that a and b are relatively prime integers (without common factors other than 1 or -1).

Case 1. Assume a is odd.

$$(a/b)^2 = 2 \tag{1}$$

Multiplying through by b^2 we obtain

$$a^2 = 2b^2 \tag{2}$$

This last equation implies that a^2 is an even integer which in turn implies that u is even (for if a were odd, then a^2 would have to be odd). This is a contradiction since a was assumed odd.

Case 2. Assume a is even (then b must be odd—Why?).
a even implies the existence of an integer c such that

$$a = 2c$$

Substituting into eq. (2) we obtain

$$(2c)^2 = 2b^2$$
$$4c^2 = 2b^2$$
$$2c^2 = b^2$$

The last equation implies that b^2 is even, which in turn implies that b is even. This is a contradiction since a was assumed even and b odd.

Conclusion: If we accept the hypothesis that 2 is the square of some rational number, then we have shown that it is possible for an odd number to be even. The latter is clearly impossible. Hence, the original assumption must be false; i.e., there is no rational number whose square is 2.

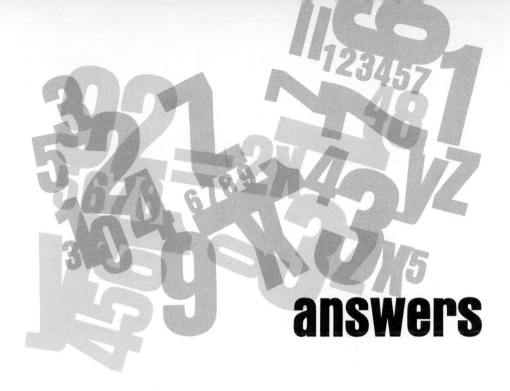

answers

EXERCISE 1   PAGE 7

1. Examples: $\{2, 4, 6, 8, 10\}$; 6; $\{4, 8, 10\}$.   3. $A = \{3, 6, 9, 12, 15, 18, 21\}$; $1 \notin A$, $6 \, \varepsilon \, A$, $7 \notin A$, $12 \, \varepsilon \, A$, $14 \notin A$, $19 \notin A$, $21 \, \varepsilon \, A$.   5. $U = V = W = X$.   7. 6.   9. A, D.
11. All are (ϕ is a subset of every set).   13. (A) $\{a, b\}$, $\{a\}$, $\{b\}$, ϕ, (4 subsets); (B) $\{a, b, c\}$, $\{a, b\}$, $\{a, c\}$, $\{b, c\}$, $\{a\}$, $\{b\}$, $\{c\}$, ϕ (8 subsets); (C) $\{2, 4, 6\}$, $\{2, 4\}$, $\{2, 6\}$, $\{4, 6\}$, $\{2\}$, $\{4\}$, $\{6\}$, ϕ, (8 subsets); (D) $\{a, b, c, d\}$, $\{a, b, c\}$, $\{a, b, d\}$, $\{b, c, d\}$, $\{a, c, d\}$ $\{a, b\}$, $\{a, c\}$, $\{a, d\}$, $\{b, c\}$, $\{b, d\}$, $\{c, d\}$, $\{a\}$, $\{b\}$, $\{c\}$, $\{d\}$, ϕ, (16 subsets). If we increase the number of elements in a set by 1, it appears that the number of subsets of the new set is double that of the old set; hence we would expect of 5 elements to have 32 subsets. The reader might like to check this assumption.   15. ϕ is the empty set; $\{\phi\}$ and $\{0\}$ are nonempty sets, each containing one element.

EXERCISE 2   PAGE 11

1. Even numbers: 306, 1008; Odd numbers: 9, 17, 29, 87, 37; Composite numbers: 9, 87, 306, 1008; Prime numbers: 17, 29, 37.   3. No; No.   5. No.   7. Yes; No.
9. $2 \cdot 2 \cdot 3$; $2 \cdot 3 \cdot 3$; $2 \cdot 2 \cdot 3 \cdot 7$; $2 \cdot 2 \cdot 2 \cdot 2 \cdot 2 \cdot 2 \cdot 2$ 11. (A) Infinite; (B) Infinite;
(C) Infinite; (D) Infinite; (E) Finite; (F) Finite.

EXERCISE 3   PAGE 16

1. (A) Variables: P, a, b; Constants: 2. (B) Variables: P, s; Constants: 4. (C) Variables: A, s;
Constants: 2.   3. (A) 11; (B) 1; (C) 27, 27; (D) 21; (E) 7, 9; (F) 25, 21; (G) 11; (H) 17.
5. (A) 31; (B) 28; (C) 16.   7. $\{16, 64, 144, 256, 400\}$.   9. 9, 16, 36, 64.
11. (A) $x + 5$, 12; (B) $5x$, 35; (C) $x - 5$, 2; (D) $2x + 3$, 17; (E) $3(x - 3)$, 12; (F) $7(x + 5)$, 84.
13. (A) $V = 30 + 32t$; (B) 30 and 32 constants, V and t are variables; (C) 286 fps.
15. (A) $d = 2t$; (B) 2 is a constant, d and t are variables; (C) 20 miles.
17. $C = 100 + 10x$; 100 and 10 are constants, C and x are variables.

EXERCISE 4   PAGE 21

1. (A) $=$, (B) $\neq$, (C) $=$, (D) $=$, (E) $=$, (F) $\neq$.   3. (A) $=$, (B) $\neq$, (C) $\neq$, (D) $=$, (E) $=$,
(F) $=$, (G) $=$.   5. $2x + 7 = 49$.   7. $x + (x + 1) + (x + 2) + (x + 3) = 54$.
9. $x(x + 10) = 50$.   11. $x + 2x = 27$.   13. $x + 3x = 68$.   15. Incorrect use of
the equality symbol.
17. $3x = 3x$ (reflexive law)
    $x = y$ (given)
   $3x = 3y$ (substitution principle)
19. $a + c = a + c$ (reflexive law)
       $a = b$ (given)
    $a + c = b + c$ (substitution principle)

EXERCISE 5   PAGE 30

1. (A) closure axiom for addition; (B) closure axiom for multiplication; (C) commutative axiom for addition; (D) commutative axiom for multiplication; (E) associative axiom for addition; (F) associative axiom for multiplication.   3. (A) commutative axiom for multiplication; (B) associative axiom for addition; (C) closure axiom for multiplication; (D) associative axiom for multiplication; (E) closure axiom for addition; (F) commutative axiom for addition.   5. (A) closure axiom for addition three times; (B) closure axiom for multiplication three times; (C) closure and commutative axioms for addition; (D) closure and commutative axioms for multiplication.   7. (A) A; (B) A, B.   9. $5 - 3 \neq 3 - 5$, $9 \div 3 \neq 3 \div 9$. In the set of natural numbers the operations of subtraction and division are not commutative.   19. (A) $abcdef$; (B) $a + b + c + d$; (C) $uvwxyab$;
(D) $a + b + c + d + x + y$.

EXERCISE 6   PAGE 35

1. (A) 5; (B) 9, 9; (C) 3; (D) 9, 7; (E) 5; (F) 2, 8.   3. (A) 35, 35; (B) 135, 135; (C) 660, 660.
5. (A) $5a + 5b$; (B) $27x + 27y$; (C) $xy + xz$; (D) $x^2 + 5x$; (E) $7y + y^2$; (F) $abc + abd$.
7. (A) $3(x + y)$; (B) $c(x + y)$; (C) $s(r + t)$; (D) $y(x + 3)$; (E) $y(7 + 8) = 15y$; (F) $x(x + 1)$.
9. (A) $6x + 6y + 6z$; (B) $ax + ay + az$; (C) $u^2 + uv + uw$; (D) $x^3 + x^2 + x$;
(E) $2y^3 + 6y^2 + 8y$; (F) $auv + buv + cuv + duv$.   11. (A) $4(x + y + z)$;
(B) $a(x + y + z)$; (C) $x(x + y + z)$; (D) $y(y^2 + y + 1)$; (E) $3t(t^2 + 2t + 3)$; (F) $uv(u + v)$;
(G) $x(5 + 2 + 3) = 10x$; (H) $ab(2 + 4 + 3) = 9ab$.   13. (A) $abx + aby$;
(B) $cu + du + cv + dv$; (C) $mr + mt + nr + nt$; (D) $m^2 + 8m + 15$; (E) $x^2 + 5x + 6$.

EXERCISE 7   PAGE 39

1. (A) 32; (B) 81; (C) $x \cdot x \cdot x \cdot x \cdot x$; (D) $y \cdot y \cdot y \cdot y \cdot y \cdot y \cdot y$; (E) 125; (F) 10,000.   3. (A) a^6;
(B) 2^3; (C) x^3y^2; (D) 3^3; (E) $2^3 \cdot 3^3$; (F) u^3vw^4.   5. (A) 1,000; (B) 10,000,000;
(C) 500,000,000; (D) 23,000,000; (E) 125,000,000,000,000.   If a natural number is
multiplied by a natural number power of 10, the product is the first natural number
followed by a number of zeros equal to the power of 10.   7. (A) x^5; (B) y^9; (C) a^3b^3;
(D) $6x^4y^4$; (E) $4uv^3w^2$; (F) 10^{11}; (G) $96 \cdot 10^{15}$.   9. (A) $588 \cdot 10^{15}$ miles, $1,176 \cdot 10^{14}$ miles;
(B) 588,000,000,000,000,000 miles, 117,600,000,000,000,000 miles.   11. $132 \cdot 10^{23}$ lb,
13,200,000,000,000,000,000,000,000 lb.   13. (A) $x^2 + x$; (B) $x^3 + 2x^2 + 3x$;
(C) $x^3y^2 + xy^4$; (D) $6a^3b^3c + 3a^3b^2$; (E) $5t^7 + 10t^5 + 15t^4 + 30t^3$.

EXERCISE 8   PAGE 42

1. 4, 7, 1, 8, 1.   3. (A) 3; (B) 2; (C) 1; (D) 1.   5. $2x$ and $4x$, $3y$ and $5y$, $6x^2$ and $3x^2$,
$7y^2$ and y^2, xy and $2xy$.   7. (A) $7x$; (B) $16t$; (C) $9y$; (D) $12x + 4y$; (E) $3u + 4v$;
(F) $11s + 3t$.   9. (A) $4x + 7y + 7z$; (B) $4x^2 + 3xy + 2y^2$; (C) $4x^2 + 5x + 5$; (D) $9x + 8$;
(E) $5x^4 + 5x^2 + 4$.   11. (A) $8x + 31$; (B) $11t^2 + 13t + 17$; (C) $3x^2 + 4x$; (D) $18t^2 + 13t$;
(E) $3y^3 + 3y^2 + 4y$.   13. (A) $9x^2y^2 + 5x^3y^3$; (B) $7x^5 + 11x^3 + 6x^2$; (C) $6x^2 + 11x + 8$;
(D) $6x^2 + 13x + 6$; (E) $2x^2 + 5xy + 2y^2$.   15. $x + (x + 1) + (x + 2) + (x + 3)$;
$4x + 6$.   17. $y(y + 2)$; $y^2 + 2y$.   19. $x + x(x + 2) = 180$; $x^2 + 3x = 180$.

EXERCISE 9   PAGE 46

1. (A) $7 > 3$; (B) $7 \neq 3$; (C) $5 \leq 5$; (D) $11 < 12$; (E) $11 \geq 11$; (F) $9 = 9$.   3. (A) F; (B) F;
(C) T; (D) T; (E) F; (F) T.   5. (A) T; (B) T; (C) T; (D) F; (E) F; (F) T.   7. (A) $\{6, 8\}$;
(B) $\{6, 8\}$; (C) $\{2, 4\}$; (D) $\{2, 4, 6\}$; (E) $\{4\}$; (F) $\{2, 6, 8\}$.   9. (A) $\{3, 4, 5\}$; (B) $\{2, 3, 4, 5\}$;
(C) $\{1, 2, 3, 4\}$; (D) $\{1, 2, 3, 4\}$.   11. (A) $10x > 40,000 + 4x$; (B) $10x \geq 40,000 + 4x$.
13. $3S + 6R \leq 800$.   15. (B) $0 < x < 6$.

EXERCISE 10   PAGE 50

1. (A) $B = \{x \mid x \le 7\}$; (B) $C = \{t \mid t > 13\}$; (c) $D = \{u \mid 4 < u \le 10\}$.   3. (A) Set F
is the set of all natural numbers x such that x is less than or equal to 8; (B) Set B is the set
of all natural numbers t such that t is greater than or equal to 4 and less than 9; (c) Set C
is the set of all natural numbers n such that $n + 7$ is greater than 5 and less than or equal
to 23; (D) Set A is the set of all natural numbers y such that $3y + 5$ is equal to $4(y + 2)$.
5. (A) 2, 3, 4; (B) 4, 5, 6; (c) 3, 4, 5, 6, 7; (D) $\le$, $<$; (E) 2, y, 7; (F) $\ge$.
7. $A = \{x \mid 0 < x < 6\}$.

EXERCISE 11   PAGE 53

1. (A)    (B)

(c)   3. (A)

(B)   5. (A)   (B)

7. (A)   (B)

9. (A) 3, 5, 8; (B) 7, 12, 16.   11. (A) 4, 5, 6, 7, 8, 9; (B) 4, 10, t.   13. x, x, N.
15. (A) 6, 7, 8; (B) 3, 4, 5, 6, 7, 8, 9, 10, 11, 12.

EXERCISE 12   PAGE 58

1. 7, 11, 13; yes.   2. (A) $x = y$; (B) $x \ne y$; (c) $4 \varepsilon B$; (D) $5 \notin C$; (E) $x > y$; (F) $x \le y$.
3. (A) $\{2, 3, 5, 7\}$; (B) $\{2, 4, 6, 8\}$; (c) $\{4, 6, 8, 9\}$; (D) $2 \cdot 2$, $2 \cdot 3$, $2 \cdot 2 \cdot 2$, $3 \cdot 3$.
4. (A) True; (B) False; (c) False; (D) True; (E) False; (F) False; (G) True; (H) False.
5. (A) $\{33, 36, 39, 42, 45, 48, 51, 54, 57\}$; (B) $33 \varepsilon R$, $47 \notin R$, $51 \varepsilon R$, $57 \varepsilon R$;

(c)    6. 10.

7. (A) 42; (B) 50; (c) 210; (D) 42.   8. (A) $3y + 5$; 17; (B) $5y - 3$; 17; (c) $4(y - 3)$; 4.
9. (A) $<$, $<$, $<$, $>$, $>$; (B) 9, 14, 17.   10. $\{25, 36, 49\}$,

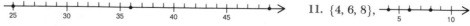   11. $\{4, 6, 8\}$,

12. (A) $\{3, 5, 7, 9, 11, 13\}$; (B)

13. (A) $D = \{u \mid 5 < u \le 13, u$ is an odd number$\}$; (B) The set is the set of all natural numbers t such that t is greater than 13. 14. (A) $<$, $\le$; (B) 4, t, 8; (C) u, 5.
15. No. If an element of the set is subtracted from an element of the set, the result is not necessarily an element of the set. 16. $(5 - 2) - 1 \ne 5 - (2 - 1)$.
17. (A) Closure and commutative axioms for addition; (B) Closure axiom for addition and commutative axiom for multiplication; (C) Closure and associative axioms for addition; (D) Distributive axiom for multiplication over addition; (E) Closure axiom for addition and distributive axiom for multiplication over addition; (F) Closure and associative axioms for multiplication. 18. (A) Closure axiom for addition twice; (B) Closure axioms for addition and multiplication; (C) Closure and associative axioms for addition; (D) Closure and commutative axioms for addition. 19. Distributive axiom for multiplication over addition. 20. (A) $7x^2 + 3x + 6$; (B) $3x^2 + 4xy + 7y^2$; (C) $10x + 3y + 7z$. 21. (A) $10a^2 + 8ab + 12b^2$; (B) $2x^6 + 13x^3 + 15$; (C) $3x^2 + 11x + 6$. 22. (A) $a(x + y)$; (B) $2x(x + 2y)$; (C) $3xy(x + 2y + 3)$.
23. (A) 2; (B) 1; (C) 1; (D) 3. 24. (A) $8x^3y^4z^4$; (B) $36 \cdot 10^{20}$; (C) $10u^6v^6$.
25. $2 \cdot 10^{27}$; 2,000,000,000,000,000,000,000,000,000. 26. (A) $=$; (B) $=$; (C) $\ne$; (D) $=$.
27. Substitution principle for equality. 28. (A) $x + (x + 2) = 36$; $2x + 2 = 36$; (B) $2[x + (x + 1)] = 5x$; $4x + 2 = 5x$. 29. (A) $x + (x + 2) = (x + 2) + 5$; $2x + 2 = x + 7$; (B) $75 = (2w + 5)w$; $2w^2 + 5w = 75$. 30. (A) $c = 400 + 40x$; (B) 400 and 40 are constants, c and x are variables; (C) $\{1,600, 1,800, 2,000\}$.

EXERCISE 13   PAGE 66

1. $-8, -2, +3, +9$.
3. (A) (B) (C)
5. (A) F; (B) T; (C) T; (D) T; (E) F; (F) F; (G) F; (H) T; (I) T; (J) F. 7. (A) $+20,270$ ft; (B) -280 ft; (C) $+29,141$ ft; (D) $-35,800$ ft. 9. (A) -2; (B) -8; (C) $+4$.
11. (A) $+\$25$; (B) $-\$10$; (C) $+\$237$; (D) $-\$17$; (E) $+23$ yd; (F) -9 yd.

EXERCISE 14   PAGE 71

1. (A) (B)
3. (A) -5; (B) -7; (C) $+5$; (D) $+5$ or -5. 5. (A) $+2$; (B) -2; (C) -2; (D) $+2$; (E) -2; (F) $+3$; (G) -3; (H) $+3$; (I) -3; (J) -3. 7. (A) -12; (B) $+3$; (C) -4.
9. (A) $\{+5\}$; (B) $\{+12\}$; (C) $\{0\}$; (D) $\{-4\}$. 11. (A) sometimes; (B) never.
13. (A) 0; (B) The set of all nonnegative integers; (C) 0; (D) The set of all nonnegative integers.

EXERCISE 15   PAGE 74

1. (A) 6°; (B) −6°; (C) −20°; (D)

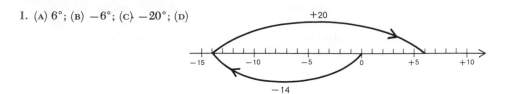

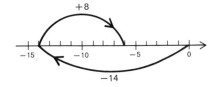

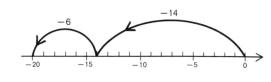

3. +18, −2, −3, +2, −4;

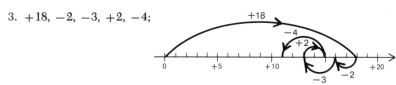

5. (A)

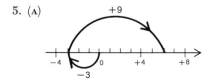

(B)

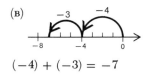

$$(-4) + (-3) = -7$$

$$(-3) + (+9) = +6$$

(C)

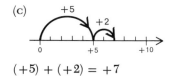

(D)

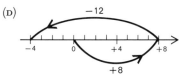

$$(+5) + (+2) = +7$$

$$(+8) + (-12) = -4$$

7. (A)

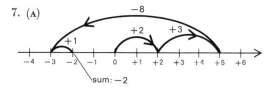

(B)

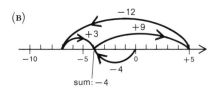

9.

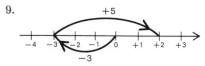

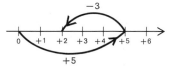

$$(-3) + (+5) = +2$$

$$(+5) + (-3) = +2$$

EXERCISE 16   PAGE 79

1. (A) $+11$; (B) $+3$; (C) -3; (D) -11; (E) 0.   3. (A) $+9$; (B) -6; (C) -11; (D) $+5$.
5. (A) -2; (B) -4; (C) -36; (D) -96.   7. (A) -5; (B) -4; (C) -48.
9. (A) $+5$; (B) -5; (C) $+16$; (D) -7; (E) $+9$; (F) -77.   11. No; 9-yd net gain.
13. Meg, with a score of $+105$.   15. (A) $-(|-9| - |+5|) = -4$;
(B) $-(|-12| + |-13|) = -25$; (C) $(|+12| - |-4|) = 8$; (D) $-(|-33| - |+12|) = -21$;
(E) 0.   17. (A) 10; (B) 13; (C) -6; (D) 0; (E) 2; (F) 14.   19. (A) always; (B) sometimes.
21. (A) 0; (B) 0; (C) $+5$ or $-(-5)$; (D) $-D$.   25. $+20$.
27. $-327 + x = -197$, $x = +130$.

EXERCISE 17   PAGE 85

1. (A) 13; (B) 0; (C) 0; (D) -10.   3. (A) -15; (B) -34; (C) -131; (D) 45.   5. (A) 14;
(B) -11; (C) -13; (D) 5.   7. (A) Theorem 3 in Sec. 16; (B) Theorem 3 in Sec. 16.
9. (A) 1; (B) -1; (C) 1; (D) -13.   11. No, $a - b$ does not necessarily equal $b - a$ for
all integers a and b. No, $(a - b) - c$ does not necessarily equal $a - (b - c)$ for all
integers a, b, and c.   13. (A) 4; (B) -8; (C) 0; (D) -6; (E) -5; (F) -5; (G) 9; (H) 2;
(I) -3; (J) -8; (K) -10; (L) 15.   15. (A) 20,550 ft; (B) 35 ft.   17. (A) \$28; (B) \$67.
19. 185.

EXERCISE 18   PAGE 92

1. (A) 14; (B) -48; (C) -63; (D) 15; (E) -8; (F) 8; (G) 0; (H) 0.   3. (A) -28; (B) -28;
(C) 36; (D) 36; (E) -6; (F) -6; (G) 8; (H) 8.   5. See answers for problem 1.
7. (A) -4; (B) -3; (C) 6; (D) 7; (E) 1; (F) -1; (G) 2; (H) 0.   9. (A) -4; (B) 8; (C) -12;
(D) 72; (E) -25; (F) 40; (G) -125; (H) 17.   11. (A) 15; (B) -15; (C) 9; (D) -9; (E) 15;
(F) 15; (G) -5; (H) -5.   13. (A) never; (B) always.   15. (A) $x^2 + x$; (B) $x^3 + x^2y$;
(C) $6x^2y + 8xy^2$; (D) $6x^3 + 8x^2$.   17. (A) $8x^2 + 3x$; (B) $5x^2 + 8x$.

EXERCISE 19   PAGE 96

1. (A) 7; (B) -12; (C) -30.   3. (A) 12, 12; (B) 8, 8.   5. (A) $8t^4 + 12t^3 + 20t^2$;
(B) $6x^3y - 6xy^3$; (C) $6a^2b^2 + 18ab^3 + 3a^2b^3 + 3ab^4$; (D) $8u^5 - 12u^3v$.

EXERCISE 20   PAGE 100

1. (A) 4; (B) 4; (C) -4; (D) -4; (E) 0; (F) 0; (G) undefined; (H) undefined.   3. (A) -12;
(B) undefined in the integers; (C) -5; (D) -5; (E) -6; (F) 0.   5. Sometimes (0/0 undefined).
7. See answers to problem 1.   9. See answers to problem 1.   11. (A) 4; (B) -6;
(C) 25; (D) 0; (E) 5; (F) -1; (G) -27; (H) -14.   13. Because the product of 0 and any
integer is 0, not -5.   15. Sometimes, $\dfrac{+4}{+2} = \left|\dfrac{+4}{+2}\right|$ but $\dfrac{-4}{+2} \neq \left|\dfrac{-4}{+2}\right|$.

EXERCISE 21   PAGE 105

1. (A), (B), (C), (D), (E), (H).   3. (A) 12; (B) -2; (C) 5; (D) 5; (E) -13; (F) -2; (G) -2; (H) -2.   5. (A) -4; (B) 1; (C) 3.   7. (A) $8x$; (B) $-2x$; (C) x; (D) $-2y$; (E) $-2y$; (F) $-2y$.   9. (A) $7x + 3y$; (B) $-5a + 3b$; (C) $4s - 6t$; (D) $2x^2 + 2y^2$; (E) $-xy - ab$; (F) $6x + 3y$.   11. (A) -11; (B) 11; (C) -13; (D) -14; (E) 0; (F) 5.
13. (A) 5; (B) 14; (C) 1; (D) 1; (E) 6; (F) -563.

EXERCISE 22   PAGE 108

1. $8x - 7$.   3. $14y$.   5. $7t - 56$.   7. $-a + 3b$.   9. $4x - 6$.   11. $4t^2 - 3t$.
13. $3x + 8$.   15. $3x - 14$.   17. $-8x^2 - 16x$.   19. 1.
21. $13x^2 - 26x + 10$.   23. (A) $3x - y$; (B) $-3x + y$; (C) $y + 2z$.
25. $10x + 25(x - 4)$ or $35x - 100$.   27. $2x + 2(x - 5)$ or $4x - 10$.

EXERCISE 23   PAGE 114

1. -12.   3. -3.   5. -13.   7. 8.   9. -7.   11. 0.   13. 3.   15. -3.
17. 8.   19. -7.   21. No solution.   23. 16.   25. 16.   27. -15.
29. No solution in the integers.   31. 6.   33. No solution.
35. $3x - 6 = 6$, $3x = 12$, and $x = 4$; $3x = 0$ and $x = 0$.   37. (A) and (D).
39. $ac = ac$ (identity property of equality)
    $a = b$ (given)
    $ac = bc$ (substitution principle).

EXERCISE 24   PAGE 118

1. 16, 18, and 20.   3. 7 ft and 11 ft.   5. 4 ft.   7. 19 in. and 38 in.   9. 5 sec.
11. 13 ft above and 104 ft below.   13. 130 min or 2 hr, 10 min.   15. 8 hr.
17. 70 hr or 2 days, 22 hr; 1,750 miles.   19. 8 dimes and 12 nickels.
21. Any four consecutive even numbers.

EXERCISE 25   PAGE 122

1. (A) $>$; (B) $<$; (C) $<$; (D) $<$; (E) $>$; (F) $<$; (G) $>$; (H) $<$.   3. (A) $<$; (B) $>$; (C) $<$; (D) $<$.   5. (A) $\{-6, -4, -2, 0, 2\}$; (B) ϕ; (C) $\{-2, 0, 2, 4, 6, 8\}$; (D) $\{-6, -4, -2\}$; (E) $\{-2, 0, 2, 4, 6\}$; (F) $\{-4, -2, 0\}$.

7. (A)   (B)

9. To the right; greater.

EXERCISE 26   PAGE 124

1. (A) F; (B) F; (C) T; (D) F; (E) T; (F) T.   2. (A) $+48$; (B) -12; (C) -245; (D) $+14{,}495$.

3.

$$|+2|$$
$$|-2|$$
$$-(+2) \quad -(-2)$$

4. (A) $+4$; (B) -8; (C) $+8$; (D) $+8$.

5. Sum: (A) -14; (B) $+6$; (C) $+6$; (D) $+2$. Difference: (A) -4; (B) $+10$; (C) -10; (D) 0. Product: (A) $+45$; (B) -16; (C) -16; (D) $+1$.   6. (A) $+5$; (B) -4; (C) -4.

7. $(-7) + (+150) + (-55) + (-60) + (+28) + (-32) + (-15) = +9$.   8. (A) -2; (B) -15; (C) $+5$; (D) -8.   9. (A) -24; (B) $+6$; (C) -18.

10. $(+29{,}141) - (-1{,}292) = +30{,}433$.   11. (A) $>$; (B) $>$.   12. (A) -5; (B) $+9$; (C) -3; (D) -33.   13. (A) $+7$; (B) $+3$.   14. (A) $\{+3\}$; (B) $\{-5, +5\}$; (C) The set of nonnegative integers.   15. Never.   16. The negative of a number is the mirror image of the number relative to the origin on the number line.   17. Part of the number symbol for negative numbers: $\overset{\downarrow}{-}7$; The binary operation of subtraction: $(+3) \overset{\downarrow}{-} (-4)$; The unary operation to take the negative of: $\overset{\downarrow}{-}(-4)$.   18. Addition and multiplication.   19. Addition, subtraction, and multiplication.   20. (C) is false; let $a = +5$ and $b = -3$.   21. The quotient would have to be a number such that the product of it and zero would yield the dividend; this is only possible if the dividend is zero, but, then, the quotient could be any number.   22. (A) 2; (B) 10; (C) -43. 23. -41.   24. (A) -2; (B) -10; (C) 0.   25. (A) $6x - 4$; (B) $-2x + 4$. 26. (A) $3t^2 - 17t$; (B) -3.   27. (A) $x - 1$; (B) $x - y$.   28. (A) $x = -2$; (B) $x = 2$. 29. (A) No solution in the integers; (B) $x = 2$.   30. $4x + 6 = -2$, $4x = -8$ and $x = -2$; $4x = 4$ and $x = 1$.

31. (A) $\{-8, -5, -4, -1\}$; $>$; (B) $\{3, 5\}$

32. (A) $A = \phi$; (B) $B = \{5\}$.   33.   .   34. $12, 13, 14, 15$.

35. Short piece, 6 ft; long piece, 12 ft.   36. 994 sq in.   37. 17 hr; 306,000 miles. 38. 438 reds, 876 roans, and 438 whites.   39. No solution.

EXERCISE 27   PAGE 133

1. $-2\frac{1}{4}$, $-\frac{3}{4}$, $1\frac{3}{4}$.   3.   .   5. (A) $\frac{7}{8}$; (B) $\frac{7}{8}$; (C) $\frac{3}{4}$;

(D) $-\frac{3}{4}$.   7. (A) $\frac{2}{3}$; (B) $-\frac{1}{4}$; (C) $-\frac{9}{4}$; (D) $\frac{3}{2}$; (E) $-\dfrac{a}{3d}$; (F) $-\dfrac{4a}{b}$.   9. (A) 9; (B) -8;

(C) $-10x$.   11. (A) $\frac{8}{15}$; (B) $-\frac{2}{3}$; (C) $\frac{1}{2}$; (D) $-\frac{8}{9}$; (E) $\dfrac{1}{z}$; (F) $\dfrac{3ad}{2c}$.   13. (A) 1; (B) 2.

15. (A) $\frac{1}{2}$; (B) $-\frac{5}{3}$; (C) $-\frac{3}{4}$; (D) $\frac{3}{2}$.

EXERCISE 28   PAGE 137

1. $\frac{3}{2}$.   3. $\frac{7}{2}$.   5. 5.   7. 0.   9. $-\frac{5}{9}$.   11. $-\frac{2}{3}$.   13. $-\dfrac{a^3}{b^3}$.   15. y.

17. $\dfrac{3v}{2u}$.   19. $-2y^2$.   21. (A) $\frac{81}{100}$; (B) $\frac{9}{4}$.   23. (A) $\frac{2}{5}$; (B) $\frac{5}{2}$; (C) $\dfrac{ad}{bc}$; (D) $\dfrac{bc}{ad}$.

25. $\frac{7}{5}$.   27. $-\frac{3}{2}$.   29. 12.   31. $-\frac{3}{2}$.   33. $\frac{2}{3}$.   35. $\frac{1}{2}$.   37. $\frac{3}{5}$ hr.   39. $\frac{3}{5}$.

41. 400 ft.   43. (A) T; (B) T; (C) T; (D) F, $2/1 \neq 1/2$; (E) T; (F) F, $(8/4)/2 \neq 8/(4/2)$.

EXERCISE 29   PAGE 140

1. 6.   3. 12.   5. 24.   7. 90.   9. 120.   11. $6x^2$.   13. $12x^2y^2$.   15 $36s^2t^2$.

EXERCISE 30   PAGE 143

1. (A) $\frac{4}{5}$; (B) $\dfrac{3y}{7}$; (C) $-\dfrac{3}{5xy}$; (D) $-\frac{4}{5}$; (E) 1; (F) $\dfrac{x-z}{y}$.   3. (A) $\dfrac{1}{12}$; (B) $-\dfrac{9}{10}$; (C) $\dfrac{13x}{6}$;

(D) $\dfrac{x^2-y^2}{xy}$; (E) $\dfrac{x-2y}{y}$; (F) $\dfrac{x+1}{x}$.   5. $\frac{5}{3}$.   7. $\dfrac{3x^2-4x-6}{12}$.   9. $\dfrac{z-x-y}{xyz}$.

11. $\dfrac{18y-16x+3}{24xy}$.   13. (A) $3x+4$; (B) $10x-9$; (C) $14x-12$.   15. $\dfrac{22y+9}{252}$.

17. $\dfrac{15x^2+10x-6}{180}$.

EXERCISE 31   PAGE 146

1. $\frac{10}{9}$.   3. 36.   5. 200.   7. 24.   9. 9.   11. 10.   13. 56.   15. 75 ft.
17. (A) $c = 0.50 + 0.40m$; (B) $3\frac{1}{2}$ miles.   19. Seventy $\frac{1}{2}$-lb packages and thirty $\frac{1}{3}$-lb
packages.   21. \$36,000; \$360; \$240.

EXERCISE 32   PAGE 149

1. 18.   3. 4.   5. 4 in.   7. \$95.   9. 1.4.   11. $7\frac{1}{2}$ lb.   13. 92.5926.
15. 14.52 years.

EXERCISE 33   PAGE 156

1. (A) F; (B) T; (C) T; (D) T.   3. (A) T; (B) F; (C) T; (D) T; (E) F.   5. (A) A, B, C;
(B) A, B; (C) A, B; (D) A.   7. (A) $0.375\overline{00}$; (B) $2.5\overline{55}$; (C) $0.538461\overline{538461}$.   9. (A) $\frac{3}{11}$;
(B) $\frac{106}{33}$.

EXERCISE 34 PAGE 159

1.

3. (A) $>$; (B) $<$; (C) $<$; (D) $<$.   **5.** $-\frac{5}{2} \leq x < \frac{3}{2}$.

7. $-\frac{5}{4}$ $\frac{3}{4}$ **9.** $-\frac{15}{8}$ $-\frac{1}{8}$

11. $-\sqrt{5}$ π

13.

15. Negative.

EXERCISE 35 PAGE 161

1. $-\sqrt{8}$ $-\frac{9}{4}$ $\frac{9}{4}$ $\sqrt{8}$

2. (A) T; (B) F; (C) F; (D) F.   **3.** (A) $<$; (B) $>$; (C) $>$.

4. $-\frac{2}{3}$ π **5.** (A) $\frac{3y}{10}$; (B) $-\frac{3}{5xy}$.

6. (A) -9; (B) $-12x$.   **7.** (A) $-\frac{25}{49}$; (B) $-\frac{4}{9}$; (C) $-\frac{25}{42}$; (D) $\frac{65}{42}$.   **8.** (A) $\frac{16}{21}$; (B) $\frac{17}{18}$.

9. (A) $\frac{2}{5x^2}$; (B) $\frac{9y^2}{10z^2}$; (C) $\frac{-9y^2 - 10z^2}{15xyz}$; (D) $\frac{10z^2 - 9y^2}{15xyz}$.   **10.** (A) $-\frac{4}{9}$;

(B) $\frac{20xyz + 135xy^3 + 6z^2}{18y^2z}$.   **11.** $-\frac{7}{3}$.   **12.** 12.   **13.** $-\frac{10}{9}$.   **14.** $\frac{1}{15}$ hr or 4 min.

15. 35.   **16.** 9.   **17.** -110.   **18.** \$80.   **19.** 2.25 qt or larger.   **20.** 1,120,000.

21. 5; 36.

EXERCISE 36 PAGE 165

1. b.   **2.** a, d.   **3.** a, c, d.   **4.** a, b.

EXERCISE 37   PAGE 166

1. chemist, 40 hr; assistant, 30 hr.   3. 75 percent.   5. $80,000.   7. 12 lb.

9. (A) 3.09 grams; (B) 324.31 grams.   11. 350 cc.   13. $T = 80 - 5.5\left(\dfrac{h}{1,000}\right)$ or

$T = 80 - 0.0055h$; 10,000 ft.   15. 0.1 in., 107.4 ft.   17. (A) GNP = NNP + (0.1)NNP
or GNP = (1.1)NNP; (B) 105.6; 52.8.   19. 78 by 27 ft.   21. 30°, 60°, 90°.
23. $2\frac{1}{4}$ cups of milk and 3 cups of flour.   25. 16.   27. 400 miles.   29. (A) 216 miles;
(B) 225 miles.   31. 250.   33. 315; 105; 105; 35.   35. 264; 330.   37. $\frac{1}{3}$ in.
39. 200,000 mps.   41. 4 ft from the 6-lb end.   43. 400 lb.   45. (A) 15 ohms;
(B) 0.3 ampere.   47. 150 cm.   49. 18 four-cent stamps and 12 five-cent stamps.
51. $5\frac{5}{11}$ minutes after 1 P.M.

EXERCISE 38   PAGE 178

1. $A(5, 5)$, $B(8, 2)$, $C(-5, 5)$, $D(-3, 8)$, $E(-5, -6)$, $F(-7, -8)$, $G(5, -5)$, $H(2, -2)$, $I(7, 0)$,
$J(-2, 0)$, $K(0, -9)$, $L(0, 4)$.   3. (See graph below)
5. $A(2\frac{1}{2}, 1)$, $B(-2\frac{1}{2}, 3\frac{1}{2})$, $C(-2, -4\frac{1}{2})$, $D(3\frac{1}{4}, -3)$, $E(1\frac{1}{4}, 2\frac{1}{4})$, $F(-3\frac{1}{4}, 0)$, $G(1\frac{1}{2}, -4\frac{1}{4})$.
7. (See graph below)   9. (A) II; (B) IV; (C) I; (D) III.

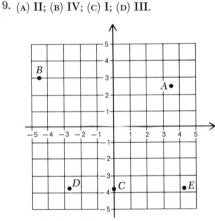

graph for problem 3

graph for problem 7

EXERCISE 39   PAGE 181

1.

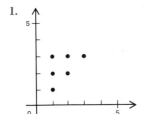

3.

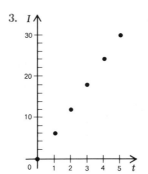

5.

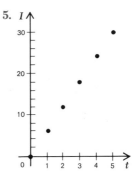

7.

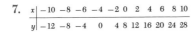

x	-10	-8	-6	-4	-2	0	2	4	6	8	10
y	-12	-8	-4	0	4	8	12	16	20	24	28

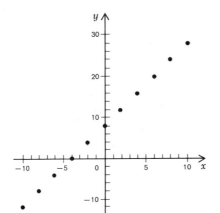

9.

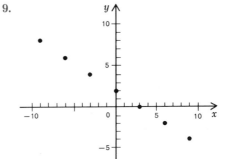

11.

C	-30	-25	-20	-15	-10	-5	0	5	10	15	20	25	30
F	-22	-13	-4	5	14	23	32	41	50	59	68	77	86

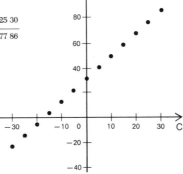

13.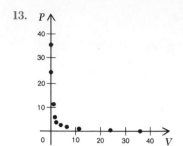

15.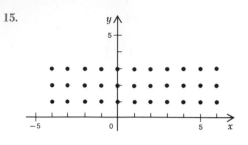

EXERCISE 40   PAGE 185

1.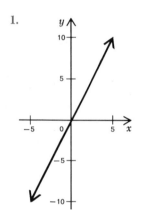

3.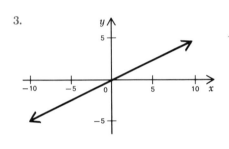

5.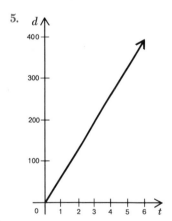

7.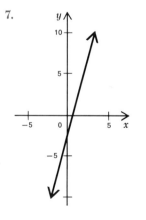

9.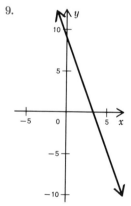

11.

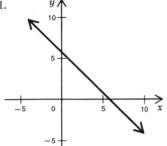

13.

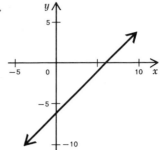

15.

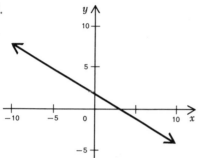

17.

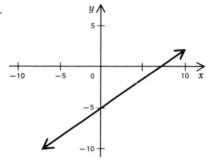

19.

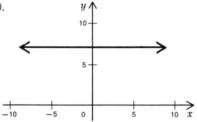

21.

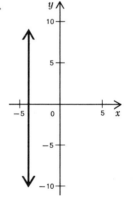

23.

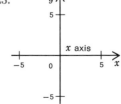

25.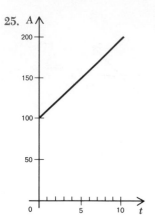

27.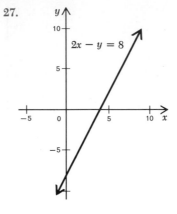

29.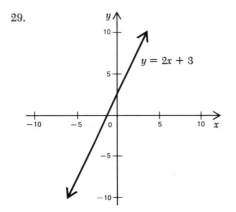

31.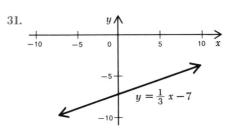

33.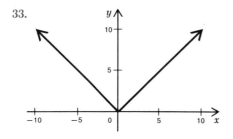

35.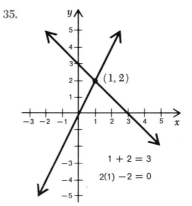

37.

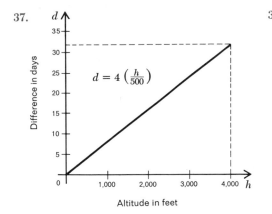

$$d = 4\left(\frac{h}{500}\right)$$

Difference in days

Altitude in feet

39.

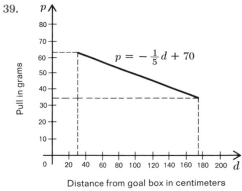

$$p = -\tfrac{1}{5}d + 70$$

Pull in grams

Distance from goal box in centimeters

EXERCISE 41   PAGE 192

1. (A)

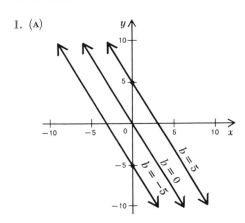

(B)

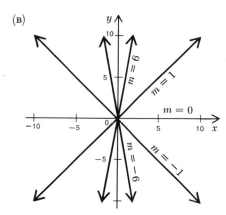

3.

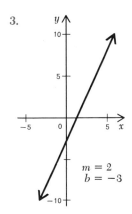

$$m = 2$$
$$b = -3$$

5.

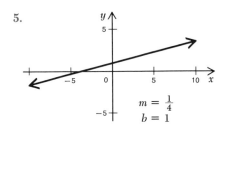

$$m = \frac{1}{4}$$
$$b = 1$$

7.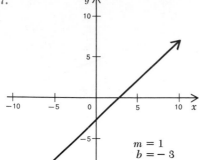

$m = 1$
$b = -3$

9.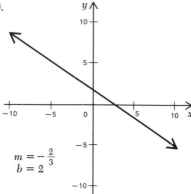

$m = -\dfrac{2}{3}$
$b = 2$

11. $y = -x - 1$. 13. $y = \frac{2}{3}x + \frac{3}{2}$. 15. $y = x$. 17. $y = -\dfrac{x}{3} - 2$.

19. $m = \frac{1}{2}$. 21. $m = \frac{1}{3}$. 23. (A) $y = \dfrac{x}{2}$; (B) $y = \dfrac{x}{3} + 6$. 25. $y = 4$.

27. $x = 2$. 29. (A) $S = \dfrac{W}{10}$; (B) (See graph below); (C) 2.3 in.

31. (A) $c = \dfrac{x}{2} + 200$; (B) (See graph below)

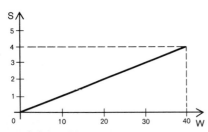

graph for problem 29B

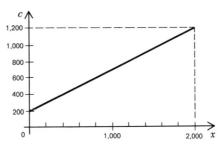

graph for problem 31B

EXERCISE 42   PAGE 196

1. $(3, 2)$. 3. $(6, 8)$. 5. $(-4, -3)$. 7. no solution. 9. an infinite number of solutions; any solution to one equation will be a solution to the other. 11. Both companies pay $175 on a sale of $2,500.

EXERCISE 43   PAGE 201

1. $(3, 2)$. 3. $(2, -4)$. 5. $(-3, -5)$. 7. $(1, -\frac{2}{3})$. 9. $(1, -5)$.
11. $(-1, -\frac{3}{2})$. 13. no solution. 15. $(-2, -3)$. 17. $(2, 3)$. 19. $(1, 0.2)$.
21. $(-6, 12)$. 23. infinite number of solutions. 25. Both companies pay $175 on a sale of $2,500.

EXERCISE 44   PAGE 204

1. $(3, 2)$.   3. $(6, 8)$.   5. $(-4, -3)$.   7. no solution.
9. Both companies pay \$175 on sales of \$2,500.   11. $(1, -1)$.
13. limes, 11 cents each; lemons, 4 cents each.   15. $2\frac{1}{2}$ hr; 35 letters together, $17\frac{1}{2}$ each.

EXERCISE 45   PAGE 205

1. 84 $\frac{1}{4}$-lb packages; 60 $\frac{1}{2}$-lb packages.   3. Typist: 8 hr, \$20; Steno: 6 hr, \$24.
5. 60 cc of 80 percent solution and 40 cc of 50 percent solution.
7. 40 sec, 24 sec; 120 miles.   9. 11 ft, 7 ft.   11. $52°, 38°$.
13. 700 student, 300 adult.   15. 927 brown, 309 blue.   17. 16 in., 20 in.
19. 3 ft from 42-lb weight.   21. $d = 141$ cm (approx.); move away from goal box;
move toward goal box.   23. 14 nickels, 8 dimes.

EXERCISE 46   PAGE 211

1. (A) 5; (B) 3; (C) 1; (D) 2.

2.

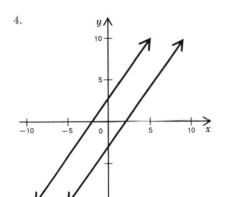

3.

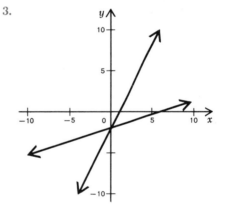

4.

5.

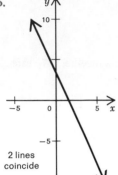

2 lines coincide

6.

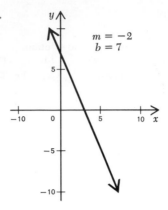

$m = -2$
$b = 7$

7. (A)

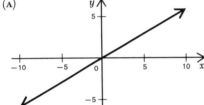

(C)

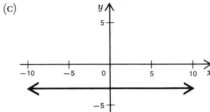

8. $y = -2x - 4$.

9. $y = -\frac{x}{2} + 5$.   **10.** $y = \frac{x}{3} + 3$.   **11.** $x = -3$, $y = 3$.   **12.** $a = -\frac{3}{2}$, $b = \frac{2}{3}$.

13. $x = 1$, $y = -4$.   **14.** $x = -6$, $y = 8$.   **15.** Milk: 2.4 cups, flour: 2.8 cups.

16. (A) $y = \frac{x}{2}$; (B) $y = x - 5$.   **17.** (See graph below)

18. (A) $E = 50 + 0.04S$ (B) (See graph below)   **19.** a, c, and d.

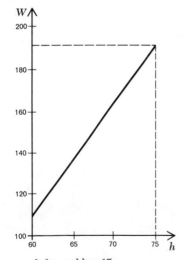

graph for problem 17

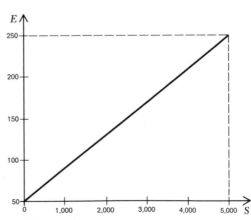

graph for problem 18B

20. $\frac{2}{3}x + \frac{y}{9} = 1$ or $6x + y = 9$.   21. 60 lb on the 6-ft end; 72 lb on the 5-ft end.

22. $l = 78$ ft, $w = 27$ ft.   23. Plane: 170 mph; wind: 10 mph.

24. 1,000 economy, 1,600 deluxe.   25. The original system is not true for any replacements of x and y.

EXERCISE 47   PAGE 217

1. (A) $<$; (B) $>$; (C) $<$; (D) $>$.   3. (A) $\geq$; (B) $<$; (C) $<$; (D) $\leq$.

5. $x > 4$ ⟶∘⟶ x (4)   7. $m \leq 2$ ⟵●⟶ m (2)

9. $x \geq -3$ ⟶●⟶ x (-3)   11. $x < 2$ ⟵∘⟶ x (2)

13. $x < -3$ ⟵∘⟶ x (-3)   15. $x < -21$ ⟵∘⟶ x (-21)

17. $x < 3$ ⟵∘⟶ x (3)   19. $x \leq \frac{2}{7}$ ⟵●⟶ x ($\frac{2}{7}$)

21. $p < 3$ ⟵∘⟶ p (3)   23. $x > 10$ ⟶∘⟶ x (10)

25. $-1 < x \leq 2$ ⟶∘●⟶ x (-1, 2)

27. $-2 \leq n \leq \frac{3}{2}$ ⟶●●⟶ n (-2, $\frac{3}{2}$)

29. $3 < x < 7$ ⟶∘∘⟶ x (3, 7)

31. $-9 \leq m \leq 9$ ⟶●●⟶ m (-9, 9)   33. (A) T; (B) F; (C) F.   35. $x \geq -\frac{3}{2}$.

37. $w < 5$ in.   39. $w \geq 155$ lb.   41. $86° < F < 95°$.   43. $b - a$ is negative. Therefore the inequality sign reverses when both sides are divided by it.

EXERCISE 48   PAGE 223

1.

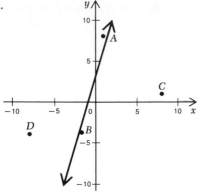

A: above
B: below
C: below
D: above

3. *P*: below, *Q*: above.

5.

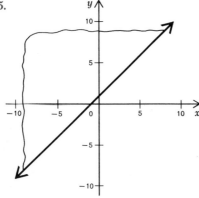

7.

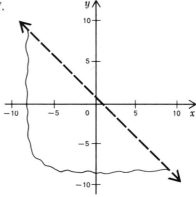

9.

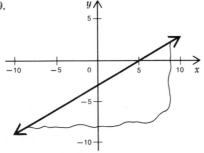

11.

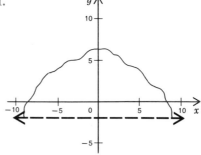

13.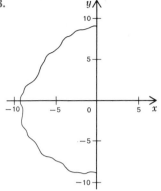

15.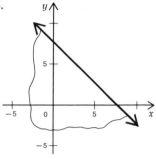

17.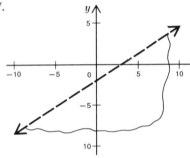

19.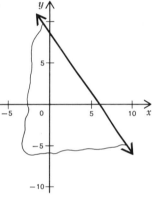

21.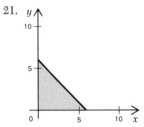

23.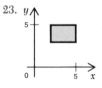

25.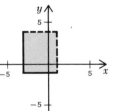

27.

29.

31.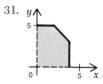

33.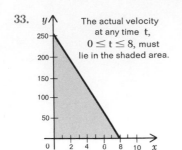

The actual velocity at any time t, $0 \le t \le 8$, must lie in the shaded area.

35.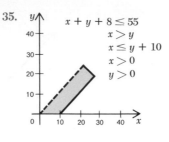

$$x + y + 8 \le 55$$
$$x > y$$
$$x \le y + 10$$
$$x > 0$$
$$y > 0$$

EXERCISE 49   PAGE 225

1. $100 + 6t > 133$, $t > 5.5$ years.   3. $\dfrac{55 + 73 + x}{3} \ge 70$, $x \ge 82$.

5. $\dfrac{W}{110} \le 30$, $W \le 3,300$ watts.   7. $1.7 \le \dfrac{V}{740} \le 2.4$, $1,258 \le V \le 1,776$.

9. $5 \le \dfrac{d}{1,088} \le 10$; $5,440 \text{ ft} \le d \le 10,880 \text{ ft}$; $1.03 \text{ mi} \le d \le 2.06 \text{ mi}$.

11.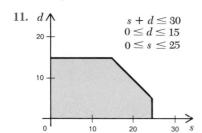

$$s + d \le 30$$
$$0 \le d \le 15$$
$$0 \le s \le 25$$

13.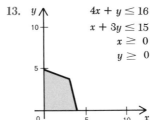

$$4x + y \le 16$$
$$x + 3y \le 15$$
$$x \ge 0$$
$$y \ge 0$$

15.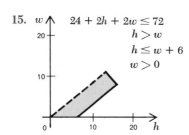

$$24 + 2h + 2w \le 72$$
$$h > w$$
$$h \le w + 6$$
$$w > 0$$

EXERCISE 50   PAGE 228

1. (A) Equivalent inequalities are inequalities with same solution set. (B) All.

2. $x > 0$

3. $x > 3$

4. $x < 4$

5. $x \leq -3$

6. $x > -12$

7. $x \geq -10$

8. $F \leq 68$

9. $x > \frac{9}{8}$

10. $-1 < x \leq 6$

11. $-40 \leq C \leq 15$

12. (A) T; (B) T; (C) T; (D) F.   13. Above.

14.
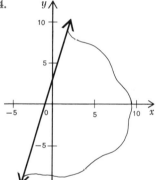

15.
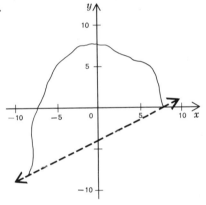

16.
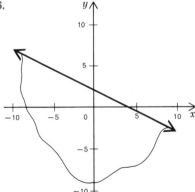

17.
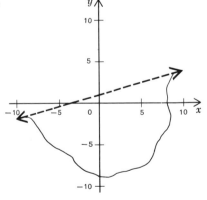

18.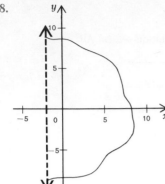

19.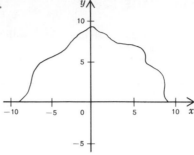

20.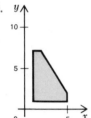

21.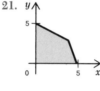

22.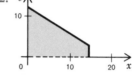

23. $5 - x \geq x,\ x \leq \frac{5}{2}$.   24. $68 \leq F \leq 77$.

EXERCISE 51   PAGE 234

1. a, b, d, f, g, h.   3. (A) b; (B) g; (C) a; (D) h.   5. $2x - 4$.   7. $-3x - 4y$.
9. $x^2 - 3x$.   11. $x^2 - 4x - 5$.   13. $2x^2 - 2xy + 3y^2$.   15. $4x - 12y + 7$.
17. $2x^4 - 5x^3 + 5x^2 + 11x - 10$.   19. $2x^3 - 7x^2 + 13x - 5$.
21. $x^3 - 6x^2y + 10xy^2 - 3y^3$.   23. $a^3 + b^3$.   25. $x^3 + 6x^2y + 12xy^2 + 8y^3$.
27. $2x^4 - 5x^3 + 5x^2 + 11x - 10$.   29. $2x^4 + x^3y - 7x^2y^2 + 5xy^3 - y^4$.

EXERCISE 52   PAGE 237

1. $3x^2 - 15x$.   3. $-5x^3 + 15x^2 - 10x$.   5. $2x^3y - 6x^2y^2 - 4xy^3$.
7. $-16m^5n^2 + 6m^3n^3 - 8m^2n^5$.   9. $3x - 2$.   11. $m - 2n$. $x - 2y$.
15. $2c(2a - 3b)$.   17. $2x(3x^2 - 2x + 1)$.   19. $-2y(x - 3)$ or $2y(-x + 3)$.
21. $5xy(2x^2 - xy - 3y^2)$.   23. $-2xy(3x^2 + 2y^2)$.   25. $(-2x^3)(4x^2 + 5x + 3)$.
27. all.   29. The set of all real numbers.

EXERCISE 53   PAGE 240

1. $x^2 + 5x + 6$.   3. $m^2 - 5m + 6$.   5. $t^2 - 2t - 24$.   7. $a^2 - 4a - 32$.
9. $t^2 - 9$.   11. $b^2 + 2b - 80$.   13. $y^2 + 16y + 63$.   15. $n^2 - 4n + 3$.
17. $x^2 - 49$.   19. $y^2 + 9y - 10$.   21. $2x^2 + 9x + 9$.   23. $2x^2 - 9x + 4$.
25. $2t^2 + 5t - 12$.   27. $5a^2 - 24a - 36$.   29. $6x^2 - 7x + 2$.   31. $4m^2 - 49$.
33. $4x^2 - 12x + 9$.   35. $16x^2 + 8x + 1$.   37. $x^2 + 4xy + 3y^2$.   39. $m^2 - n^2$
41. $6x^2 - 13xy + 6y^2$.   43. $12m^2 + 17mn - 5n^2$.   45. $a^2 - 2ab + b^2$.
47. $4x^2 - 12xy + 9y^2$.

EXERCISE 54   PAGE 244

1. $(x + 2)(x + 3)$.   3. $(m - 3)(m - 4)$.   5. not factorable.   7. $(x + 4y)(x + 5y)$.
9. not factorable.   11. $t(t - 2)(t - 10)$.   13. $(2x + 1)(x + 3)$.
15. $(2x - 3y)(x - 2y)$.   17. not factorable.   19. $y(3y - 4)(2y - 3)$.
21. $2x(x^2 - x + 4)$.   23. $(2x + 3y)(3x + y)$.   25. $(n - 2)(n + 4)$.
27. $(x - 6y)(x + 2y)$.   29. not factorable.   31. $(2s - 1)(s + 3)$.
33. $3x(2x - 5)(x + 1)$.   35. $(2u - 3v)(3u + 4v)$.   37. not factorable.
39. $(5x - y)(3x + 4y)$.   41. $(x - 3)(x + 3)$.   43. $2x(x^2 + 4)$.
45. $(3y - 5)(3y + 5)$.   47. $xy(2x - y)(2x + y)$.   49. not factorable.
51. $4(x - 3)(x - 4)$.   53. $3xy(x - 2y)(x - 3y)$.   55. 6, 10, 12.

EXERCISE 55   PAGE 248

1. $x - 2$.   3. $3x^2 - x + 2$.   5. $\dfrac{3t^2 + t - 2}{t}$.   7. $2m^2 - mn + 3n^2$.
9. a.   11. $x + 2$.   13. $x + 5$.   15. $2x - 3y$.   17. $x - 5$.   19. $2x - 3$.
21. $m - 2$.   23. $4x - 1$.   25. $y - 3$.   27. $x^2 + x + 1$.   29. $x - 4, R = 3$.
31. $4a + 5, R = -7$.   33. $4x + 6, R = 25$.   35. $x^2 - 3x - 5$.
37. $x^3 - 2x^2 + 4x - 8$.   39. $x^2 + 3x + 8, R = 27$.

EXERCISE 56   PAGE 250

1. a, c, d, f.   2. (A) c; (B) a.   3. $12x^2 + 12x - 7$.   4. $x - 7$.   5. $6x^2 - 7x + 2$.
6. $12x^2 + 2x - 13$.   7. $6x^2 + 11x - 10$.   8. $27x^4 + 63x^3 - 66x^2 - 28x + 24$.
9. $x + 3$.   10. $3x + 2$.   11. $(3x - 2)(x + 3)$.   12. $(3x - 2)(3x + 2)$.
13. $-2x + 20$.   14. 0.   15. (A) $x^2 - 2xy + 3y^2$; (B) $\dfrac{x - 3}{x}$.
16. (A) $(-2ab)(3a + 4b)$; (B) $(5x - 4y)(5x + 4y)$; (C) not factorable; (D) $(x - 5)^2$;
(E) not factorable; (F) $2x(2x + 1)(x - 3)$.   17. (A) $4t - 3, R = -2$; (B) $4x^2 - 2x + 1$.
18. all.

EXERCISE 57   PAGE 254

1. $\frac{8}{3}$.   3. $\frac{2}{9}$.   5. x^2u^2.   7. $\frac{c^3d^2}{a^6b^6}$.   9. $\frac{a^2}{2}$.   11. $a + 1$.   13. $\frac{1}{m}$.

15. $t(t - 4)$.   17. $6 - 3x$.   19. -1.   21. $\frac{(x - y)^2}{y^2(x + y)}$.   23. all but one.

25. Answer: 108,642.   Let $x = 108,641$ and write the other numbers in terms of x, then simplify.

EXERCISE 58   PAGE 257

1. $\frac{2x + 5}{3y}$.   3. $\frac{x - 1}{x}$.   5. $\frac{1 - b}{a^2}$.   7. $\frac{12x + y}{4y}$.   9. $\frac{2 + x}{x}$.

11. $\frac{x^2 - xy + y^2}{x^3}$.   13. $\frac{y^2 + 8}{8y^3}$.   15. 5.   17. $\frac{1}{x - 1}$.   19. $\frac{a + 2}{a + 1}$.

21. $\frac{-(x + 7)}{(2x + 3)(x - 1)}$.   23. $\frac{x - 5}{(x - 1)^2(x + 1)}$.   25. $\frac{3x - 5}{x - 3}$.   27. $\frac{x^2 - 6x + 7}{x - 2}$.

29. $\frac{2}{x + y}$.   31. $\frac{5a^2 - 2a - 5}{(a + 1)(a - 1)}$.   33. $\frac{-17}{15(x - 1)}$.   35. $\frac{5t - 12}{3(t^2 - 16)}$.

EXERCISE 59   PAGE 259

1. $\frac{x}{2}$.   3. $\frac{x + 3}{x(x + 2)}$.   5. $\frac{1}{x - 3}$.   7. $\frac{2a}{8a - 1}$.   9. $\frac{1}{y - x}$.   11. $\frac{x - y}{x + y}$.

13. $\frac{5}{3}$.   15. $\frac{1}{1 - x}$.   17. $v = \frac{c^2(v_1 + v_2)}{c^2 + v_1v_2}$.

EXERCISE 60   PAGE 263

1. $x = -6$.   3. $m = 3$.   5. $K = \frac{4}{13}$.   7. $y = 4$.   9. No solution.
11. $E = 5$.   13. No solution.   15. $x = -11$.   17. $s = 2$.   19. $D = 1$.
21. $t = -4$.   23. $-1, 2$.   25. 92.6 United States cents.   27. 400 mph.

EXERCISE 61   PAGE 264

1. $b = 60$ cm, $m = 2$.   3. $f = 12$ cm.   5. $a = 1$ sq in.   7. $L = 10$ in.
9. Air: 1,101 fps; Water: 4,954 fps.   11. $3\frac{3}{5}$ hr.   13. 1.5 hr.   15. $R = 4.4$ ohms.
17. $R_2 = 4$ ohms.   19. $r = 3\frac{1}{2}$ percent.   21. 36.

EXERCISE 62   PAGE 270

1. $I = A - P.$ 3. $r = \dfrac{d}{t}.$ 5. $t = \dfrac{I}{pr}.$ 7. $\pi = \dfrac{C}{D}.$ 9. $x = -\dfrac{b}{a}.$

11. $t = \dfrac{s + 5}{2}.$ 13. $y = \dfrac{3x - 12}{4}$ or $y = \tfrac{3}{4}x - 3.$ 15. $E = IR.$ 17. $L = \dfrac{100B}{C}.$

19. $m_1 = \dfrac{Fd^2}{Gm_2}.$ 21. $h = \dfrac{2A}{b_1 + b_2}.$ 23. $F = \tfrac{9}{5}C + 32.$

25. $f = \dfrac{ab}{a + b}$ or $f = \dfrac{1}{\dfrac{1}{a} + \dfrac{1}{b}}.$

EXERCISE 63   PAGE 272

1. $\dfrac{2xy}{ab}.$ 2. $\dfrac{2y^4}{9a^4}.$ 3. $\dfrac{x}{x + 1}.$ 4. $\dfrac{(d - 2)^2}{d + 2}.$ 5. $-1.$ 6. $x = -3,\ x = 2.$

7. $\dfrac{2q^2 - 15pq + 8p^2}{20p^2q^2}.$ 8. $\dfrac{-1}{(x + 2)(x + 3)}.$ 9. $\dfrac{2}{m + 1}.$ 10. $\dfrac{5x - 12}{3(x^2 - 16)}.$

11. $\dfrac{4 + y}{2x - y}.$ 12. $\dfrac{x - y}{x}.$ 13. $m = 5.$ 14. $x = -2.$ 15. No solution.

16. 1, 2.   17. 175 mph.   18. $R = \dfrac{W}{I^2}.$ 19. $L = \dfrac{2S}{n} - a.$ 20. $f_1 = \dfrac{ff_2}{f_2 - f}.$

21. $r = \dfrac{A - P}{Pt}.$ 22. $W = \dfrac{E^2}{R}.$

EXERCISE 64   PAGE 277

1. 7.   3. 5.   5. 12.   7. 2.   9. 5.   11. 3.   13. 5.   15. 7.   17. 2.

19. 7.   21. 6.   23. 7.   25. $24 \times 10^{22}.$ 27. $\dfrac{y^6}{3x^4}.$ 29. $x^9.$ 31. $a^{10}b^{10}.$

33. $x^8y^{12}.$ 35. $27a^9b^6.$ 37. $2c^8d^4.$ 39. $\dfrac{m^5}{n^5}.$ 41. $\dfrac{a^{12}}{b^8}.$ 43. $\dfrac{x^6y^3}{8w^6}.$

45. $\dfrac{y^3}{16x^4}.$ 47. $-\dfrac{x^2}{32}.$ 49. $-\dfrac{1}{a^8}.$

EXERCISE 65   PAGE 282

1. 1.   3. $\tfrac{1}{4}.$ 5. 9.   7. 1.   9. $10^{11}.$ 11. $10^2.$ 13. $10^{17}.$ 15. $4/10^8.$

17. 2^6 or 64.   19. $1/10^{12}.$ 21. $2^6/3^4$ or $64/81.$ 23. $1/10^4.$ 25. $\tfrac{1}{30}.$ 27. $\tfrac{1}{25}.$

29. $\tfrac{36}{13}.$ 31. 1.   33. $a^{12}.$ 35. $1/(8c^3d^6).$ 37. $(9x^6)/y^4.$ 39. $x^6/y^4.$

41. $(2x)/y^2.$ 43. $n^2.$ 45. $(4x^8)/y^6.$ 47. $1/(x + y)^2.$ 49. $1/(xy).$

51. $(xy)/(y + x).$

EXERCISE 66   PAGE 284

1. 5.2×10.   3. 7×10^{-1}.   5. 3.4×10^2.   7. 8.5×10^{-2}.   9. 6.8×10^3.
11. 7.23×10^{-4}.   13. 4.27×10^{13}.   15. 5.87×10^{12}.   17. 3×10^{-23}.   19. 37.
21. 7,100.   23. 0.837.   25. 0.0004.   27. 2,510,000,000.   29. 0.00000059.
31. 93,000,000.   33. 0.0000000000000000000000017.   35. 4.2×10^6, 2.2×10^{27},
2×10^{-20}, 6×10^9, 2.5×10^{-5}.   37. 3×10 or 30.   39. 3×10^{-4} or 0.0003.
41. 6.6×10^{21} tons.   43. 10^7, 6×10^8.

EXERCISE 67   PAGE 289

1. 9.   3. -2.   5. $\sqrt{5}$.   7. $-\frac{2}{3}$.   9. $-4x^2y^3$.   11. $-\dfrac{3m^2}{2n^3}$.   13. $2\sqrt{2}$.

15. $\sqrt{3}/3$.   17. $\sqrt{3y}/(3y)$.   19. $2m^2n^2\sqrt{6m}$.   21. $2x\sqrt{3x}$ 23. $\dfrac{7\sqrt{2}}{2}$.

25. $\dfrac{2x\sqrt{3xy}}{3}$.   27. $\sqrt{a^2 + b^2}$.   29. $-\dfrac{\sqrt{2}}{3}$.   31. $\dfrac{\sqrt{6}}{3}$.   33. $\dfrac{\sqrt{6mn}}{2n}$.

35. $\dfrac{2a\sqrt{3ab}}{3b}$.   37. $\dfrac{\sqrt{2}}{2}$.   39. $-x\sqrt{x^2 - 2}$.   41. 3.464.   43. 0.577.

45. 12.245.   47. -4.062.   49. ──────•───┼───•──────▶
                                        -2 0   2 x

51. ──────•───┼───•──────▶   53. 1.58 sec.   55. (A) 5 mps; (B) 18,000 mph.
      $-\sqrt{7}$ 0 $\sqrt{7}$ m

57. Because the square of any real number is positive.   59. $-$.   61. yes, yes.
63. $5^{1/2} = \sqrt{5}$.   65. Going from step 1 to step 2 is not valid.

EXERCISE 68   PAGE 292

1. $8\sqrt{2}$.   3. $3\sqrt{x}$.   5. $4\sqrt{7} - 3\sqrt{5}$.   7. $-3\sqrt{y}$.   9. $4\sqrt{5}$.   11. $-2\sqrt{x}$.
13. $2\sqrt{2} - 2\sqrt{3}$.   15. $2\sqrt{x} + 2\sqrt{y}$.   17. $\sqrt{2}$.   19. $-3\sqrt{3}$.
21. $2\sqrt{2} + 6\sqrt{3}$.   23. $-\sqrt{x}$.   25. $2\sqrt{6} + \sqrt{3}$.   27. $3\sqrt{2}$.   29. $-\sqrt{6}/6$.
31. $5\sqrt{2xy}/2$.   33. $2\sqrt{3} - \dfrac{\sqrt{2}}{2}$.

EXERCISE 69   PAGE 294

1. $3\sqrt{3} - 12$.   3. $2 + 3\sqrt{2}$.   5. $2\sqrt{3} - \sqrt{6}$.   7. $5\sqrt{2} + 5$.   9. $x - 3\sqrt{x}$.
11. $2\sqrt{2} - 1$.   13. $6 + \sqrt{x} - x$.   15. $9 + 4\sqrt{5}$.   17. $2 - 11\sqrt{2}$.
19. $23 - 8\sqrt{5}$.   21. $18 + 13\sqrt{2}$.   23. $4x - 12\sqrt{x} + 9$.   25. yes.
27. $\dfrac{3 - \sqrt{3}}{3}$.   29. $\dfrac{-2 + \sqrt{7}}{2}$.   31. $2 - \sqrt{2}$.   33. $\sqrt{5} - 2$.   35. $2\sqrt{6} + 4$.

37. $\sqrt{3} - \sqrt{2}.$ 39. $\dfrac{x + 2\sqrt{x}}{x - 4}.$ 41. $3 - 2\sqrt{2}.$ 43. $5 + 2\sqrt{6}.$

45. $\dfrac{x + 5\sqrt{x} + 6}{x - 9}.$

EXERCISE 70   PAGE 296

1. (A) 32; (B) $\frac{1}{27}$; (C) 1.   2. (A) $\frac{1}{64}$; (B) 8; (C) 81.   3. $6x^5$.   4. $2/x^5$.   5. $16m^8n^{12}$.

6. $\dfrac{8x^6}{27y^9}.$ 7. $-\dfrac{1}{a^4}.$ 8. $y^3/x^2.$ 9. $4x^4y^2.$ 10. $\dfrac{4A}{B^2}.$ 11. $\dfrac{4a^8}{b^8}.$ 12. (A) 1;

(B) $\dfrac{m^4 + 1}{m^2}.$ 13. 12.   14. $\dfrac{x^2 + 2xy + y^2}{x^2y^2}.$ 15. 0.072.   16. 2×10^{-3}, 0.002.

17. 1.036 cc.   18. $a^2 = b.$ 19. $2mn\sqrt{2n}.$ 20. $\dfrac{-\sqrt{5}}{2}.$ 21. $\sqrt{3}/3.$

22. (A) xy; (B) $\sqrt{x^2 + y^2}.$ 23. $\dfrac{x\sqrt{5}}{5}.$ 24. $4\sqrt{3}.$ 25. $\sqrt{5xy} - 2\sqrt{x + y}.$

26. $\dfrac{5\sqrt{6}}{6}.$ 27. $2\sqrt{2} - 13.$ 28. $2x + 2\sqrt{6xy} + 3y.$ 29. $\sqrt{3} - \sqrt{2}.$

30. $\dfrac{x - 4\sqrt{x} + 4}{x - 4}.$ 31. 1.183.   32. All nonnegative real numbers.

EXERCISE 71   PAGE 302

1. 3, 5.   3. $\frac{1}{2}$, -2.   5. $-\frac{3}{2}$, $\frac{2}{3}$.   7. 0, $-\frac{5}{3}$.   9. $\{3, 2\}$.   11. $\{0, 3\}$.
13. $\{6, -2\}$.   15. $\{0, 2\}$.   17. $\{\frac{1}{2}, -8\}$.   19. $\{-5, 5\}$.   21. $-\frac{1}{2}$, 3.
23. Not soluble by factoring.   25. -2, 4.   27. -6, 2.   29. $-\frac{1}{2}$, 2.   31. Not
soluble by factoring.   33. -2, 5.   **35.** -3, 3.   37. $x^2 - 8x + 15 = 0.$
39. $x^2 + x - 2 = 0.$ 41. $2x^2 + 3x - 2 = 0.$ 43. length: 11 in.; width: 3 in. Note:
length $= -3$ in. makes no sense so it must be discarded.   45. $\frac{2}{3}$ or $\frac{3}{2}$.   47. 1 ft.

EXERCISE 72   PAGE 305

1. $\pm 2.$ 3. $\pm 5.$ 5. $\pm\sqrt{5}.$ 7. No solution in the real numbers.   9. $\pm 3\sqrt{3}.$
11. $\pm 2\sqrt{3}.$ 13. $\pm\frac{3}{2}.$ 15. $\pm\frac{4}{3}.$ 17. $\pm\sqrt{10}/2.$ 19. $\pm\sqrt{3}/3.$ 21. $\pm 2.$
23. 5, 1.   25. $-2 \pm \sqrt{3}.$ 27. No real solution.   29. $\dfrac{1 \pm \sqrt{5}}{2}.$ 31. $\dfrac{3 \pm \sqrt{6}}{2}.$
33. $b = \pm\sqrt{c^2 - a^2}.$ 35. 70 mph.   37. 40.64 min.

EXERCISE 73   PAGE 309

1. $4, (x + 2)^2$.   3. $9, (x - 3)^2$.   5. $\frac{9}{4}, (t + \frac{3}{2})^2$.   7. $\frac{25}{4}, (x - \frac{5}{2})^2$.   9. $-2 \pm \sqrt{2}$.

11. $3 \pm 2\sqrt{3}$.   13. $\dfrac{-3 \pm \sqrt{13}}{2}$.   15. No solution in the reals.   17. $\dfrac{3 \pm \sqrt{3}}{2}$.

19. $\dfrac{-1 \pm \sqrt{13}}{6}$.   21. $\dfrac{-m \pm \sqrt{m^2 - 4n}}{2}$.

EXERCISE 74   PAGE 313

1. $a = 1, b = 8, c = 3$.   3. $a = 1, b = -4, c = 8$.   5. $a = 2, b = 3, c = -1$.
7. $a = 2, b = 6, c = 3$.   9. $a = 3, b = 0, c = -5$.   11. $-4 \pm \sqrt{13}$.

13. $5 \pm 2\sqrt{7}$.   15. $\dfrac{-1 \pm \sqrt{5}}{2}$.   17. No real solution.   19. $\dfrac{2 \pm \sqrt{2}}{2}$.

21. $\dfrac{-3 \pm \sqrt{17}}{4}$.   23. $3 \pm \sqrt{7}$.   25. $\dfrac{3 \pm \sqrt{11}}{2}$.   27. $\dfrac{\sqrt{5} \pm 7}{2}$.   29. True.

31. True.   33. 4.61 by 2.61 in.

EXERCISE 75   PAGE 314

1. $3, -5$.   3. $\dfrac{3 \pm \sqrt{13}}{2}$.   5. No real solution.   7. $0, 2$.   9. $\dfrac{3 \pm \sqrt{33}}{4}$.

11. $\frac{3}{2}, -2$.   13. $0, 1$.   15. $\dfrac{3 \pm \sqrt{13}}{2}$.   17. $\pm 5\sqrt{2}$.   19. $4, -7$.   21. $-50, 2$.

23. $t = \sqrt{\dfrac{2d}{g}}$.   25. $r = -1 + \sqrt{\dfrac{A}{P}}$.   27. $\{-3\}$.

EXERCISE 76   PAGE 315

1. 20.   3. (A) 2,000 and 8,000; (B) 5,000.   5. $p = \$2$.   7. 3 in., 4 in., 5 in.

9. $\dfrac{-1 + \sqrt{5}}{2}$.   11. 12, 14.   13. -7 or 8.   15. 55 mph.   17. $10\sqrt{2}$ ft, 14.14 ft.

19. 180 fps, 122.76 mph.   21. 2 hr, 3 hr.   23. 2 mph.

EXERCISE 77   PAGE 321

1. ± 9.   2. $0, 2$.   3. No real solution.   4. $\pm 2\sqrt{2}$.   5. $\dfrac{-1 \pm \sqrt{5}}{2}$.

6. $\frac{1}{2}$, -2.   7. $\frac{3}{2}$, $\frac{2}{3}$.   8. $\dfrac{1 \pm \sqrt{5}}{4}$.   9. No real solution.   10. 5, -3.

11. $\dfrac{-3 \pm \sqrt{57}}{6}$.   12. $\frac{3}{2}$, -2.   13. $2x^2 - 5x - 3 = 0$.   14. True.   15. 3, 14.

16. 6 by 5 in.   17. 5 in., 12 in.

EXERCISE 78   PAGE 328

1. Domain: all real x, $-3 \le x \le 8$; range: all real y, $-2 \le y \le 7$; the relation is a function.   3. Domain: all real t, $0 \le t \le 9$; range: all real d, $-3 \le d \le 3$; the relation is not a function.   5. Domain: $\{-6, -4, -2, 0, 2, 4, 6, 8\}$; range: $\{3\}$; the relation is a function.

7. Domain: $\{-2, 0, 2\}$
   Range: $\{0, 2\}$
   The relation is a function.

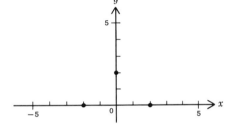

9. Domain: $\{1, 2, 3\}$
   Range: $\{1, 2, 3\}$
   The relation is not a function.

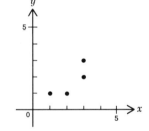

11. Domain: all real x, $0 \le x \le 6$
    Range: all real y, $-4 \le y \le -1$
    The relation is a function.

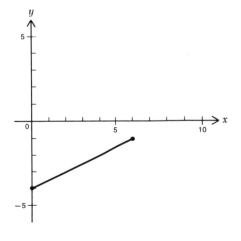

13. (A) Range: {0, 1, 16}
　　The relation is a function.

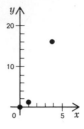

(B) Range: {−2, −1, 0, 1, 2}
　　The relation is not a function.

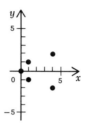

15. $C = 2x, x \geq 0$.

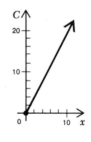

17. $C = 300 + 50x, x \geq 0$.

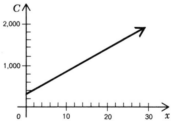

19. $A = 100 + 4t, t \geq 0$.

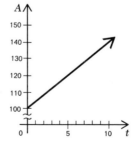

21. $A = x^2$, $x \geq 0$.

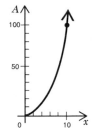

23. $d = 16t^2$, $t \geq 0$.

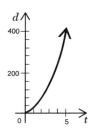

EXERCISE 79   PAGE 331

1. 3, 13, -37, -7.   3. 12, 0, 12, 3.   5. $2a + 5$, $2c + 5$, $2a + 7$.
7. 3, 11, 3, $h^2 + 2h + 3$.   9. 3, 0, does not exist.   11. (A) 7, (B) 54, (C) 32.
13. (A) $1 - 2h$, (B) $-2h$, (C) -2.   15. $8 + 2h$.   17. (A) $f(t) = 30t$, $t \geq 0$;
(B) 30, 300, 30.   19. $f = \{(-1, -4), (0, -1), (2, 5)\}$.   21. (A) yes, (B) yes, (C) no.

EXERCISE 80   PAGE 335

1.
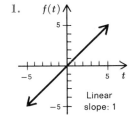
Linear
slope: 1

3.

Quadratic

5.
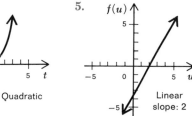
Linear
slope: 2

7.
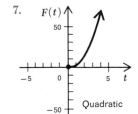
Quadratic

9.
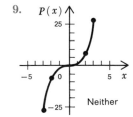
Neither

11.
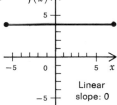
Linear
slope: 0

13.
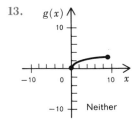
Neither

15.
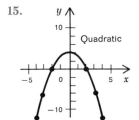
Quadratic

17.
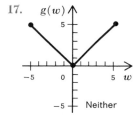
Neither

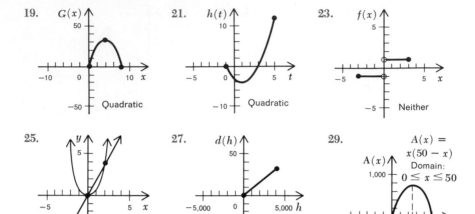

19. $G(x)$ Quadratic

21. $h(t)$ Quadratic

23. $f(x)$ Neither

25. (graph) Quadratic

x	y
0	0
2	4

27. $d(h)$

29. $A(x) = x(50 - x)$
Domain: $0 \leq x \leq 50$
$A(x)$
Maximum area for 25×25 ft

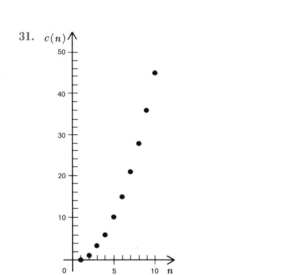

31. $c(n)$

33. First two are linear; the last four are quadratic.

EXERCISE 81   PAGE 339

1. $-2, 2$.   3. No real solutions.   5. $3, -1$.   7. No real solutions.   9. 5.
11. 0, 6.   13. (B) 0 (time when object leaves ground); 6 (time when object returns to ground); Domain: $0 \leq t \leq 6$; Maximum height: 144 ft.   15. ± 1.4.   17. 1.3.

EXERCISE 82   PAGE 341

1. A relation is any set of ordered pairs of elements.   2. *a* and *c*.   3. (A) Domain: all real numbers x, $-4 \leq x \leq 4$; Range: all real numbers y, $-1 \leq y \leq 3$. (C) Domain: $\{-5, -3, 0, 3, 5\}$; Range: $\{-3, 2, 5\}$.

4. (A)

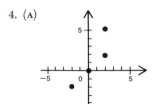

(B)

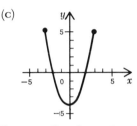

(C)

Domain: $\{-2, 0, 2\}$
Range: $\{-2, 0, 2, 5\}$
Not a function.

Domain: all real numbers.
Range: all real numbers.
A function.

Domain: all real x, $-3 \leq x \leq 3$
Range: all real y, $-4 \leq y \leq 5$
A function.

5. g is linear and h is quadratic.   6. $7, 3, 11, 7 - 2a$.   7. $0, 15, 10, 2e^2 - e$.
8. (A) 2, (B) -8, (C) $t^2 - 2t + 2$.   9. $h^2 + 4h + 1, 4 + h$.

10. $C(x)$

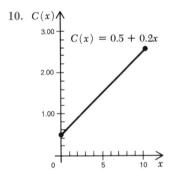

$C(x) = 0.5 + 0.2x$

11. $f(t)$ Quadratic

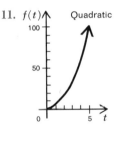

12. u

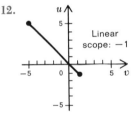

Linear
scope: -1

13. $G(t)$

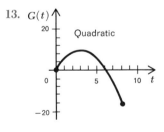

Quadratic

14. $h(x)$

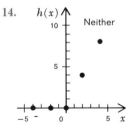

Neither

15. $f(x)$ $f(-2) = 0$
$f(4) = 0$

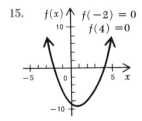

16. $x = -2, 4$; see problem 15.

EXERCISE 83   PAGE 350

1. Q, Q.   3. Q, Q.   5. I.   7. Q.   9. Q.   11.

x \ y	Q	I
Q	Q	I
I	I	Q

13. I, I.

EXERCISE 84   PAGE 352

1. 2.   3. 6.   5. 2, 2.   7. 1, 6.   9. 1, 1.   11. 5, 5.   13. 4, 4.   15. 4, 4.
17. 5, 3.   19. 4, 2.   21. 4.   23. 4.   25. 0, 1.   27. Yes.   29. $\bar{0} = 0$,
$\bar{1} = 6, \bar{2} = 5, \bar{3} = 4, \bar{4} = 3, \bar{5} = 2, \bar{6} = 1$.   31. 5, 5.   33. 2, 2.
35. 6, 6.   37. 5, 5.

EXERCISE 85   PAGE 355

1.

$x \oplus y$

x \ y	0	1	2
0	0	1	2
1	1	2	0
2	2	0	1

$x \odot y$

x \ y	0	1	2
0	0	0	0
1	0	1	2
2	0	2	1

2. 0, 0.   3. 1.   4. 2, 2.   5. 1.   6. 2, 2.   7. 1, 1.   8. 1, 2.   9. 2, 2.
10. (A) 2; (B) 0.   11. $Q = 0, I = 1$.   12. Yes.   13. Yes.   14. Yes.
15. $\bar{0} = 0, \bar{1} = 2, \bar{2} = 1$.   16. $0'$ does not exist, $1' = 1, 2' = 2$.   17. 2, 2.
18. 2, 2.

index